Doctor in Bolivia

H. ERIC MAUTNER

Doctor in Bolivia

CHILTON COMPANY — BOOK DIVISION
Publishers
Philadelphia   New York

Published in Philadelphia by Chilton Company,
and simultaneously in Toronto, Canada, by Ambassador Books, Ltd.

LIBRARY OF CONGRESS CATALOG CARD NUMBER 60-8820

MANUFACTURED IN THE UNITED STATES OF AMERICA
BY QUINN & BODEN COMPANY, INC., RAHWAY, N. J.

To the memory of my sister Bertl,
one of the victims of Nazi madness

Contents

Doctor in Bolivia

1

I Leave La Paz—and, I Hope, the Past—to Begin My Job as Health Officer

I was leaving, leaving La Paz at last. I should have been eager and enthusiastic, all the things people should be when they are taking a new and
interesting course in their lives, but I wasn't. I was nervous and apprehen-
sive. As if a dentist had told me there was nothing wrong with my teeth,
that he just wanted to check them over, and all the time I *knew* he was
going to hurt me terribly. I leaned back in my seat, the brakes moaned,
and the station wagon that was taking me and other passengers to the airport came to an abrupt stop.

A huge black limousine pulled up noiselessly beside us, a luxurious
vehicle filled with sleek, expensively dressed men and women. I imagined
that it belonged to one of Bolivia's fabled tin-mine kings, and I couldn't
suppress a twinge of resentment. Even here in La Paz, the capital, it was unusual to see such a car so early in the morning—much more unusual, for
that matter, than what had brought us to a halt. A flock of llamas, at
least fifty or more, was pouring into the intersection, throwing traffic into
confusion, and bringing everything to a dead stop. The ancient trolley
coming down the hill toward us barely made it. Thundering beneath a
shower of sparks from overhead wires, it almost crashed into the ambling
llamas before its small wheels ground to a stop on the worn tracks.

The noise, the shouts, the horn-tooting alarmed the graceful animals;
they craned their long necks anxiously and looked about with their large,
mournful eyes. Coming in from the sidewalk, a barefoot Indio in a wide,
bleached sombrero, ragged trousers, and a torn shirt tried to keep the llamas
together with pathetic rallying cries and wooden gestures. He moved listlessly and ineffectually, and I was not surprised. His jaws were working,

and I knew he was chewing coca leaves, which was all many Indios had for breakfast. The cocaine in the leaves accounted for his dull, vacuous face, his blunted motions and general inefficiency.

Now a llama broke away from the sprawling flock and leaped onto the curb where a *chola,* an Indio woman, sat by her little newspaper stand. She wore a stiff felt hat, a shawl of blazing red, and several multicolored skirts. The animal's headlong plunge knocked her sprawling, spilled her newspapers all over the sidewalk, and she, like the Indio pursuing the llama, began to whimper pathetically. Just behind her a shopkeeper was hanging a huge, dried snakeskin over the vicuna blanket already draped over the frame of his shop door. The short bald man turned slowly and gazed without much interest at what was a commonplace spectacle in La Paz. Looking past the whimpering *chola,* he saw me sitting in the station wagon and looking his way.

"Well, doctor!" he called out, his face brightening, and walked over to the station wagon window with the slow, deliberate steps of all Europeans in turbulent La Paz. I lowered the window so we could talk—the llama traffic jam not having cleared—and now he looked worried. "You're not leaving us, are you, doctor? Why didn't you tell me?"

It was a good question. The truth was I hadn't known definitely about my appointment as provincial health officer, even after a series of interviews with the authorities, nor of my departure for the interior until an hour ago—and this after three weeks of agonized waiting during which I had been put off from *mañana* to *mañana* by the agents of Bolivia's only airline. They always shrugged off my queries. The weather over the Cordillera was bad or the plane was undergoing repairs. It was also common knowledge that the run to Santa Morena, the province's only airport, was unprofitable, and the government had to use pressure to make the airline schedule the trip at all. As for my assignment, I knew it was a difficult post and paid little; naturally the native Bolivian doctors preferred to practice in the cities, where the work was less strenuous and much more lucrative.

Had I wanted to practice in the city—and I wasn't sure I did—I couldn't have done so. Foreigners were legally forbidden to enter private medical practice. They could, however, work as government employees wherever the officials chose to send them. Oh, I might have been tempted to practice in La Paz, if it were permitted, but, discounting the apprehension which came over me now and then, I was looking forward to my new job. There was something romantic and adventuresome in the idea of a jungle

2

doctor and, subconsciously, I was probably relieved that the laws of Bolivia left me no alternative.

All this crossed my mind as the little man waited for my reply, and he promptly cut in before I could find suitable words.

"So your appointment finally came through, eh? I knew it would if you remained patient long enough." He laughed. "Anyway, you'll like it out there. It is always warm and—not like here—there is enough oxygen in the air to breathe. It is not high. You won't have to rest after every step as you do in La Paz. And the people are so friendly. Why, thirty years ago when I came to Bolivia, we had to travel across the Cordillera by foot and mule. What a trip!" He made a face. "And today you go by plane in a few hours. Ah, the llamas are out of the way. Good luck to you, doctor!"

We had just time for a quick handshake before the station wagon jerked to a start. The big black limousine was already halfway up the hill, and the rear guard of the llamas was disappearing down a side street, leaving behind that strong, fetid odor that always dismayed me. How could such beautiful, graceful creatures smell so awful? But the Indio trailing them didn't seem to mind. Probably the cocaine dulled his smell as well as the rest of his senses.

The shopkeeper waved at me from the curb. Thirty years was a long time, but I hoped he knew what he was talking about. I had heard people refer to the region I was headed for as the "Valley of Death," full of malignant diseases and dangerous wild animals. Nor had they neglected to remind me that life in the Province was crude and primitive, and that my patients would be ignorant, backward, and superstitious people. Well, we would soon see who was right—the alarmist, the optimistic shopkeeper, or the doctor and his dreams of romance and adventure.

We rode on to the plaza where the government buildings, the big stores, the movie houses, and the old cathedral were. From here a long avenue led past the railroad station to the highway that wound upward along the slopes of the Andes Valley in which La Paz nestled. I could feel the atmosphere thinning out as we climbed, and the station wagon's engine rattled protestingly, complaining at the work it was forced to do in the rarefied air. Looking back as we reached the highest point, I saw La Paz, the capital in the sky, spread out before me. From the distance it was a beautiful sight; the llamas had no smell, the Indios were picturesque, and the city beckoned. Now I felt another pang at leaving.

The station wagon rumbled up the road to the airport, which was really no more than an airstrip built on a plateau surrounded by jagged, thrusting

3

mountains. The pale blue sky was startlingly low; so low it seemed that I had only to reach up to grab a piece of it. Heaven and earth were molded together. But the plane was waiting, and we hurried toward it. It was warming up, the big Junkers' three engines roaring away, Indios sweeping the great wings free of snow. Real snow only ten degrees south of the equator! We got out of the station wagon, and again doubts assailed me.

The passengers were checked off one by one, our baggage weighed, and we stood around waiting for take-off time. I was so wrapped up in my hot-and-cold thoughts about the future that I paid no attention to the men and women about to make the trip away from civilization with me. Just then a taxi scrambled up the road to La Paz, pulled into the airstrip, and stopped close to me. I looked up as someone called my name. Herbert, big and stooped and with his pipe, as always, in his mouth; Karl, older than the rest of us and serious, and Karl's attractive wife, Maria.

"Martin," she said now, breathlessly, "we just had to come to see you off."

I was touched and also annoyed. Leave-takings were a waste of emotions, always arousing uncalled-for sentimentalities.

"She's right," said Karl, echoing his wife. "We had to come."

"I still can't believe you're going," said Herbert. "Why, you belong to us, and you mustn't be alone. Isn't Bolivia far enough from Europe? Isn't La Paz small enough a town for you? *Must* you bury yourself in the jungle?"

Why should they want to keep me in their "magic" circle of drifting, haunted refugees? I wondered. Why did they have to make things harder for me? Of course, Herbert was different. He was the strong one. Stronger than any of us. He was tense when tenseness could be of an advantage; relaxed when the occasion called for it, and he could sleep when sleep was in order. He was always in control. So then let him stay in La Paz, in civilization with its movies, radios, and newspaper headlines.

"It's all decided now." I sighed resignedly. "I'm going."

"But you belong to us," Herbert went on. "We think and speak the same language. It isn't good for you to be alone out there."

This angered me, and I wanted to hurt him. I had heard all this before. It was my turn to needle.

"Have you heard from your wife lately, Herbert? I thought she was supposed to follow you from Sweden to La Paz. I understand there was an airmail delivery yesterday. You must have some word by now."

Instead of wincing, as I had expected, Herbert looked elated.

"I did hear from her. Soon, very soon, she will join me in La Paz."

4

"Good," I said, regretting my meanness. "I'll be looking forward to meeting her." The loud-speaker blared that it was time for departure. I felt more uncertain than ever, but put up what I hoped was a good show for my friends. "They're calling for passengers to go aboard. Good-by, and don't worry about me. And all the best to all of you."

We shook hands all around and embraced. Maria kissed me on the lips, and I felt a tremor of desire. It had been so long since Lisa in Paris. Lisa! Who was I to twit Herbert about his wife?

"Write," Maria said in my ear, over the roar of the motors. "Write as much and as often as you can. You mean a lot to us."

In an instant, it seemed, the airstrip was just a narrow thread and my friends dark specks upon it. I saw La Paz as a toy village, then the valley in the Andes was left behind, and we were over the mountains. The Illimani, tallest peak of the Cordillera, loomed ahead, growing larger by the second. We went past the great, icy mountain at 20,000 feet and all around us the lesser peaks of the Cordillera raised whitened, snow-covered heads. Forbidding and self-sufficient in their frigid beauty, the mountains shielded a score of small lakes, all of them as blue as a baby's eyes.

I looked back through the window, and now the whole Cordillera moved into my field of vision, summit by summit, topped by the Illimani. Like schoolgirls in an old-fashioned dance, standing in line and holding hands, each in her white hat and wide hoopskirt, the lesser peaks all seemed guarded and chaperoned by the duenna Illimani. Then the Cordillera faded slowly into the blue mist, and I leaned back into my seat.

I was on my way in spite of everything. I had done what I wanted to do, I exulted, feeling childishly proud and happy. It was the same feeling I had experienced as a small boy when I built myself a rugged cabin from old pieces of lumber. It stood in the corner of the backyard, hidden by shrubs, and when I was in it, I reigned unmolested and free. On the other hand, when I had had enough and wanted company or food, all I had to do was walk back to the house. Interesting and challenging as the new life I was heading for might be, I was not sure that my European medical education had prepared me for it in any way. The Cordillera was a formidable barrier. As I understood it, the plane made the trip to Santa Morena perhaps twelve times in a six-month period, and not at all during the rainy season. To cross the mountains by foot or mule was impossible, a legendary feat. So for months on end there might be no way of getting supplies or assistance. Nor, as with my cabin, could I just call it quits when I had enough and retire to civilization.

The mountains were a spiritual barrier as well. Behind them lay the

Pacific Ocean, the Panama Canal, the Atlantic, Europe, Austria—and hell. Just thinking of my homeland made me ill. Nazi Austria was not the Austria in which I had been born, grown up, and studied. The new Austria wanted nothing to do with Jews like me, and I wanted nothing to do with it. My God, what a relief to have left that nightmare behind me. The insults, the beatings, the jails, the concentration camps, the killings . . . Then Paris and despair, the sweetness of Lisa, but still the overwhelming despair. It was there I had met Herbert, Karl, Maria, and the others. We were all alike, bruised, bloody, and beaten inside and out. We had been torn up and uprooted and, as with trees, our bundles of roots were raw, sensitive nerve ends, twitching and cringing.

We hadn't known what to do with ourselves and our lives—our new lives into which we had been forcibly propelled, healthy and alive by the grace of God, but that was about all. We had made the rounds of the consulates in Paris, and it was a shock to learn that we were not particularly wanted anywhere. After all, who were we? What did we have to offer? And who cared anyway? It was in Paris that we had finally heard at the Bolivian consulate that that government needed agricultural workers, and we all decided to take our chances and go to Bolivia. Even then we had to slip a sum, amounting to some forty dollars apiece, under the table to get our visas. And that, too, was a shock. Our Nazi world was corrupt, and it pained us to find that the free world was corrupt in its own way.

Then that damn boat ride, all of us jammed in like cattle, seasick, crowded, miserable, and practically at each other's throats. We were free at last, but we didn't know it, didn't appreciate it, didn't know what to do with it. We still guarded our passports and documents with our lives. Why, I remember after landing at the port town of Arica in Chile and taking the train, high over the Andes to La Paz, when old Goldstein lost his documents. He was a worrier, the documents meant life, identity, reason—everything—and he kept them in a yellow briefcase clutched close to his bosom. Somehow, during the train trip, he had lost them and promptly gone crazy. He made a terrible commotion, ran up and down the cars screaming about his loss, and probably had visions of himself being dragged off and sent back to the Gestapo.

His torment communicated itself to all of us. My own heart almost stopped as I fumbled through my clothes for my own precious documents. If I lost them, I'd lose myself—just like Goldstein, who was out of his head now. Then a big fat Bolivian border policeman came through the cars, collared Goldstein, and it was some time before he got the whole story minus hysteria and carrying on.

"So what?" he said with a snort. At this Goldstein and his frantic friends erupted again, but the border guard shushed them. "I said so what if you lost that junk. You are here now, so why do you need documents? Nobody's going to kick you off the train, send you back, or anything like that. This is a free country, friend."

He couldn't know the force and impact of his words. He was right. We were so touchy that we got stupidly excited over little things which, in this country—praise be!—were meaningless. This was freedom. Here a person counted as a person, a man was a man without having to have thirty documents, permits, and what-have-you to identify, justify, and prove his right to life and manhood. The train stopped later on at a way station high up in the mountains, and we all filed out into the snow, breathed deeply of the free rarefied air, and got drunk on it. We couldn't get enough.

Then came La Paz, finding a place to live, and a job. It was every man for himself now, and the trouble was that too many of us were not whole men. We were still the uprooted, amputees bound to the past, ghosts with no haunted houses to haunt. That was why I was glad I had left La Paz. Yes, in the jungle I would find myself. I saw it as a place of opportunity now, where there was still scope and need for a man's knowledge and his will to work. A job was waiting for me there, a position of responsibility in the new world, where I would no longer be just a card with a fingerprint. Of course, I warned myself, it wouldn't be easy. The jungle might treat a man as viciously as the Nazis, but it wouldn't hide its savagery and terror behind a flag of culture and the myth of the super-race. Danger in the jungle would be clean and honest; there might be pain and fear, but not, I was sure, that searing mental anguish that had left so many of us transplanted refugees paralyzed during those last agonizing, useless years in Europe.

From one angle, the window next to me was like a mirror. I saw my own chin stick forward, firm, resolute, resolved. Some women I'd known had called this chin of mine a fraud. It seemed soft and sensitive, they told me, even though I could be hard at times. But then how little they knew me—and how little I knew myself. They had called my mouth deceiving, too, almost feminine, they claimed, and hardly shaped to say some of the surprising things I sometimes said. But nobody could call my nose feminine. It was so large, a real eagle's beak. Ah, was there ever a man or a woman who was truly satisfied with his face?

Abruptly, contrasting my displeasing features with what I knew had become my displeasing—even ugly—nature, I dozed off for a while. I

7

awoke to find the plane flying through thick clouds. The pilot and copilot were flying by instrument with experienced, almost bored calm; the navigator-radio operator, earphones on his head, was bent over his charts. It seemed to me the plane was wallowing through the sky. It carried a heavy cargo load, my own big wooden crates of medical supplies, which had been furnished by the government, accounting for much of it. Only God knew how long these supplies would last—or how long they would have to last. All I could hope for was that they had packed what was most needed in the jungle.

I yawned, and my eardrums popped and popped again. The plane moved on sluggishly, monotonously. A mashed-potato white ceiling glistened above us, and below a carpet of gray cloud hid the ground. The motors roared with a million splinters of sound as I hovered between waking and sleeping. When my eardrums wearied, the noise seemed to fade; when they recovered a little, the racket assaulted them afresh.

Cars, buses, trains, ships, airplanes. I had begun to feel I had been in flight all my life, and there had been no other sounds than roaring engines, hooting whistles, grinding wheels, and the up-and-down crashing of the waves. Of them all I preferred the train. Its noise was not deafening, but rather friendly, and could be separated into the roll of the wheels over worn rails, the soft rattle of old windows, the asthmatic panting of the ancient locomotive that hauled us across Europe into the comparative safety of France. But I had come to hate the sound and motion of all transport, none perhaps as much as the stomach-turning seesaw of the ocean liner that had brought us over to Arica in Chile.

To be uprooted wrenched one's entire life and being out of context. I knew that uprooted trees could be successfully transplanted almost anywhere, but it took care, special precautions, time, and, above all, endless patience and perseverance—all qualities that many refugees significantly lacked. To give up one life and begin another took resilience and resourcefulness and courage. Too bad the knack of successful migration had not been taught to us Jews as far back as kindergarten. (We should have been born with the instincts of birds.) We ought to have been hardened and toughened, taught to have no sensitivities, no scruples, no yearnings for stability and security. And what had I been taught? I had been soaked in the philosophies of Plato and Kant at a time when the world was governed by perverted laws of supply and demand. A crazed, hysterical time dominated by the economics of scarcity, the credo of master races which demanded the extinction of "inferior" races, visas, dictators, *lebensraum*,

8

an associated garbage festering on the minds of men like social abscesses. In this new era, the individual was the least important component and, at the same time, the most vulnerable, since every one of us was burdened with the anachronism of a sympathetic heart hammered ceaselessly on the remorseless anvil of the times.

I dozed off again, then a stinging concussion quivered my eardrums and burned into my throat. I was wide awake now and aware that we were descending. The plane was diving through the thick gray blanket, we were enveloped in it like cotton and, for an instant, I thought we were crashing. I held my breath and we shot out into clear, blinding air with the earth below incredibly bright and studded and incrusted with emerald green. I pressed my nose against the cold window, and my bird's-eye view of the jungle filled me with sudden joy. Whatever my doubts, I was among the privileged ones to be allowed to see and experience this beauty.

A winding line approached at top speed, broadening finally into a river whose yellow waters flowed and undulated toward an uncertain horizon. The bright green patches became the lushly luxuriant crowns of great trees. Looking around the plane, I saw the navigator's mouth working. His black eyes danced with the pleasure of achievement. Here was proof of his sound navigation—finding a pinpoint like this—and his finger pointed excitedly to the window. As we continued on down and down, I could feel the heat creeping into the plane, and the landscape faded into the lighter green of parched grass. There were trees and vegetation everywhere except in one place, where I could make out a straw-thatched cabin surrounded by a deep green patch of woods and a glistening, half-moon-shaped pond.

Some lonely settler makes his home here, I thought, beginning to build a picture of the tragedy that had forced this lonesome, world-weary hermit to desert civilization entirely. He is staring up open-mouthed at the plane now, remembering the wonderful time he once had in La Paz, the sights he saw, the women, the gaiety. And he is filled with anguish and regret. But the navigator was still pointing excitedly and shouting something. I could almost read his lips. Surely, this little patchwork of nothingness could not be a jungle village. It simply couldn't be so!

The roar of the motors at low altitude was unbearable. The heat inside the plane had grown suffocating. The navigator's lips kept forming two words.

"Santa Morena. Santa Morena. Santa Morena."

2

I Arrive in Santa Morena; My First Case; I Meet Pierre and Don Socrates; My New House; The Boys Who Burned the Candle at Both Ends

The realization so numbed my senses that a few minutes passed before I was aware that my fingers were cramped into fists and I was muttering "My God, my God" over and over again to myself. Herbert had been right again, and I *was* burying myself in the jungle. Santa Morena was a pinpoint in nothingness, and I should have known it. I was a fool! What had I expected, anyway? A town, a resort, some spa? As we swung over the village, I saw a few bare green streets, shacks, houses, and cabins with thatched roofs.

Santa Morena was tiny and now I doubted that Rojas, the capital of the province, was much larger. And I laughed to myself briefly, a healthy thing in my present state of shock. Prague was big, so was Vienna, so was Paris. And La Paz, which I had thought of as a small backward town on arrival, now appeared as cosmopolitan as Paris, as gay as old Vienna. What did it really matter? This was journey's end for me, my destination, and it was time to turn and face facts, with my back to the wall if need be.

Sweat prickled my body as the plane circled the yellow meadow which was the airstrip. I saw a crowd of people straggling along the outskirts of the village, then gather into a small dark knot as they awaited the machine, their only means of contact with the outside world. The women wore dresses of funereal black, but their parasols, bobbing over their heads, were all shades of bright red and purple. The men wore romantic sombreros, just as the books said, and they looked tanned and stolid. All my qualms returned now, and I wished that those same books had told me how I should

10

act toward these people, these strangers, in the next few minutes. First impressions must be vital out here.

The wheels touched, the plane bounced, the wheels touched again, and the plane rolled on to a smooth stop. My God, was I the only one getting off at Santa Morena! I stood up on shaky legs, walked down the cabin as waves of heat swam in to smother me, hesitated at the door, and clamped a smile on my tense, set features. Then, clutching my suitcases, I stepped down from the plane into the concentrated rays of the torrid tropic sun. They hit me like a club. I shrank back, reeled with dizziness, and was afraid I was going to faint. "The blazing sea of a tropical noontime . . ." The hackneyed description was sickeningly valid.

I took another grip on my suitcases, looked about me dazedly, blinking and self-conscious and sweating all over under the gaze of the silent villagers, who studied me as if I were an illustration in a mail-order catalog come to life. From their midst a man approached me, and nothing could have startled me more. I dropped my bags and simply stared openmouthed at this Falstaff, wearing a straw hat *à la* Maurice Chevalier, a pajama jacket, linen trousers, and dusty black shoes. His belly was a big, wobbling bulge, and his little eyes, in his porcine face, were so deep a blue they almost seemed black. His lips moved. He was obviously speaking to me, but I couldn't hear a thing. The plane's engines had thoroughly deafened me. He repeated himself and I shrugged helplessly.

"I am Doctor Martin Fischer," I said.

At least that was what I thought I said, because I couldn't hear my own words, and I hurriedly fumbled in my breast pocket for my letter of introduction from the government officials. The man took my letter without bothering to read it, repeated whatever he had said in the first place, then, seeing I still did not get it, lifted one arm and pointed to a group of people standing around a dried cowhide that was spread out on the grass. Through the tangle of interested spectators I could just make out an elderly gentleman sprawled on the cowhide, wearing a European-style dark suit, a fedora, a white shirt, and a black tie. As I looked his way, the onlookers moved back respectfully, and he was raised and supported into an upright position by an Indio, who now sat bracing his back against the old man's. Apparently his only duty was to keep his master from slumping over.

Falstaff gestured again and I got the idea. I dropped my suitcases and went over to the man. It was odd being plunged into my job when I had barely set foot in Santa Morena, nor was the place in any way suitable for a consultation and I felt self-conscious and ill at ease. A cursory examination made it clear that the elderly gentleman was very ill. His respiration was fast and shallow. Under his burning wrist I could feel a rapid and irregular pulse. Evidently his heart was not standing up to the strain imposed by the fever and what was ailing him. He seemed unaware of either me or his surroundings, almost past delirium. I looked at his face carefully and pulled down his lower eyelids. Whose insane idea had it been, I wondered angrily, to drag this dangerously ill man to the airstrip? Why couldn't the idiots wait until I went to his house to see him?

I got down on my knees and took off the man's coat, first freeing one arm, his upper body, and finally the other arm. I pulled his shirt and vest up to the shoulders just as two small brown hands, evidently feminine, appeared to grab the shirttail protectively, holding it back so the material would not drape over the naked back. I stared at the small hands, then moved my eyes past the slim wrists and graceful arms until they met two burning black eyes set into a pretty brown face. It brought me up short, but this was no time to ogle an attractive girl. Quickly I went back to the sick man. I was going to put my ear to his back, but I was still sound-deaf, and I had to depend on my tactile sense rather than on the tell-tale sounds of percussion and auscultation for my diagnosis. I had had good training. Touch alone was enough to tell me that only a small part of one lung still had air in it.

I stood up, squinting against the glaring sun and feeling the sweat running down inside of my city clothes. "He has double pneumonia," I said. Everyone stared and, since I could not hear my own voice, I repeated myself in Spanish. "Double pneumonia, I said!" They all seemed to jump as I spoke and I realized I was screaming. Just then my deafness began to slip away and I heard a squeaky, high-pitched voice. It came from Falstaff, looming at my side, and I was astonished. I was even more astonished to hear him speaking in French.

"We thought he had pneumonia. They are taking him to La Paz to be cured. His brother and niece are going with him."

To cover my astonishment I glanced for an instant at the sick man, the blazing sun making his blue lips appear purple beneath the fluttering wings of his nostrils. But what a difference a voice makes! My Falstaff was gone, replaced by the chief eunuch in an Oriental harem. I blinked. The huge plane squatting on the meadow back of me, the Indios lugging cargo back and forth, the sick man on the cowhide, the people around him, the hypnotic sun, the ridiculously inappropriate voice speaking—of all things—French, a language out of the past—it was all so unreal, a dream. Then the fat man's meaning hit me.

"Taking him to La Paz!" I exclaimed. "Do they want to kill him? He needs oxygen, and La Paz is so high that even healthy people don't get enough air. Why, he won't survive the trip if they go. He'll die en route."

The fat man turned to the pretty girl and the older man who stood worriedly beside her. They were both dressed for traveling, these last two, and I assumed they were the sick man's niece and his brother. All of them chattered earnestly in Spanish for a while, then looked at me uncertainly as the spectators shifted feet. Then the girl's father came up to me.

"Do you think you could cure *El Chileno*—I mean my brother here?"

"I could try," I said nervously. This was a very sick man, but there was always an outside chance. "But he must be taken out of this sun immediately and brought home."

"How long will it take and how much will it cost?"

What questions! What was I supposed to be, a merchant-prophet or a physician? I was almost tempted to say, "How the hell do I know?" or some such thing. You didn't bargain at death's door; you got to work fast. These people would have to learn that it was not proper or even ethical to speak of money at such moments. Nor did good doctors guarantee cures.

"I assure you," I explained righteously, "that money is the last thing on my mind." It was the wrong thing to say. The doubt that had been so evident in this man's expression was now superseded by outright distrust. That made me even more irritated. "But the idea of taking anyone as sick as this man to La Paz," I went on uncomfortably, "is absolutely out of the question."

A heated discussion began among the same three, as the Indio again propped the sick man against his strong back. Although the tone of the argument was violent, I noted that not one of the participants so much as gestured.

"I don't even care to go to La Paz," said the girl stridently. Then to make sure she was understood in the hubbub, she shouted, "If he wants to, Papa can go alone with uncle. I believe what the doctor says." And then she threw me a glance of such frank intimacy and unmistakable curiosity that I could feel myself blushing.

"It's absolutely out of the question, *loco,* to take him to La Paz," I repeated defensively. But the moment the words were out of my mouth I knew again that I shouldn't have said them. These people had little enough confidence in me already. Still, I couldn't help adding, "The trip will kill him."

That did it. A few minutes later *El Chileno,* his clothes falling off him, was carried off to the waiting plane. I hadn't time to protest or remonstrate,

13

nor would it have done any good. Shaken by both the heat and the experience, I started back for my bags. The fat man waddled after me hurriedly.

"Please forgive these ignorant people," he said in French. "And now let us go to the pueblo."

He took one of my bags and I the other, then led the way. The crowd broke into small groups behind us. When we reached the narrow path at the border of the airstrip, we had to walk single file.

"The pampas are hot today," said the fat man, puffing and wheezing, his voice as high-pitched as ever. "Very hot."

"What are the pampas?" I asked in my ignorance.

My eunuch showed no surprise or even mockery. He stopped, turned a half-circle and made a sweeping gesture.

"From here to the east it's at least a thousand kilometers to the Brazilian border, and then from there to the Atlantic Ocean it's a few thousand more kilometers—all flatland, grass, and virgin woods. We call them the pampas." He pointed to the airplane, which had taken off with roaring engines a few minutes earlier and was now dwindling toward the bluish line on the horizon in the direction it had come. "That is the Cordillera. From there to Santa Morena the Andes slope gradually. We are in the foothills. In floodtime people come from all around to the safety of the pueblo. And then, you know, on the other side of the Cordillera there's the Pacific Ocean."

We had stepped off the path while he was talking, and all the others had passed and gone ahead of us. We went on, passing some shrubs which gave off an overpoweringly sweet fragrance, and he jerked a sausage-like thumb at them.

"Smell the wild vanilla? In the big cities they're willing to pay high prices for the stuff. Here we're too lazy to pick it."

I was only half listening because, physically and mentally, I was thoroughly uncomfortable. Sweat was pouring off me, and my underwear was glued to my skin. Thinking of *El Chileno,* I was filled with nagging self-reproach. Somehow I hadn't handled the situation properly. The chances of his pulling through, had he remained here, were doubtful enough, but the flight would only hasten his death. Damn it, what an ignominious beginning. The path widened, and there was now room for us to walk side by side. The fat man seemed to guess my thoughts.

"Too bad, but I really think that the flight and altitude will go hard for *El Chileno.* Well, it can't be helped. If he dies, it will prove you were right and help your prestige."

Which also meant that, if by some miracle he survived, my prestige

14

would suffer. This kind of reasoning left me gasping. And he was so cheerful about it all.

"Wait a minute now. Did they really expect me to give them a fee schedule with a complete prognosis right there and then?"

"Cash is rare in these regions, doctor. You might have mentioned some reasonable sum, but I think they were bent on the trip anyway." He chuckled. "Especially Carlotta. There's a girl for you! Her uncle's sickness was the answer to all her prayers. She's been dying to see the glamor of La Paz, you know, and they're not so rich. Just making the trip will use up just about everything they own. But Carlotta—well, now it seems she's found a greater attraction here." He looked at me knowingly. "I saw how she looked at you."

I didn't know how to take this fat clown or what to make of him, so I wisely said nothing. We walked on and, after a while, he spoke again.

"I came to Bolivia through the Chaco, the place where they fought the war with Paraguay, you know."

"That's interesting," I said absently.

The fat man seemed pleased to have gotten any answer at all. Fat man, Falstaff, eunuch. Funny, he hadn't even introduced himself, and I wasn't up to asking his name. It was *so* enervatingly hot.

"How long were you in La Paz?" he went on.

"About six weeks and—yes, six weeks."

"You speak Spanish quite well for that short time. You'll know it even better soon." His voice trailed off, and I didn't bother telling him that I'd known the language earlier. We walked on farther without speaking, then he said, "I'm supposed to leave with the cattle for the Brazilian border one of these days. But they asked me to stay on so I could talk to you in French, in case you didn't understand Spanish."

"Why French?" I said in surprise.

"Because Don Socrates, to whom your letter of introduction is addressed, received a cable that a doctor from France was going to be the new health officer of the province."

"Oh, I came from France all right, but I am certainly not French."

We passed more vanilla shrubs, then continued on into a cleared place. I was really tired and sticky. All around the pampas glistened like heated silver, the air sizzled, and I fried in it. We approached a small pond—I imagined it was the half-moon-shaped one I'd seen from the air—and started across some planks over it.

"This is the *currichi* of Santa Morena," the falsetto voice explained. "The people here say that whoever has drunk of its waters once always return to it."

"One of the local legends?"

"It could be true, but I don't see how. Look at the filthy, slimy stuff—and they think it has magical restoring powers. Oh, they believe everything here. You'll see."

A thin man, one I recognized from the airstrip spectators, was waiting for us at a point beyond the *currichi* where the path widened.

"Don Pierre," he said to me in Spanish, indicating the fat man, "is a lawyer from Austria, doctor. Did you know that?"

"Von Wien?" I burst out unwittingly in German, forgetting my exhaustion. "How extraordinary!"

Pierre's globular cheeks turned a mottled crimson. "Are you an Austrian?" he asked in German, sounding alarmed.

"Of course, and from Vienna. Like you, eh? That's incredible, to find a fellow countryman out here. Absolutely incredible!"

I began to chatter away about Vienna and Austria, but Pierre kept his mouth shut and marched along under a strain. It seemed a strange way for him to act toward a compatriot. I didn't understand the man at all. The path broadened again, the shrubs thinned out and disappeared, and we were on a grassy lane which turned into a grassy street. A few cows lazily made way for us. Farther on there were sidewalks of hard, dry-packed earth, then a row of gray mud-walled houses with shaggy thatched roofs.

In twos and threes the people returning from the airstrip ahead of us left the mainstream and disappeared into the open doors of the houses. Curious children remained behind to stare at the newcomer. They wore short linen trousers, faded shirts, and sombreros of felt or straw. From time to time an Indio man arose from his seat on the sidewalk in front of a house, stared, pushed back his sombrero, and scratched his thick black hair and his neck. It was plainly a gesture of embarrassment, and just as plain that here the Indios were even more of an inferior class than in La Paz. We slowed at the end of the street at the plaza, a square fenced with barbed wire.

"I will take you to Don Socrates first," said Pierre. He pointed to a house at the corner. "He is our leading citizen." He looked at me. "You'll probably be staying with him. There are no hotels in Santa Morena, except for the gambling house—and I wouldn't recommend that."

"I see," I said agreeably, but I didn't.

We went into Don Socrates' house and on into a big room, whose entire width was spanned by a hammock. From it a tall man, well beyond middle

16

age, arose and came toward me smiling, with his arms extended in welcome. He had silver-gray hair, a large, black, flowing mustache, and sparkling black eyes. He wore light, rumpled trousers of some bleached material, and the collar of his faded shirt was open at the throat.

"What a pleasure to see you at last, doctor," he said warmly. "We have been expecting you for the past two weeks. Forgive me for not being at the airport to greet you, but the sun is hard to take at this time."

He was in good health, his handshake strong, and I felt that his inability to take the sun could be traced to some social reservation—something to do with protocol—rather than any physical weakness.

"Come," he went on with a royal gesture of invitation. "Come sit down in the hammock."

Pierre watched as I went over and sat gingerly on the swaying hammock. Don Socrates clapped his hands and a brown-skinned, barefoot girl with jet-black hair appeared at the door in the back of the room.

"You called, Papa?" she said in a flat monotone.

"Daughter, bring a few glasses of the new *chicha,*" said Don Socrates brusquely.

This young girl couldn't be the old man's daughter. Her dark complexion, her black hair, her nose, lips, and cheekbones were distinctly Indio. Not a trace of European blood here, and yet Don Socrates had a Greek name and was unquestionably Caucasian. And her submissive tone and air, and Don Socrates' curtness. Why this "Daughter–Papa" business? Pierre was quick to notice my bewilderment.

"Confusing, isn't it, doctor? But all the natives—from grandparents down to toddlers—call their patrons 'Papa' and 'Mama.' And, in turn, they call their servants 'Son' and 'Daughter,' *hijo* and *hija.* It's all very homelike and loving, but all the Indios are no more than slaves."

He said this in German, which struck me as tactless, but Don Socrates only smiled, showing his tobacco-stained teeth.

"*Hágame el favor,* and sit down comfortably. You must be tired. One must get accustomed to the heat of Santa Morena."

Don Socrates made conversation, I gave one-syllable replies, and looked about me. It was a Spartan room. Two wooden trunks along each wall and a simple table with several stools completed the room's furnishings. The stools, I saw, had cowhide seats, cracked and worn with age. Now the girl brought a tray of glasses filled with a yellow liquid in which kernels of corn bobbed like miniature buoys. When she offered Don Socrates the tray first, he scowled in disgust and sternly motioned toward me. His demeanor, his patrician manners were worthy of a nobleman. Don Socrates was supposed to be the richest man in the area, and his lordly airs were out of place in these barren surroundings, but he certainly carried it off well. I liked this man right off.

We toasted each other and drank, and I can't say that I liked *chicha*, whatever it was. My taste buds were numb, and the heat was getting me again. Not a breeze stirred in the room and the air was stale and over-heated. I struggled to stay alert.

"Oh, yes." Pierre waved the letter I had given him. "The doctor brought this from La Paz for you, Don Socrates."

"It's from your provincial representative in Parliament," I explained. "He urged me to get in touch with you, and said I could count on your help and advice. I understand he's a good friend of yours."

"Yes, indeed." He looked flattered. "And thank you."

Don Socrates then took the letter, walked across the room, and began poking about in one of the trunks. From among linens, clothes, and odds and ends, he dug out a pair of old-fashioned eyeglasses, sat down, and began to read contentedly.

"I know these letters of recommendation," said Pierre. "They're always much too long, and they don't mean a thing."

To my embarrassment he spoke in German again, but Don Socrates did not seem to mind. He read the letter carefully and, when he had finished, smacked his lips as if he had just bitten into something delicious. Ah, what a wonderful man this politician in La Paz was, he exclaimed. Always so helpful to his constituents, and every few years, especially before an election, he even came down and visited the province. Don Socrates looked to see what I made of this gesture, which he considered truly magnanimous, and I said the representative was a fine man.

"Doctor," Don Socrates went on earnestly, "we are so grateful to have you here. You cannot imagine how important it is for us to have a real doctor in this province, one who is responsible to the government. All we have now are the *curanderos*—they're not responsible to anyone and they're not even doctors. Why, these quacks kill people, I tell you."

I had been hoping to have to do no more than exchange amenities before I could be excused and retire to rest, wherever I was billeted. But now I seemed to be in for a long session, and I had to put all my will power to work against the paralyzing heat to say my piece.

"The authorities in the Ministry of Health know that, Don Socrates. I had several talks with them about it before I came, and I have been in-

18

structed to check on everyone who sets up to cure people. Naturally, I don't want to hurt anyone's feelings. I will try to work with the *curanderos*, but if they refuse to co-operate, I will do everything I can to stop their practice."

"Good, good. You must certainly do just that, doctor, and I assure you that all the intelligent citizens will be on your side."

Don Socrates glanced at the letter again, and Pierre leaned toward me and spoke again in German.

"A pretty speech, but you better take it with a grain of salt. Don Socrates means well, and he's more levelheaded than most around here, but he is being much too polite. He hasn't told you that there are a lot of people who think they can get along very well with their *curandero*, just as they always have, without having some *gringo* meddling in their affairs. You'll have to be careful, doctor. Some of these people are very important, too."

I was about to make a comment as the Indio girl came in diffidently, a big tablecloth in her hand. She waited at the door until Don Socrates happened to look up from his letter. He nodded to her, and she proceeded to spread the yellow cloth on the table. On it she placed four spoons of different patterns, four crude matching forks, and one knife. I noticed this as we sat down, and Pierre felt it necessary to explain in loud German, obviously taking enjoyment in Don Socrates' failure to understand a word.

"He has a handsome *estancia* in the country. There they eat on beautiful heavy damask tablecloths and use fine silverware. You'd be surprised at the difference."

I was approaching the point where nothing could surprise me, but the meal was better than I would have imagined. We had soup that was palatable, in spite of its rank cowfat smell, fried meat that was really good, and bananas, sliced lengthwise, fried in fat and sprinkled with brown sugar. I was being honored, and I forced myself to eat, although the heat had cut my appetite. Nevertheless, Don Socrates apologized for the frugality of the meal.

"We have bread only once a week. We would have had some if we'd known you were to be here today." He explained that his wife and daughter were at his *estancia* in the *campo*, the family country seat, as it were, and he planned to send a messenger to summon them home now that their highly honored guest had arrived at last. "You know yourself, doctor, how uncertain the flight schedules are. We never really know when the plane will come."

"How well I know! I waited for three weeks, and every day they said *mañana.* I had all my business settled with the government, then had to sit around waiting for the plane. It was always engine trouble or bad weather over the Cordillera. Now I understand that they will come regularly every two weeks."

"Agh! They've been saying that for the past ten years. They really treat our province badly. Promises, always promises. And they don't keep them."

His face was wrinkled with disgust, and he was shaking with anger. In spite of his dignity and surface calm, I saw him now as a mercurial and emotional man.

"I have a house for you," he went on, changing the subject. "Your supplies are already being delivered there."

"That's good of you."

I tried to sound polite and grateful, but I resented it. I would have liked a chance to choose my own house. I felt I was being manipulated as I had been in La Paz, Paris, Austria—in fact, all my life. But Don Socrates seemed to read my mind.

"You see, it's not easy to get hold of a suitable house for a short time. After all," he explained convincingly, "you have to have a place to stay, and this house, which is just opposite, belongs to a good friend of mine. I talked to him just before he left for Brazil to sell his cattle. His house isn't completely finished, but it is livable."

This time my "thank you" was more than purely formal. Here was a good, understanding man. Don Socrates poured a glass of water for himself and looked at me.

"You must be thirsty, doctor. How about some water?"

"Is it filtered?" I asked.

Pierre, who had spoken little, grinned, and Don Socrates hesitated before replying.

"This water is from the *currichi,* which has a current containing purifying plants that kill all the germs. *Salud!*"

He drank, and I gulped down the water he had poured for me. It was warm and did taste like water, that much I could say for it, but I didn't believe a word of the germ-killing element. All the books were filled with warnings against drinking unboiled or unfiltered water in the tropics. Accordingly, one of my most precious possessions was a filter, which was in one of my supply crates. But until I could get it out, what was good enough for Don Socrates and the others had to be good enough for me. Of course I lacked their local immunity, and it would be just like the new *gringo* doctor to come down with typhoid fever, dysentery, or whatever.

After dinner, Don Socrates and Pierre took me across the street to see the house I was to live in. The mud walls were solid and the thatched roof completed. The window frames were already built in, but gaps and holes around them awaited the mason. The dirt floors inside were still soft, not trampled down hard as in Don Socrates' house. A few dilapidated stools stood around, their cowhide covers worn and hairless, and in one corner there was a wooden bed on which lay rumpled blankets. It looked as if someone had been sleeping on it recently. I noticed a pottery vessel and a tin cup standing in a little puddle on the window sill nearby. The one other room was bare.

As we looked around, the *agente* from the airline arrived, accompanied by two Indios carrying my boxes and extra suitcases. I told them to put my luggage in the empty room. Don Socrates came in with me to help oversee the unloading and, under his watchful eye, they discharged their duties as quickly as possible. After they left, he fingered the white fabric curtaining the room's one window.

"This type of cloth is used for mosquito netting as well as for curtains."

"Are the mosquitoes bad down here, Don Socrates?"

"After the rainy season, yes. But we are used to them."

Pierre gave a sort of negative grunt, but Don Socrates seemed not to hear him as he rolled a cigarette. Both men seemed preoccupied now, and I was puzzled. We were all standing around as if we were waiting for something, but what? Aha, I decided, they have something up their sleeves. And I was worried.

"Doctor," said Don Socrates after a time, "there is a special reason why I am so happy that you have finally arrived. Two young men, one of them a son of mine, have been seriously ill for some time. They have a terrible eruption of a kind that even we, who have unfortunately had enough occasion to see all kinds of diseases, have never seen before. It is a great scourge and gives me shame. So much that I have kept the boys locked up so nobody could see them."

Well, I thought, a disease with severe eruptions. Hmm. What could it be—plague, pest, or smallpox? According to the books, these were prevalent in the region.

"Where are they?" I said brightly. "Let's go see them."

"You think you can help them?" He was so eager.

"It depends." I smiled. "Oh, Don Socrates, about going on to Rojas. How long will it take to prepare for the trip there?"

"About a week." He shrugged. "Maybe two."

"So much time? And how long does the trip itself usually take?"

"It depends on the weather and on your horses. I have gone to Rojas in two days of comfortable riding. Now these young men—" I started for the door, and he held out his arm. "They're right here," he said excitedly, certain that the doctor's willingness to help was synonymous with a cure. "I had them hidden here. I mean, just until you came. Then I sent a message for them to retire into the shed out in the patio."

I swallowed hard and wiped the sweat from my forehead with the back of my wrist. Wasn't this just dandy now? These youths, sick with "a terrible eruption," had slept in this bed and drunk from that cup. Now I was expected to use these same articles, and no one here thought anything of it. As health officer, I ought to protest here and now, I ought to—wait a minute! Better to go easy. My perspective was still warped. After all, I had been in La Paz only that morning, and my plane flight seemed to have brought me back a hundred light-years into time.

The shed Don Socrates had mentioned was nothing but a straw thatch set on four low beams. There were no windows, but walls of interwoven palm branches let in a little light. As the three of us came in, a young man with eyes as black and intense as Don Socrates' got up from an old, wobbly stool, and another young man pushed himself up from a cowhide spread on the dirty floor. If there was to be a formal introduction, I thought wryly, then I'd have to shake hands and embrace each of them as was the custom here. Well, if the *currichi* table water hadn't infected me by now, nothing would. But I was lucky. Don Socrates explained that I was the doctor, and there was only tense silence all around as I concentrated on the hands and faces of the two young men.

Eruptions almost the size of hazelnuts polka-dotted their features, and they both had large red blotches on the palms of their hands. If it were smallpox, these men would be deathly sick, with a high fever, and surely unable to stand. These two seemed to be just sullen, frustrated, and annoyed at their imprisonment. Then it would have to be one thing: the most likely diagnosis was secondary stage syphilis. All the same, from all I'd been told in La Paz, there was supposed to be so much of that disease around that even a layman like Don Socrates would recognize it. So I could be wrong. This could be one of those mysterious tropical diseases.

"All right," I said, with the exaggerated heartiness of one not too sure of himself. "Now take off your shirts." Both chests were covered with the same kind of eruptions. Then I'd have to go farther, but it didn't have to be a public demonstration. "May I ask you both to leave for a minute?" I said, turning to Don Socrates and Pierre.

22

The old man's eyes popped and his face was comic with astonishment. *"Con mucho gusto,"* he said simply and obeyed like a soldier.

Pierre lingered by the door before following him. "Don't look so surprised," he said in German. "Don Socrates is the boss around here. Nobody ever sends him away, and nobody has any secrets from him."

So I had committed another in what seemed a long line of *faux pas* to come. Angry at myself, I barked at the young men, "Come on, pull down your pants!"

They obeyed meekly and hurriedly, and I found what I had hoped to find. The primary lesions had not healed, and they clinched the diagnosis. I was about to tell them that it was all very simple, but then I changed my mind. Better to make this one a little dramatic. Teach them a lesson.

"Is it possible that both of you may have fooled around with the same girl?"

They stared at me stonily, then one of them finally broke the silence. "Neither of us have had anything to do with girls for many months now?"

"You haven't, eh?" I said skeptically.

Both of them swore to it, and my diagnosis flew out the window if I believed them. If it wasn't syphilis, then it must be some unusual tropical disease of which I'd never heard. It had to be that, and I was off to a fine start—first antagonizing the crowd at the airport over *El Chileno* and now incompetent when I had a chance to redeem myself. Oh, damn it all anyway! I motioned to the men to pull up their trousers, stroked my chin and pretended to look thoughtful, and stepped outside into the blazing afternoon sun. I saw Pierre standing in the shadow of a tree whittling on a stick, while Don Socrates lounged beneath the overhanging thatched eave of the house and chatted with a neighbor.

"What have they got?" Pierre asked.

"I'm not sure. It could be something rare."

"We thought so, too. I wish you could cure those fellows though. It's just what you need to build your reputation."

"Don't rub it in!" I snapped.

"I'm not, doctor," he said pleadingly. "I'm on your side."

"Then tell me this: is there anyone else in Santa Morena who has the same eruptions?"

"No. We've checked all over, especially with the girls."

"What do you mean? Those boys told me they haven't been with a woman for many months."

"Many months!" Pierre squeaked, and I had to laugh at his expression.

23

"Why, we had to put a watchman here to make them stay inside the last few nights. These two are the worst hellers in the village. Every night just like bulls in a herd. And not just with one girl, with two or three one after the other."

"Well, well." I smiled with pleasure. "This *is* interesting."

What liars they were, I thought, and what a fool I was to believe them when all the evidence was there before me to convict them. At this point Don Socrates ran over, eager to hear what I had to say.

"Can you do anything, doctor?"

"I'm going to cure both of them." I gave it the full Paul Muni as Dr. Pasteur treatment, grave and sincere as I fought the urge to laugh. "But it will take a little time, you know. The first thing is to make the eruptions disappear, then the rest of the cure can begin."

Don Socrates' eyes shone with admiration, Pierre goggled at my easy self-assurance, and I took delight in the impression I had made. Now was a good time to get a few things clear.

"About that trip to Rojas, Don Socrates. My orders were to go there as soon as possible. That's why I wonder if I really need a house."

"Of course you do, doctor! I know about your orders, and the subprefect down there has already sent messages on your behalf. But it will take time to prepare, as I told you, and Santa Morena needs you for now."

"All right then. Now I'll get something for those poor fellows."

I went into the house, unpacked one of the labeled supply crates, and quickly prepared two injections of salvarsan. The boys looked fearful as I came near them with the intravenous needle, but with Don Socrates watching they behaved well. After I had finished, I explained that they might have a reaction: the blotches might get bigger and they might run a high fever before they were cured. Don Socrates stayed with my patients in the shed, and I went back inside my house with Pierre.

"I hope it will work out like that," he said doubtfully.

"Still worried about my reputation, eh?" I said in German. "I'm afraid I have to disappoint you. It's just the second stage of syphilis, nothing extraordinary."

Pierre shook his head. "I don't know, but this isn't like *El Chileno's* case. His family is poor and commonplace. Don Socrates is rich and important. That's why I hope you're right. In all the time I've been here I've never seen eruptions as bad as those."

I noticed an elderly, clean-shaven Indian standing outside the door of

24

my house. He was scratching the back of his head as Don Socrates spoke to him.

"Doctor, this man has been my *mozo* for forty years. He is trustworthy and dependable. I shall leave him here to help you, and I'll come later. I'm going to stretch out awhile in my hammock."

He waved, then left, and I got busy unpacking. The *mozo* helped me pry the lid off the crate containing the filter and other necessities. We moved the cot into the corner of the large room, as far away from the window as possible, and I put out a few personal things I would be needing. As we worked, Pierre walked about restlessly, sniffing here and there like a dog investigating a new home.

"You've got to have a hammock," he announced. "They're an institution here. Yes, in these regions you can't live without a hammock."

"I'll buy one when I get to my permanent quarters."

"Nonsense! You need one right now. Besides, you won't be in your permanent quarters for some time."

"I thought Don Socrates said it would be a week or so before we started for Rojas."

"A week or so. *Ach!* He could have said *mañana,* and that can mean tomorrow, next month, or never." I stared at him and he laughed. "Oh, relax, countryman, you still have plenty of time until *mañana.*"

3

My First Night in Santa Morena; I Watch a Poker Game; I Try to Sort Out My Impressions; I Begin My Jungle Career; Don Socrates as My Medical Assistant; I Am Paid in Cows; My Patients' Complaints; A Talk with Pierre

As night descended on the village, enveloping it in mellow darkness, I sat in front of Don Socrates' house chatting with the villagers come to pay their respects to the new *gringo* doctor. They were all men, of course, since the women never ventured out alone, and now words flew back and forth from behind the glowing tips of *cigarillos*. The topic under discussion was Europe, evidently chosen in order to give the newcomer a chance to say something.

It was an interesting choice and especially thoughtful of them, except that my fellow conversationalists seemed to have only the dimmest notion of the monumental events that had racked the Continent during the past decade. They knew as little of the immediate details as the French police in Paris who, before and during World War II, had continually harassed refugees as "dangerous" Germans rather than looking on them as persecuted Jews badly in need of help in their flight from Hitler. They even displayed a peculiar objective admiration for the Nazis, the conquests in the name of the super-race, the concentration camps, and the pogroms. Say what you will, they seemed to be thinking, you've got to hand it to these people—they're efficient, they get things done, they show results. Of course, on the surface, these villagers politely pretended to be sympathetic, but it soon became clear to me that their interest in international affairs was superficial and purely a matter of courtesy. I was flattered by their hospitality, but I couldn't help wondering what they would talk about when I was truly accepted as a member of the community.

Only a few of the men had ever ventured from home even as far as La Paz and, so far as affairs across the sea were concerned, they were like spectators watching a game they didn't understand, able to enjoy the novel and bewildering sport without fear of being either hurt or in the least involved. Soon the conversation drifted around to topics that really interested them, such as the market price of cattle at the Brazilian border, the scarcity of hard cash, the complex problems of transportation, and the cavalier treatment the national government accorded their province. From time to time someone lamented the province's isolation from the rest of the world, but the complaint didn't ring true to me, and I gathered that they weren't too dissatisfied with things as they were.

I was still so worn out from the heat and the tumultuous events of the day that I was unable to form a clear picture of any of my companions. I was like a traveler who had come down from his hotel room after a long day on the road and was trying to get some ideas of his surroundings. They all seemed robust good fellows, amiable and pleasant and undemanding. I did notice that Pierre was absent and questioned Don Socrates about it.

"Pierre does not like to go out at night," he explained curtly.

Several of the others nodded sagely at this, and I did not pursue the subject. There was more here than met the eye, but Don Socrates had not spoken sarcastically, nor was there the least malice or contempt for the balloon-shaped, high-voiced Viennese expatriate, who could so easily have been made the butt of cruel jokes. Then one of the men made some loud suggestion, which for some reason I didn't catch. It found an immediate response, and he and four others went inside to the *sala*. The Indio *sirvienta*, summoned by a clap of Don Socrates' hands, was ordered to get a cloth for the table.

"Would you like to join us in a little poker game, doctor?" Don Socrates asked, following the others inside and pulling up a chair at the table.

"*Gracias,* no," I said, not feeling alert enough to play good poker. "But I would like to watch."

The housemaid came in with the same tablecloth on which we had eaten, spread it over the tabletop, and put two homemade candles diagonally opposite each other at the corners of the cloth. After she lighted them, the room was immediately filled with the same sickening cowfat smell of the soup I had eaten twice that day, for I had also had supper with Don Socrates and,

27

item for item, it had been a repetition of lunch. The crude candles were mounted on wooden blocks incrusted with wax drippings, and they evidently had been in use a long time. They had no sooner been lighted than a host of insects congregated about their flames, batting about, getting their wings burned, and falling on the cloth like shot-down fighter planes. In the flickering light and the close atmosphere of the small room, the men dragged their chairs to the table, while I sat to the side on an upturned barrel one of them had brought in from outside.

Don Socrates got up from his chair and began rummaging around in the same trunk that had produced his spectacles earlier. To my surprise, he pulled out a pack of cards, brand-new and still in its glistening cellophane wrapping. He removed the transparent covering with relish and riffled the crisp, fresh cards like a professional gambler in a casino. The cards in themselves were comforting to me as a reminder that not everything out here at the edge of nowhere need be faded, old, and unmatched.

More conversation preceded the game, and I took advantage of it, the room being so overwhelmingly sticky and close, to go out on the porch with the excuse that I wanted to look at the moon. It was a good idea. The sky was a deep, velvet-dark dome studded with sharply etched stars. The moon spread a soft magic light over the thatched roofs. Music in a minor key seemed to fill the air, either the combined chirping of thousands of crickets or perhaps just a plain ringing in my ears. Suddenly I felt cheerful, almost happy. I was like a young man who had returned to the playground of his joyous boyhood. My doubts were still there, but submerged now against the tide of respect of the people of Santa Morena, their courteous hospitality, and the undeniable confidence they had aroused in me.

I was worlds removed from the flesh-peeling, nightmare past. The sky was the same, the moon, and the stars—and I was the same. But what a difference! Take that night in Paris last winter when an official of the French Security Police had descended on my little apartment without warning. It seemed it was illegal for foreigners in Paris to work. I must therefore immediately give up assisting French doctors at the hospital. But why—?

"Because somebody has complained," snapped the hatchet-faced official. "Besides, you are an *étranger* and do not possess the required papers. It can go hard for you if you persist."

"But it's only orderly work I am doing," I protested. "No more than giving injections, helping with the anesthetic, and practically emptying bedpans. That sort of thing."

But he was adamant. Nothing would pacify him, and he even threatened to deport me. God, the shame and humiliation of it! Lisa, the lovely,

28

sympathetic companion of those miserable Paris months, had been in the apartment with me, and I could still feel my degradation. Poor Lisa had been so pale as the man stormed at me. She wept after he left, and we became involved in the old argument. Why take such risks? I didn't have to work. She had money.

"Oh, Martin darling, I've told you and told you that I earn enough for both of us. I don't understand your pride. You are so wonderfully unconventional in so many ways, and then so old-fashioned and stubborn over money. And you *know* I'm yours. I love you, Martin, I've gladly given you everything, body and soul, and yet you have to make an issue over a few francs."

The poor, sweet girl just didn't understand—and I couldn't make her. It just wasn't the money. I *had* to do something. I was a doctor. I just couldn't sit around and live on her money. It was a time when love was not enough to take the place of self-respect, a reason for living, and personal identity. A man couldn't go on living as a cipher, which was what we refugees had become.

I looked up at the sky and the muscles of my tense face relaxed. The past was over and done with. I was in Santa Morena, embarked on a new life, and I had best forget it for my peace of mind. I smiled at the stars. How wonderful for once not to be a superfluous *étranger* in a distraught, war-torn country, a refugee unwanted and on the run. To belong, to be an equal among equals with a place in the sun, a job, responsibilities—ah, it was good, I exulted. Herbert, Karl, Maria, I thought, all our wishes of the last few years have been fulfilled here in one, single eventful day. If only I could show you, let you share it all with me. Abruptly, I got up and went back inside to my top of the barrel seat by the poker table.

The game was well along, and my attention was drawn to one of the players, a young man who must be barely twenty. During the general conversation outside, I remembered that he had sat quietly in the background in deference to his elders, hardly opening his mouth. Now he was a full-fledged member of the group. He bet with assurance, raised and raised again, showing no respect at this point for Don Socrates' white hair or great *estancia* in the country. All the men kept their hats on, tipping them back slightly only when they had to squint close to the candlelight to identify a card. Each time they leaned close to the candles, they set the clouds of insects around the flame into an uproar of buzzing and wheeling, and clouds more fell to their deaths on the sticky wooden blocks and were interred in a tomb of transparent wax.

These men were all gamblers and competitors, unveiling their cards with such staged deliberate slowness and tension that my nerves tingled at least as much as theirs. They played with furious concentration, pausing only to take out a small sack of tobacco, a roll of papers, then expertly rolled a *cigarillo* and licked the edge of the thin paper to seal it. After a while the *sirvienta,* without being bidden, brought in a tray with three small cups of thick black coffee and a flat plate of brown sugar. One of the cups, I noted, was of chipped porcelain, the others of battered tin.

The three oldest men were served first. After they had finished, they wiped their mouths with the backs of their hands. The maid then took the empty cups back into the other room and—surely without bothering to wash them—brought them back with coffee for the other two men, who hadn't been served, and myself. I took only a sip. It was pungent, unbelievably strong, more like liquid mud with a fierce coffee flavor.

These men all seemed well heeled, so far as poker was concerned. They all had big bundles of money in front of them, which seemed to contradict the scarcity of cash Pierre had spoken about in connection with medical fees and the same scarcity the men had lamented earlier. None of these lacked for money certainly, and I was close enough to see that the bills ranged from five to twenty pesos in denomination, good money in a country where a fine meal was available in the capital for ten pesos. (The peso was then the equivalent of about one or two American cents. At the official rate the Bolivian currency was, of course, worth more. But who ever paid the official rate anywhere?)

Again my mind wandered off. Strange, I thought, how all the people (from nearly every country in Eastern and Central Europe), who had crowded our British ship on the voyage from France to South America, had learned to deal in only one currency: American dollars and cents. We too had played poker on board. Oh, not during the first two weeks as the wild waters of the Atlantic whipped our faces and wrecked our stomachs, but later on after we had passed through the Panama Canal and the soothing waters of the Pacific had permitted something like a social life on that crowded cattle boat. We had played poker for American pennies. Once in a while a real dollar bill appeared, always to be greeted with respectful murmurs. It was a sliver of a great personal secret, because the amount of American money owned by an immigrant was his greatest and deepest secret.

Watching these five dedicated gamblers, utterly immersed in their game, I was reminded of a Pole on the boat with whom I had become friendly. As a matter of fact, he was friendly with everyone, still youthful, in spite of his gray hair, and with an irrepressible sense of humor. Shortly after we arrived in La Paz, he had picked out a likely bench in the plaza, the park just opposite the presidential palace, and with his forty-odd American dollars had begun a promising banking business. Anyone with dollars for sale—of course, no one had many—could get a quick exchange from him at a price slightly weighed in his favor. But if we needed a few dollars to send to a relative (the government refused to supply dollars for this purpose because it needed them for vital imports), our man always had the dollars. And, amazingly enough, in a few weeks this cheerful, enterprising Pole had gone on, from his initial capital of forty dollars, to just about controlling the entire Bolivian black market in dollars. He too was a gambler, and a clever one.

I watched the game a little longer, then my fatigue overcame me. I got up from my barrel head, bade the players good night, but they were so intent on their poker they barely heard me. Only Don Socrates looked up.

"Will you be so good as to look in on our young patients, doctor?" he asked. "I'll check later before I go to bed."

In the heat of the game he had apparently forgotten that this was a hush-hush subject, but again none of the players paid any attention to this exchange. I went out, crossed the street, then walked on behind my house to the shed in its patio. The young men sprawled on the cowhide, their cheeks burning with fever, their eyes no longer sullen but hot and brilliant. The salvarsan had begun to work. They were sick now, but in a short time they would be well. I would have at least one cure to my credit. My reputation would no longer hang entirely on the life or death of that sick old man, *El Chileno*. I made sure my patients were comfortable, then went into my own room.

I put clean linen on my bed, undressed, blew out the lantern that had been lighted for me, and lay down. But, for all my weariness, sleep would not come. This had been a remarkable day and left me with almost too much to think about. Just the time then to put my thoughts on paper when it was all fresh. Without bothering to light the lamp, I got out my flashlight, found paper and pencil among my things, and began to write sitting on a small box and using a crate as a desk. By the beam of the flashlight I put down the date and "Dear Herbert . . ."

If I had gone right on, I might have been all right, but I hesitated, my darting, surging thoughts battled for an outlet to explain the wonder of the day, and suddenly I couldn't get anything at all down on paper. As I procrastinated, telling myself I was sorting out my impressions, one thought leaped uppermost in my mind, flashing like an electric beacon and thoroughly chilling me. What difference did it make whether I wrote tonight, tomorrow, or not at all? Who cared really? And there was no regular postal service, no letter box. The next plane was due to visit Santa Morena in two weeks. That is it *might;* it could just as well be three weeks, four weeks, or longer. No one knew for sure, and whatever I wrote would be stale long before it was delivered.

How could I have been so happy and content a little while ago? How childish of me! I got up and shone my flashlight around the bare room, the dark hollow ceiling, the whitish supply crates, the lifeless mosquito netting in the other room. The cold, dispassionate beam seemed to show me only one dreadful thing: I was alone, alone, so alone, and panic gripped me like a sudden cramp in the belly. Just like in Paris at that big, dimmed-out movie theater, half empty in the early afternoon. Watching Tom Sawyer's adventures was a pleasant distraction from the worries surrounding my impending departure for the New World. It was good fun, and I enjoyed it until Tom became lost in the caves, wandering about the dark caverns in terror. Then I, a grown man, had jumped out of my seat and rushed down the endless aisle to daylight pursued by a nightmare.

The big, sun-filled avenue had slowly calmed my nerves, but here in Santa Morena there was no avenue jammed with leisurely people in which I could lose myself. Here I could only run into a deserted and desolate jungle village, the end of the road for me, a place where I must face things and stop running once and for all. I shouldn't feel this way, shouldn't be torn apart by my ambivalence. Wasn't this what I had sought? To be as far as possible from so-called civilization, from a cruelly refined and brutal world. Then what the devil was I afraid of?

I lay down on my bed again and gave up any attempt to sleep. It was close to midnight by my watch. Just then, against all logic, a rooster's crow cut through the monotonously vibrant chirping of crickets, surged defiantly on the night, and was immediately taken up by what seemed every other rooster in the village. The village air rang with their clarion calls, then suddenly they stopped as quickly as they had begun. The blessed quiet lasted only a few minutes, then jungle sounds took over—a patchwork of snorting, roaring, barking, and squeaking, all strangely distorted and impossible for me either to identify or ignore.

How much easier this would be to take if I weren't alone. The memory of Lisa came back to torture me. Ah, to soothe my bitterness in her arms again, to forget everything in those long, passionate nights of love as I had during those empty months in France. I twisted and turned on my hard bed, my restless hands tingling at the thought of how they had caressed Lisa's body, played on her as on the strings of a responsive instrument, pressed her close to my heart, and cupped her perfect breasts in lustful tranquillity. Stop it! I commanded myself. For God's sake, stop it! Think of today. Think of Pierre, that poor overblown eunuch.

Never in my experience had I met anyone like him. What was he doing here? How did he fit in? He was Viennese like myself, and we seemed to have so similar a background and childhood that we might have been long-time friends and confidants. Mentally, however, he was miles away from me. I could no more understand him than I could grasp this strange new world of insufficient china, wealthy gamblers, fresh playing cards in a cellophane wrapping, and plain old secondary syphilis.

Or Don Socrates, a patriarch and sage in a setting that most city persons would have assumed to be poverty-stricken, yet he moved with such dignity and assurance that everyday luxuries seemed unimportant. He felt himself so much the aristocrat that one had to believe him. And if the men were unusual, what about the women? Take that girl, Carlotta, at the airstrip. Come to think of it, besides Don Socrates' Indio *sirvienta,* she was the only woman I had come in contact with. Carlotta was pretty, but she appeared temperamental. And Pierre had said she was not going to La Paz just because of me. Well, well. There might be something here.

I shifted positions on the bed and stared about me, where the moonlight drowned the barren room, the place I lay, my suitcases, and the crates in unearthly silver light. From outside came the endless cricket chirping with other sounds which I could now distinguish as the clump of cows and the lighter, faster steps of the horses that grazed on Santa Morena's grassy streets. Night thoughts, solitary night thoughts, were poisonous. I longed for someone with which to talk over all that had happened, the things and people I had seen, and it was time I accepted the cold, stark fact of my aloneness.

I was twenty-eight years old. I had been graduated from medical school three years ago. If it hadn't been for the Nazis, I might well have married. After all, many of my friends and classmates had chosen to take wives for precisely the same reason I had chosen to remain single. When the Nazis had overridden Austria and immediately persecuted and made pariahs of them, some of my friends had vaulted into marriage to avoid that corrosive loneliness which now consumed me. Their wives, at least, would share their exiles with them, make them feel a little less lonely, while I . . .

In my mind's eye I reviewed the girls I'd known who might have accepted me as a husband. How would they—or Lisa—have reacted to Santa Morena, Don Socrates, Pierre, and the sterility of life in La Paz? How would they have stood the seasickness and cattle-boat conditions of the Atlantic crossing, the weary merry-go-round in Paris to get a visa to South America? What would they have thought of the soup that smelled of cow-fat, the unfiltered water from the *currichi,* or this bed I was lying on which had recently been occupied by two syphilitic young men.

It was one thing to love and live in domestic bliss—if there really were such a thing—when things were going well. In trying times—oh, what ugly scenes I had witnessed in Paris, on the boat, and in La Paz between people who were sworn to cherish each other in times of adversity, "in sickness and in health, . . . till death us do part," and all the rest. Bad times had not strengthened these marriages; indeed, it had weakened and cracked them to the breaking point. Perhaps it was better to suffer alone than to suffer twain.

Big nose to the contrary, I had been often referred to as good-looking and handsome. I wasn't too sure about this, but it was flattering and I was human enough to like it. Even if it was true, I wasn't convinced that being personable was an unmixed blessing. A handsome man comes to consider his good looks as a sort of vested interest; he expects dividends and returns without effort on his part. He becomes passive, his aggressiveness becomes blunted just when he can least afford it. I wondered if this was what had happened to me, and whether it would affect my life in these next two vital years.

I was a doctor; I had that, and no one could take it away from me. In normal times—had they really ever existed?—it was considered both solid achievement and a blessing for a middle-class European to graduate from medical school. But not now, and certainly not here in no man's land. A medical degree made a pseudobourgeois out of a man. He was obligated to a certain standard, state of mind, and attitude that no longer had any foundation in fact. At one time he could have waited; there was no hurry, and circumstances would eventually permit expectations to catch up with reality. But now the abnormal was the normal, and he was permanently out of step with life. The Nazis naturally didn't give a damn, but neither did the English or the Italian shipping companies—how they clipped us for steerage passage to freedom! We were expected to be grateful and, in addition, a doctor like myself was supposed to be cultured, tactful, and always considerate of others.

How odd, then, that *El Chileno's* family hadn't expected these qualities

34

in me. They didn't mind discussing money at the very moment that seemed to me inappropriate. Well and good then. I would not be noble and self-effacing beyond demand. I would have asked for much less than they imagined anyway. And I needed every penny. The small salary I was drawing from the government wouldn't cover my living expenses in the first place. I was expected to bolster it by charging fees of those patients who could afford to pay them.

Nobility would only be a drawback here, an empty, self-defeating gesture. My profession's code of generosity and sacrifice above and beyond the call of duty would only strike these down-to-earth people as shrewd *gringo* trading. They would probably have less suspicion of my motives if I demanded money, rather than making it a secondary consideration. And I was sure they would have much more confidence in me as a trained man working for his daily bread even as they did.

It mattered little that it went against the grain and meant unlearning all the Old World morality that had encompassed me since childhood. If I was to succeed here—and I certainly hoped to—I'd have to do it. I'd simply have to acquire a completely new set of values, one that made practical business sense in the anachronistic and colorful world I had chosen to practice in. I yawned and looked at my watch. Nearly three o'clock. Time to sleep and long past time to put away fears—and the past.

I would be all right here. I would make it alone. I had built a new cabin in the corner of my backyard. It might be crude and primitive, but it suited my needs. And, although my new visitors and playmates were older than those who had frolicked in my Vienna retreat, most of them, to my jaundiced European eye, were just as innocent and childlike. Yes, the field seemed wide open for good and interesting medicine.

This comforting thought put me to sleep for the few hours of rest that remained.

*   *   *

I could easily have slept late, but I felt I had to set an example for myself and Santa Morena. I was up at seven, shaved with cold water, and avoided looking at my sleep-lined face. I had just begun unpacking the crates as Don Socrates came in, looking refreshed and affable. Staring hard at the rings around my eyes, he murmured the usual polite greetings, spoke of the poker game, and offered a modest disclaimer of skill at being the biggest money winner.

"I had a lucky night, that's all. Oh, about the boys. I have seen them and you were right, one hundred per cent. They had a high fever the whole night, but they feel better now. Which reminds me, doctor, that I have a *compadre* here that I want you to meet. His little son is sick in bed, and his father wants you very much to come and examine him."

"Right now?" I said, glancing at my equipment spread all over the dirty floor. "I have a lot to do here."

"Yes, right now. Just leave everything as it is. Nobody will touch a thing, I assure you. I'll vouch for my *mozo*. He'll guard it well. First I want you to have breakfast with me, though."

Twenty minutes later we walked down the street to a thatched-roof house as small as and even more rudimently furnished than my own. The curious black eyes of ragged Indio children followed us as we passed, and I felt self-conscious in my black business suit and carrying my doctor's kit. Don Socrates' *compadre* was evidently a poor man. Several beds stood in the *sala,* and a couple of cowhides were spread on the dirt floor, rumpled pillows and linen on them betraying their use. The sick boy lay on a wooden bed, which was curtained off by the folded side wall of grayish mosquito netting. He was as inanimate as a doll, his skin yellowish, his little arms and legs no more than sticks, his head seeming overlarge, and his belly badly swollen.

The boy was two years old, his mother explained in a singsong voice. "He has worms," she added impassively, looking so weary, worn, and old that she might have been the child's grandmother. She held a baby in her dirty arms and was well along in another pregnancy, expecting an addition to a family that already had too many members. The other youngsters, ranging in age from three to about twelve, crowded the bare room and watched in fear as I applied my stethoscope to the emaciated chest of their bedridden brother.

"What is it?" asked Don Socrates, after I had completed my examination. "Is it worms as she says?"

"His mother's diagnosis is correct so far as it goes, but the child is also terribly anemic. I'll have to get some medicine from my house."

"The child's father is very poor," he told me, as we walked back. "He only has a few head of cattle, hardly enough to make ends meet."

I nodded at the obvious. "And every year a new child," I said, half to myself. "It doesn't seem right."

"That is the way of things here, doctor." Don Socrates said with a shrug. "But they do the best they can with what they have."

It was no answer at all; it was the best kind of answer, and it was also a truthful and routine answer to a stilted remark I should never have made.

36

I was annoyed at my typical *gringo* reaction, but I had to admire Don Socrates' forbearance unless—and this was probably the case—it all meant nothing to him, because he was used to poverty, squalor, and never-ending childbearing on the part of people who simply followed their instincts in everything.

My house was surrounded by boy and girl Indios, all of them peeking through the windows at the newcomer's house and probably the same children who had stared at me on my trip to the sick boy. Undoubtedly they were taking advantage of my absence to get a good look at the *gringo's* possessions and the way he lived. Well, I felt just the same about them. They flew away as we approached, and I went in and poked through the various crates until I found the vitamins and vermifuges the boy needed. I was on the point of starting back with them when Don Socrates said it was unnecessary so long as it was a matter of taking them by mouth. He told me to give my instructions to the *mozo,* that he would repeat them word for word, and his *compadre* (whom I had yet to meet) would do exactly as prescribed.

I wanted to get my house in order, so I passed everything on to the *mozo* as directed. Considering the local diet and sanitary habits, this would certainly not be the last case of worms I would see. Nor would it be the boy's last bout with the disease, even if the treatment cured him this time—or he had the luck to live another year. Maybe that's why these people had so many children, it occurred to me cynically.

Unpacking the crates, sorting out my supplies, and finding a place for everything took time and proved a wearisome business, nor did I lose my audience. They were so wide-eyed and curious at the spectacle that I hadn't the heart to turn them away and rather struggled to ignore them. As the afternoon shadows grew longer and the heat of the sun lessened, white-skinned youngsters joined the Indio children, jamming the doors and windows, and the crowd on the sidewalk outside grew steadily. A short time later, as a procession of men and women arrived to consult the doctor, my house seemed to be surrounded by all of Santa Morena, plus all the Indios in the area.

By then Don Socrates had joined me again, took it on himself to serve as receptionist-intermediary, and showed no surprise whatsoever at the sudden influx of patients. I was appalled at their number, how to line them up and treat them in proper order, but this extraordinary man promptly took over as my assistant and organized my office. Pointing at this one, ordering that one, Don Socrates made the room with the one closed-off window the examining and treatment room. The crates were all opened and unpacked now, and two of them were put together to serve as a temporary table. Don Socrates looked about him with satisfaction, then called to his *mozo*.

"*Hijo,* go to the house and bring the *tinaja* from the patio. It should be full of water. If not, see that it is."

The *mozo* was back in a few minutes with an Indio girl, balancing a large earthen jar on her head. Heavy with sloshing water, she took it down carefully and placed it on a crate. At Don Socrates' direction, she tilted the narrow neck and poured water into a basin held by the *mozo*. I added a few drops of sterilizing lysol, and the old man amazed me by calmly beginning to wash syringes as if he had been doing so every day of his life. We were set to go now, but the *gringo* doctor was steaming and uncomfortable in his dark city woolens. All the men awaiting examination wore light linen suits, and I felt I ought to change before going into action.

I excused myself, went into the next room, and took out of my suitcase the khaki outfit that the so-called travel expert in La Paz had said was absolutely essential for the tropical jungle. A long-sleeved khaki shirt with matching riding breeches, plus high, knee-length boots (protection against the rattlesnakes lurking under every bush) were *de rigueur* "out there." I slipped into the new clothes hurriedly, feeling neither cooler nor more comfortable, but, after all, experts were experts.

As I went back to the examining room, Don Socrates shot me a quick glance of astonishment, but said nothing. So tactful were these people, I had discovered, that they would as soon say nothing if I had appeared in just an athletic supporter or, perhaps, being an ignorant *gringo* capable of anything, stark naked. I wished now that I too had had the sense to buy a light linen suit, but there was no time to pay attention to my clothes. There was work to be done—work that I knew well how to attend to— and Don Socrates' mustache bristled proudly and his fierce old eyes shone with pleasure as he dispensed medicines and bandages in accordance with my instructions.

Many of my patients were Indios, and I was startled at how so many of them showed the pallor of anemia through their pigmented skins. As I had suspected, worms, malaria, and the lack of a well-balanced diet containing the necessary vitamins were obviously taking their toll. The women, especially, showed an acute fear of tuberculosis and, aware that loss of weight was the classic symptom of the consumptive, begged me for something

38

to put on flesh. *"Engórdame,* doctor," they pleaded, one after the other. "Make me fat!" Even more startling was the uniformly bad state of their teeth. All of them seemed to have a mouth full of crooked, decayed, and festering teeth crying for extraction.

"Can you pull teeth, doctor?" asked Don Socrates, as I made a checklist of those needing dental care. "I own some forceps, and people do come to me for extractions, but I don't like to do them. I'll give them to you if you like."

"Thank you, but that's not necessary." Luckily I had considerable skill in pulling teeth, and I remembered now how some of my colleagues in medical school had laughed when I took a dental course. "I have forceps, and I know how to use them."

"That's wonderful. Of course, there is a dentist who spends a few weeks with us every year, but it is much better having a doctor who can do everything."

We lined up the dental patients outside the house under its overhanging, thatched eave. I attended them quickly, one after the other, making sure they all rinsed their mouths with lysol water, and the floor was soon splashed with bloody rinse water spilled out of the basin. We had saved them until last, and now my back was stiff and my arms ached as I put away the forceps and turned away from the improvised dentist's chair. A buzz of excitement from outside caught my attention, and Don Socrates looked around with me at a fat, old Indio, with large Mexican-style whiskers and a *serape* across his shoulders, who stood weaving in the doorway flanked by his sons and daughters. He was wheezing and breathing heavily and, as I stared, he motioned toward his heart.

I smiled both in welcome and encouragement and, thus assured, his children assisted him inside and lifted him up onto the crude examining table. His pulse was weak—I had no cause to doubt his self-diagnosis—and I immediately set about administering cardiac stimulants. At this, his children discreetly withdrew to the doorstep and stood there scratching their heads in embarrassment, anxiety showing faintly in their dull eyes.

The old Indio seemed to respond to treatment, but complained of a dryness in his mouth. My audience eagerly watched my response as I pondered his complaint. His pulse was still weak, I noted. I thought for half a minute, then had an idea that was not exactly in accordance with the textbook. I went over to my suitcase, took out a bottle of whisky, and poured several fingers of liquor into a tumbler. As if the sun had broken through a thunderhead, the Indio's swarthy face brightened, and he all but snatched the glass

39

from my hand. He drank it down in several gulps, lay back complacently, and smiled. In minutes his pulse had improved so markedly that he was able to sit up, licking his lips and apparently rejuvenated. Then he lay down again, apparently hoping for more of the same good medicine.

Two Bolivian gentlemen came in, sniffing disdainfully. They looked at my heart patient and the other Indios still clustered about disapprovingly, but took off their sombreros and greeted me politely.

"Doctor," said one of them, "we would like to buy some castor oil and some sodium bicarbonate."

"I see," I said, pretending to consider their request.

This wasn't a drugstore; I had been given to understand in La Paz that I was supposed to dispense medicine, not sell it. I stroked my chin thoughtfully, looked to Don Socrates for some lead and, after he nodded his head in firm assent, had no choice but to satisfy the men. Hardly knowing what to charge, I upped what I thought to be the retail price in La Paz, and the deal was closed to their satisfaction. Then one of them confounded me by expressing disappointment that I did not have on sale vaccines for injecting horses and mules to protect them from the virulent pest *mal de caderas*. What was I then, doctor, surgeon, dentist, *and* veterinary? Don Socrates saw my bewilderment.

"Tell them you have ordered the ampules," he whispered. "They will come with the next *avion*."

I repeated this matter-of-factly, and the pair earnestly requested that I save a few ampules for them when the shipment arrived. I agreed, at a nudge from Don Socrates, and the two men brushed through Indios as if they weren't there and went out, clutching their little packages of drugs. I had no time to question my assistant about the transaction, because nearly all the people who came in within the next half-hour wanted to buy drugs —and some wanted things in no way connected with my profession. One *caballero* was indignant because the doctor had not brought along any of that fancy silk so popular in the pueblo just now. I looked at him blankly, and he explained it was the kind Don Jaime had bought in La Paz. Why, he had been so certain the doctor would have a bolt or two, and he had even promised his señora he would bring some home. Ah, she would be so terribly disappointed.

At this point I no longer needed a cue. More as a joke than anything else, I assured the brazen fellow that I expected a shipment on the next *avion*. I looked at Don Socrates as I said it, and I was sure he gave me a wink. My statement went down easily, and the *caballero* offered to pay

40

in advance for four yards. I explained that this was unnecessary, then he stared greedily at my sun helmet, which was lying on a nearby crate, and offered to buy that. It was an effort not to laugh.

"Señor," I said pleasantly, "I bought that helmet for myself, to protect me from your burning sun down here. But if you find you *must* have it, then perhaps I will get along without it and give it to you."

Don Socrates coughed discreetly, I excused myself, and my customer busied himself with the reserve flashlight I had placed next to my pith helmet while unpacking.

"Don't give him the helmet," he advised. "Sell it to the man, but don't forget any merchant who imports from as far away as La Paz charges exactly double what he has paid for any item. One hundred per cent then."

I blinked. This business of being a doctor-merchant prescribing at a general store confused me, but it had its amusing side. The customer gladly bought one of the flashlights and the helmet at a one-hundred-per-cent markup. There was no haggling, and Don Socrates beamed like a department store manager who has made a big sale. My Indio patient was ready to leave now. I wanted him to take a small bottle of digitalis drops with him, but he shook his head when he saw it wasn't liquor. There was a question of payment for services rendered, and Don Socrates rushed into the breach to negotiate terms. This took a minute or two, the old Indio gave me a grin and fervent *"Gracias, gracias,"* and bowed himself out to his kinfolk, who happily welcomed him into their midst.

He was so grateful that I hoped that Don Socrates hadn't clipped him for a one-hundred-per-cent markup, too. I watched the old man walking away, refusing the help of his children, and doing a little strutting to show that he was his old self again—at least for the time being. The crush of patients had eased or, more likely, Don Socrates was holding them off.

"You've been a tremendous help," I told him warmly. "I don't know what I would have done without you, but still I don't think that old Indio should pay anything for his treatment. He is a poor man and I am a servant of the government."

"Not at all, doctor, and don't look so puzzled. You don't know these people as I do, and appearances are deceiving. The old man is one of the few Indios who have an *estancia*. He is shrewd and his cattle are famous. He refused the drops because he wants injections. He told me he will come back the day after tomorrow for more treatment, although I believe he is more attracted by the liquor you served him in the big glass." He smiled mischievously. "And he must pay—they must all pay what they can, or your practice will be abused. His fee will be two of his best five-year-old oxen." My eyebrows rose at this, and Don Socrates motioned for me to hear him out. "Of course, if you don't want them, I'll pay you cash for the pair right now. And, let me remind you, for this man's oxen you get almost double the usual price."

Not only was I a doctor, druggist, and merchant, but on top of everything I was also a cattle owner. It was all overwhelming, and I was speechless. Don Socrates went over to the window and stared across at his house at the corner of the plaza. Shadows of the oncoming evening bathed its walls, and it struck me that our medical session had been an extended one. The old man sighed, his mustache drooped now, and fatigue flickered on his face. He went to the door and announced to those still waiting outside that the doctor had worked enough for his first day, they could come back tomorrow. My remaining patients (or were they customers? I wondered) thanked him and left quietly.

"You know, Don Socrates," I said with a smile, "you are an excellent doctor yourself, as well as a fine businessman. It's been an interesting day, and I have learned a great deal."

"Thank you, doctor." He bowed in extravagant self-mockery, but I could tell that he was pleased all the same. "And now I'll make a bargain with you. You teach me how to be a *medico,* and I'll teach you a thing or two about trading and cattle. Out here it is important to be able to distinguish between a two-year-old ox and a three-year-old, to tell good cows from bad ones."

"So I'm to be an *estanciero,* eh?" I said half seriously. "I never thought of myself as a rancher or cattleman. Maybe I'll get used to it."

"You will," he said. "You will indeed. Nobody can afford to be ignorant about cattle out here, doctor. In times when hard money is scarce, cattle is our accepted currency. And you would be surprised at the scarcity of cash in these regions."

"Then most of my fees will be paid in cattle?"

"Undoubtedly. This afternoon I also accepted four five-year-old oxen as your fee, not counting the two from the rich Indio. I'll gladly keep all your animals on my ranch until you dispose of them. I have good hopes that you will soon have your own ranch."

His sincerity was disarming. "Good enough then. I hope so, too. Not that I know the first thing about operating a ranch."

"You will learn, doctor. I tell you that you will learn many things down here."

How right he was, how much personal meaning was contained in these

42

words, I had no way of knowing at the time. And it was just as well. Don Socrates excused himself in the usual polite terms, and it was only after he left that I realized that I too was exhausted. I slumped into a chair, watching the shadows lengthen on the mud wall of my house, then began to chuckle as I thought of all the ludicrous possibilities inherent in my new financial arrangements. I amused myself writing such imaginary bills as: to Don Carlos for antisyphilitic treatment, four heifers; to Doña Margarita, for gynecological services, one half an ox, and to Don Alfredo, for removing a splinter, the left front leg of a two-year-old cow.

* * *

Relaxed and musing enjoyably along these lines, I heard a knock on the door, and Pierre popped inside before I could say, "Come in." I understood why when I saw the reluctant puppy on a rope behind him. The puppy was whining in protest, refusing to walk, and being dragged along on its bony behind.

"*Qué tal,* countryman," said Pierre, looking disgustedly at the door as he looped the rope over the doorknob. "I have brought you a gift."

He waved a fat arm at the unhappy animal, and eased his bulk down carefully on the biggest packing crate while I looked over his "gift" with mixed feelings. If ever there were an unprepossessing dog, this was it. The tips of his ears were torn, leaving raw wounds still clotted with blood. He was so thin every rib on his little body stood out clearly against his filthy coat. If he were washed, I thought, the white cross patch, which I could just make out on his chest, might contrast nicely with his black fur. The puppy looked at me searchingly, as I appraised him, then flopped down wearily, turning his back to us.

"I know he's ugly," said Pierre, "but don't let that bother you. He's a tiger hunter and he's called 'Daguero.' That's the Indian word for black." The puppy jerked his head to look at us. "See? As I said, *es feo,* but that is nothing."

"Who needs a dog, Pierre?"

"He has a big head for a six-week-old pup. And those dark, melancholy eyes. Do you find him appealing?"

"I said who needs a dog? Didn't you hear me?"

"I heard you, and you need one. Why? To have someone to talk to, doctor. Someone to keep you company, to look at you while you pace the room at night because you are suffocating in the heat under your mosquito netting."

"Oh, come on, it's not that bad."

43

"It's worse—and please remember I speak from the benefit of years of bitter experience. So be hot and lonely with him, not all alone."

I wasn't sure I needed or wanted a dog, certainly not so forlorn a creature as this, but I felt I ought to show my gratitude for Pierre's friendly gesture. I got out the same whisky bottle I had used on my heart patient—it was one of a half dozen given to me as a farewell gift by Herbert and which he liked to call friend-makers—and Pierre's eyes widened under their puffy lids. The precious golden liquid had risen high in the water tumbler before he modestly squeaked the required "Enough." Then, his hand shaking, he raised it to his lips and downed the contents at one gulp. It seemed to revive him and, when he spoke now, to roughen and deepen his falsetto voice almost into manhood.

"I haven't had a drink like that for a long, long time. *Hombre,* you are going to be a good doctor!"

I knew he wanted another drink, and his eyes drifted down to the suitcase, which lay open at my feet. It was from its churned-up depths that I had exhumed this particular bottle a second time. He bent down before I could stop him and grabbed a photograph that had come to the surface. An old-fashioned one mounted on cardboard, it showed a little boy with big eyes, a forced see-the-birdie! smile—a hurt-looking, sensitive boy wearing a wide stiff collar and a bow tie.

"Is that you?" said Pierre incredulously.

I snatched it out of his hand and quickly buried it with the rest of my personal stuff in the suitcase. Pierre was bewildered, to say the least, and I was furious with myself. To cover my rudeness, I poured him another drink and took something else from the suitcase.

"Here's something a lot more interesting," I said, holding out a scroll. "It's my diploma."

"Your what?" He sounded both wary and puzzled.

"My diploma. They gave it to me when I was graduated from medical school. It shows my degree."

"May I see it?"

"Why not?" I shrugged. There was really nothing to the damned thing. Big letters, a seal that had once, long ago, made a big impression on me—even given me great pride and joy. But those times were gone, and the document had lost most of its importance; it had all the value of an expired driving license, since practically not a single foreign country recognized it as a permit to practice medicine. "Look at it, Pierre. Take a good look."

44

Pierre didn't notice my bitterness. He read it carefully, evidently impressed.

"A diploma. You're a real doctor then. I tell you it's unbelievable."

"What do you mean? Did you think I was an architect?"

"Of course not, but a doctor, a real doctor in this godforsaken hole. *Hombre,* what you must have on your conscience!"

"What the devil are you getting at?" I snapped, bridling.

"Now, easy, wait a minute," Pierre spluttered in his high-pitched voice. "Don't look so wild, doctor. You scare me. This is a remote corner of the world, that's all. Why, we had a fellow here once—he'd been a janitor and a floor sweeper in a drugstore some thirty or forty years ago—who knows?—and he called himself a doctor. You wouldn't believe it, but he became Santa Morena's *curandero*. People respect him and come to him for cures from far and near. You'll see for yourself. As for me, when I had the misfortune to come here some twenty years ago, I happened to mention that I had a brother who went to law school in Vienna. And then—would you believe it?—all of a sudden they made a lawyer out of *me* and everyone began asking Pierre for legal advice.

"That's the way it works out here, doctor. No license, no diploma—just what a fellow can do or perhaps get away with. When I heard they were getting a doctor in Santa Morena, I couldn't swallow it. I thought uh-huh, a doctor my foot. I figured maybe you were a druggist. That something *had* to be wrong."

"I see," I said amiably, to take him off his guard. "It's quite understandable." Then I pounced. "There wasn't anything wrong with you, was there, when you left Europe? Did you have anything on *your* conscience?"

"Nothing, actually. But when I was a young man, a little girl on our street got into trouble and some rumor mongers pointed at me. So my father bought me a ticket to Argentina, and that was that."

He said the words automatically, as if he had said them before, and his manner implied a certain complacency and pride. It was contemptible and nauseating; at the same time it was infinitely pitiful—the poor bastard! If he had really been the offender at the time, he must have had a different hormonal structure and a different voice. Perhaps the story was his way of letting me know that this was the case.

Pierre coughed. "I think what I really meant to say was that, twenty years ago, any doctor with a diploma from a European medical school could have hung out his shingle in any big town on this continent."

"Well, twenty years is a long time," I countered. "You probably haven't heard, but doctors just can't practice everywhere these days. There are too many of them, and the value of human life has greatly diminished anyway."

"Strange. Very strange."

"Not really. If you keep fresh materials out of the market, the existing commodity retains its current high value. That's the law of economics. A lawyer—even one like you—should know that."

"Then I hope the germs infesting the people in this jungle do find out about your law of supply and demand." He chuckled, but it came out as a cough. "They might move to La Paz."

"Ah, Don Pierre, we must be fair. The doctors in the cities of South America must protect themselves just as, I imagine, the *curanderos* do in the jungle. They're even stricter about newcomers in European cities. It isn't only in my profession. It's that way everywhere. You've got to see the other fellow's point of view—it's the old story of the ins against the outs."

A startling change came over the fat man. He contracted all over, as if seized with cramps, and a painful grimace drew his small eyes back into folds of overlapping flesh.

"*Hombre,* you make me sick," he said, his high-pitched voice only a whisper. "You have suffered, they pushed you around, then they threw you out. You still see the other fellow's point of view, and he sees only his own. And where does that leave you? At the end of nowhere in this hole. I tell you, you make me sick."

If I made him sick, then truly there was a lot about Pierre that thoroughly nauseated me. But I was a doctor, and even transplanted and ostracized doctors have been trained to be objective. I turned away from Pierre, crossed to the door, and leaned against the frame. Late as it was in the day, the sun was still strong enough to make me squint. The plaza had a hauntingly familiar empty look about it. One corner of the enclosed area was formed by a giant, age-old tree. The three strands of barbed wire, glittering menacingly in the sun, wound around the great trunk and went straight to the corner where Don Socrates' house stood. Now I had it; the enclosure was exactly like so many in the concentration camps. All it lacked were the guards pacing up and down, the big searchlights, and the machine gun posts at the corners.

"Barbed wire!" I muttered to myself.

"What's wrong with it?" Pierre broke in. "It keeps the cattle out and provides the villagers with a cleared space for parades and *fiestas*. Do you object to barbed wire?"

46

"Not so much here, but it is a symbol of something I cannot forget. The whole world is fenced in barbed wire now, Don Pierre, and no trespassers are allowed anywhere. I have been pushed on and on, passed from hand to hand along with other unwanted people, and this godforsaken hole, as you call it, is my last stand. That's why I choose to see everything here as fresh and new, good and beautiful. I have to do that. Don't you see?"

Pierre just stared.

"I assure you there are hundreds of thousands of people who would consider me lucky beyond belief just in being here in Santa Morena with a job and the right to live. You can't understand what it means because you don't know the Europe of today. A diploma means nothing, but here documents, papers, and visas are of no importance, because there is nothing to fear from the police, no prosecution, no terror on the streets. And that barbed wire out there—where I have come from, it's used to herd people inside and keep them there. That's modern civilization. Here, barbed wire is for keeping cattle out. That's the jungle—and what a difference!"

Pierre's chin dropped. "You are my fellow countryman and my friend, I hope and trust. We are very much alike, you know, and I do not want to offend. But there are difficulties in the jungle, too, doctor. Where people live, where you have a roof over your head and your job to do—for ordinary souls it is perhaps enough, but not for expatriates like you and me. Once you have these precious things, plus enough to fill your stomach, it is precisely then that the trouble begins. And I tell you these troubles will all be in yourself. You will see what I mean very soon.

"That's why I say don't be too fair. It doesn't help, doesn't get you anywhere. It only makes a martyr out of you—and martyrs are out of style here. There's no public for them. And you, doctor, you see too much of the other fellow's point of view. If you don't tell him off sooner or later, you'll only end by killing your own spirit."

The fat man's high-pitched voice cracked with emotion, and I found myself putting an arm across his flabby shoulders.

"You could be right. Any way you look at it, I have plenty to learn. But come on, let's have another drink to our friendship."

"Do you still like me in spite of my hateful outbursts?" he asked.

"Perhaps more," I said strongly. "Anybody can make easy friendships, Pierre, where nothing is demanded but a smile. It's the hard ones that take and endure."

The look he gave me more than made up for everything.

4

Daguero Accepts Me; The Curandero *Abandons Santa Morena to Its Fate; Pierre Gives Me the Facts and So Does Don Socrates; The Ball in My Honor; The Question of Carlotta; Arnaldo Straightens Me Out on Love in the Jungle*

I think I was immediately attracted to Daguero because he did not rush our friendship. As any dog of character would, he protested the change of house and master. He did not whine or carry on that first day with me, but he refused food, acted thoroughly dispirited, and at night lay in the patio, close to the back door, with the rope still around his neck. I tried feeding him by hand in the morning, but again he was shy and only sniffed tentatively at my fingers before turning away. I petted him, left a bowl of broth by his side, and was surprised some time later to find it empty, licked clean by a tongue that was amazingly big for such a small fellow.

After that, I took off the rope, and it did not take him long to find his place and become my friend. He stalked cautiously around his doctor-master's house, sniffing at the furnishings, acquainting himself with the equipment, crates, and suitcases, and slowly accustoming himself to the smell of antiseptics which, at first, had made him wrinkle his black nose in alarm. I did not try to hurry our friendship, but let him take the lead. It was Daguero who finally chose his sleeping place close to my bed. He lay there during my afternoon *siesta* (a feature of Santa Morena life as in nearly all tropical countries), and also insisted on sleeping there at night. So I gave in and spread a sackcloth on the spot, officially declaring the place as Daguero's bed. My *mozo* disapproved.

"A dog should sleep outside and watch the house, doctor," he said respectfully. "Only people sleep inside."

The Indio woman, who cleaned and cooked breakfast for me, also disapproved. She had been assigned to my service by Don Socrates, slept in a hut in the patio, and came and went about her duties saying little but expressing much with her black eyes. How she looked at me when I shared my breakfast of fried tongue and fat-fried bananas with Daguero. I believe I enjoyed being frowned on; I was a newcomer, a foreigner, a *gringo;* I hadn't counted on either myself or my ways being readily accepted, just as the natives had probably counted on disapproving of me, and neither party was prepared to give in until time cleared away doubts, suspicion, and novelty.

Daguero, although still a puppy, soon began to take his position as the doctor's dog with great responsibility. He announced the arrival of patients and those who came after office hours received an especially boisterous greeting. His alarm system was more in excitement than anger, as he set his long legs in a watchdog stance, jamming his big paws hard into the dirt floor to brace himself. Ears and tail erect, he barked lustily, turning from time to time to give me a How-am-I-doing? look.

He was still too thin, but his black coat took on a beautiful sheen as he began to fill out. He was a good companion now, and I appreciated Pierre's thoughtfulness in giving me Daguero. He was fun for me and, for him, everything was fun. He played with sticks, romped in the long grass, chased the shadows of birds flying overhead. The chickens in the street particularly delighted him. He would chase, almost catch one, then it would escape in clumsy flight, leaving the little dog stiff in his tracks and utterly confounded, one ear flopping, the other pricked high, and his tail a frozen exclamation point. He looked so ridiculous that I had to laugh aloud. Betrayed by the chicken, his ears and tail drooped, he stared reproachfully at me for laughing, then stalked sadly back to the house to flop on the floor and snap indignantly at flies. Daguero was good for me.

* * *

There are two ways of avoiding an inevitable showdown; either by denying that one exists or by avoiding the other party altogether. As Pierre had told me, Santa Morena had its own *curandero,* the former drugstore janitor, and I had been given to understand that he was a worthy man and one much esteemed by the people. For this reason I had looked forward to a social meeting, a cordial exchange of views, and a sort of medical truce

49

with him. In fact, through Pierre, I had sought one. But now, shortly after my arrival, I was told that the man had deliberately left the village without a word.

The action was more expressive than any words might have been. He was washing his hands both of Santa Morena and me; there obviously wasn't room for both of us in his opinion, and I was clearly in the wrong for invading his territory. No one exactly said as much, but I could feel it—and I could see it in the faces of some of the people. I was annoyed and spent a lot of time wondering if I should have handled the problem, the conflict of medical interests differently, perhaps by going directly to him on my arrival. In any case, I resented his taking the cowardly way out and, at the same time, cleverly managing to put me in a bad light as an unwanted, interfering intruder on his domain.

It was still early in the morning. I had breakfasted and was taking it easy lying on the new hammock, which I had purchased on the advice of Pierre. The heat was already suffocating, and my clothes felt spongy with sweat. I felt my cheeks, wincing at the nicks that seemed to cover them. Shaving was an ordeal in the tropics. It wasn't so much the question of hot water as of having a sharp blade. They seemed to lose their edge almost immediately, and every blade I had brought along was already dull and rusty. I could see where I would put off shaving for days at a time or perhaps grow a beard. Anything was preferable to that torture.

A tail thumped the floor at my feet, and I leaned over to stroke Daguero, who lay relaxed watching me. I was thirsty all of a sudden and longed for something cold and refreshing. The Indio woman had left some oranges on the table, and I bit into one and sucked the juice. It had a flat, insipid, warm taste, just as if the fruit had been baked in an oven. I put it aside, and my daydream returned to tantalize me. What I wouldn't give for a refrigerator, even a simple icebox, with a frosty bottle of ice-cold, sparkling soda.

The hammock swung under me as I got up and went to the door. The sun was climbing. In another hour it would reach the thatched roof of the bamboo-walled schoolhouse. Soon after, the sun would be partly hidden by its gable, and then the patients would begin coming. I felt restless and wandered outside. The shutters of Don Socrates' house were still shut, but the door of the house adjoining mine was open. The village's notary public, Don Antonio, who had been part of the reception committee that met me at the airstrip, had his office here. It was a crude general store as well, and he sold hardware, dry goods, and candy. He even had a shelf of medicines, and Don Antonio was proud of his stock of bicarbonate of soda, castor oil, and other cure-alls. The store was Pierre's usual hangout, I had learned, and I wasn't surprised to see him appear in the door.

As I hadn't seen him in a few days, I hurried to meet him, but he only waved his arm absently and started off across the plaza. It was hardly a walk; he weaved and staggered just like a drunk, and I didn't know what to make of it.

"There's our *amigo*," I said to Daguero, who was at my heels, and in a few strides I had overtaken him. He stopped then, rocking back and forth, and stared at me blankly. He was panting, and his features were ash gray. "What's the matter with you?" I said worriedly.

He shook his head and offered no resistance as I guided him back to my house and eased him onto the hammock, the ropes creaking in protest to his great weight. I tried to check his pulse but, beyond speech as he was, he only shook me off. In a minute or so he had regained his breath and summoned up a sickly smile.

"It happens to me from time to time. Think nothing of it."

Considering the oppressive heat, plus the strain on his heart from having to pump blood through his enormous body, such a collapse was not too surprising. All the same, I thought, looking at him closely, am I deluding myself, giving him the benefit of the doubt because I like the man? Could it simply be that he's as drunk as he appeared staggering across the plaza? I sniffed for liquor on his breath, but could detect nothing. The poor fellow looked so miserable I felt I had to cheer him.

"It's good to see you, Pierre," I said heartily. "You haven't been around for a while and I've really missed you. I suppose you've been busy with your herd, getting it together and all that. The dry season won't last much longer, will it?"

Pierre made a deprecating gesture, and his eyes roamed the room, seeking the suitcase that held my liquor. I caught his meaning and couldn't ignore the desperation in his eyes. It wasn't right, medically or otherwise, but what else could I do for the man? I poured him a glass of whisky, he drank some, and immediately seemed more at ease. Then I remembered that business of the *curandero* that had worried me. Anything to get Pierre's mind off his own troubles—and then I was curious myself.

"Which reminds me—about the *curandero*. I wanted to meet the man. Did you give him the message I asked?"

"*Claro.* Of course, Martin."

"And did you keep on with it?"

"Yes, certainly. I did as you requested."

"He's had three weeks. Why didn't he come?"

"Oh, he's a damned fool. What do you care?"

"Only, from what I've heard, that he left the village either last night or this morning."

"I might have known." Pierre broke into squeaky staccato laughter.

"What's the joke? I wanted to talk to the man and reach some kind of understanding, at least before leaving for Rojas. Now I can't, and it puts me in an awkward position with the people here. That's probably what he wanted anyway."

Pierre took another sip of his drink, tried to sit up, but fell back groaning, struggling to save the remainder of his whisky from disaster.

"Look, countryman, the *curandero* says you are his enemy, so let the damned fool go. When he needs you, he'll come running and call you *'querido hermano'*—that means beloved brother, you know."

"I know," I said impatiently, "but I want to stop the quack before he does more damage. I just found out that before I came he tried burning the eruptions on those two fellows in the isolation shed in my patio—Don Socrates' boy and the other one who has syphilis. He can't cure patients that way; he can only make them worse, perhaps give them a fatal infection with his filthy instruments. He does the same thing with the Indios—burns their sores, says they're cured, and all the time the disease festers in the blood.

"I've got to put a stop to it!" I said heatedly. "If I let him go on, then I'm not doing my job. There might even be a terrible epidemic, and then what would the health authorities in La Paz say?"

Pierre gathered saliva in his pursed lips and spat on the ground in front of the hammock. His scowl matched the distaste of his derisive action.

"The devil take the health authorities in La Paz! All the authorities for that matter! They don't know how the people live here. And they don't give a damn. Has any of their excellencies ever been here? Never! And, listen to me, don't start a fight with the *curandero*. He has a number of the village's outstanding citizens on his side, and they can make it hard for you." He rocked back on the hammock. "Now let's talk about something else, eh?"

"All right," I said, thinking hard on what he had told me.

"Did you know that Don Socrates' family is back from the country? I think you'll be meeting his daughter soon."

He gave me a lascivious wink, and I immediately decided not to play the game his way.

52

"Well, if she's anything like her father, I'll look forward to it. I think a lot of Don Socrates."

Pierre wasn't to be put off. "How are you doing with the girls here? The others may say things about you, but not the girls." His little eyes narrowed as he smirked. "You know, they're all after you, especially Carlotta, the girl who gave you the eye at the airstrip, remember? She has asked me about you several times. She says you are *simpático* and must be *muy hombre*."

Again he winked meaningfully. It was too bad, but whenever Pierre even so much as remotely touched on the subject of sex, he was repulsive. Perhaps his own loss of masculinity had made it an obsession.

"You have big ears, Pierre. I haven't heard a thing myself," I said evenly. "But what about Carlotta's uncle, *El Chileno*? How is he?"

"They haven't heard so far as I know. Her father hasn't even sent a telegram."

"That could mean he's all right," I said, for the sake of conversation more than anything else. "Anyway, I hope so."

"Don't give it a thought, doctor. You've made yourself a good name here already. *El Chileno's* fate doesn't matter in the least."

I should feel flattered and assured, but I wasn't. That could be the very reason the *curandero* had abandoned Santa Morena, simply to kill the good feeling building up toward me.

"Tell me more, Pierre. What do you know about my good name?"

"Oh, as you must know, there's been talk about you." He looked at me. "Some say you're a Jew, others say you're not."

I stiffened and felt a flush spreading and prickling over me, under what had come to seem a permanent layer of sweat.

"Why not?" I said, unable to sound anything but defiant and truculent. "Why couldn't I be a Jew?"

"Probably because you don't look like one." Pierre chuckled. "For them a *judio* has always been a hunchback with a dirty beard like Fagin in Dickens' *Oliver Twist*. At least that was up to the time when the newspapers began to carry so many stories about the Jews. Now they're confused."

So the stories about the Jews had them confused? They got newspapers perhaps once a month in Santa Morena, I had been told, and during the rainy season, when isolation was complete, none at all, and the Jewish persecution had them baffled, did it?

"Even here, is that the way it is?" I sighed. "I thought that in the jungle at least I would escape Europe and the Jewish problem."

"You never escape anything anywhere." Pierre stared into his glass. "Nowhere in the Americas can you escape Europe. The Indios are the only real Americans, and look what's happened to them. Why, more than half of the *estancieros* are first-generation immigrants from Europe. Even Don Socrates is one."

"No," I said, unbelievingly.

"What do you mean, no? Don Socrates is a Turk, or a Syrian, or something like that from the eastern part of the Mediterranean. And if you don't believe me, ask him. And his friends have the same background. Me, I'm from Austria, just as you are. Do you want more? About three days from here on the river, a Berliner used to live. He's been dead five years now. Then, there is even a Yankee around here, but I never met him."

"A Yankee from Brazil?" I said sarcastically.

"You know what I mean. Nobody really belongs here except the Indios. The others just come and then call it *their* country."

"Where do you belong, Pierre?" I said.

He was about to answer as a shadow fell across the door. Don Socrates stood there smiling, and Pierre gave a great heave and a grunt, peeling himself out of the hammock with suddenly acquired strength.

"*Hasta luego,*" he said, and bolted outside past Don Socrates, lurching off across the plaza, a hiccough trailing him like a distant echo.

Don Socrates and I looked at each other, then he came over and sat on the hammock at my invitation.

"Is he mad at you, Don Socrates? Have you two had a fight?"

"Mad at Pierre? Fight with him?" There was far more regret than disgust in his tone. "Ah, who is going to fight with that poor devil?" He caught sight of Daguero, his eyes lighted up, and he seemed to jump at the chance to change the subject. "How your dog is growing, doctor? *Magnífico!* He is just what you need and will guard your house, that one."

"Pierre is sick, isn't he?" I persisted. "That herd he has—frankly I don't see how on earth he can stand that trip to Brazil."

Don Socrates opened his mouth to answer, thought better of it, and pulled at the ends of his mustache for what he considered a decent interval before veering off in another direction.

"Doctor, I thought you would want to know that the subprefect has sent most urgent word for you. He wants to know when you are going to arrive in Rojas."

"When?" I said, taken aback. "Now I am in trouble. You will have to be my witness that I'm not to blame. You know, Don Socrates, that I

54

wanted to go on to Rojas right away." This had no effect and I added, "After all, that was where I agreed to go for the health authorities in La Paz. I have an obligation to them."

Don Socrates' bushy eyebrows shot up in astonishment.

"If I didn't know it, I would probably be surprised." There was disappointment in his tone, and I was puzzled. "Really, doctor, this fear of authorities is beyond me. After you are here awhile, you will learn that they are in La Paz for the purpose of serving you, and for no other reason. You elect them and they are your officials, not the other way around. And by that I mean not only the officials in La Paz." He made a little grimace. "I'm not afraid of the subprefect of Rojas. I don't jump when he says jump —and he knows better than to say it to me. But I really came here to urge you to stay on with us in Santa Morena, and—"

"But, Don Socrates, I can't—"

"Wait one minute, let me finish. Here in Santa Morena we have the only wireless station in the province. Although it does not work throughout the whole year, that's better than no station at all, isn't it? And here, too, we have the only airstrip in the province where a plane can land. That means that La Paz is not too far away. But Rojas is—it's a few days from here—a hard trip, I assure you. And down there, during the rainy season you cannot travel at all."

It was hard to refuse, but I wasn't made that way. A course had been set, a direction plotted, and my obediently methodical European mind balked at changes without a direct order. It was taking too much on myself after being given definite instructions as to what to do.

"I'm flattered, Don Socrates. Who wouldn't be? But let me go on to Rojas. After I have been there a few weeks, well—maybe—perhaps I may come back to Santa Morena. My superiors in La Paz have treated me well, and I feel I must comply with their wishes. And that's the truth."

Like Pierre before him, the old man drew saliva up into his mouth, but he went politely to the door to spit his protest, although he did look just as disgusted as Pierre. The scorn of these men for authority intrigued me. I realized that I envied them. While they spat on it, from experience I cringed and scurried.

"Your superiors—bah!" Don Socrates wiped his mustache. "In La Paz they do not know how or even *if* we exist. And our pueblo is just as good as the capital." He sighed. "But we'll do as you say. Since you want it, we'll get some carts ready for the trip."

In line with his reasoning it was shameful how relieved I felt at not having to defy authority any further. For the moment, the heat seemed a little less oppressive.

"Muchas gracias, Don Socrates," I said casually. "I knew you would see my point. Oh, there's another thing I wanted to ask you. You know Santa Morena's *curandero* well, I imagine. Why did he leave town without talking to me? I really meant well asking him to come to see me."

"Bah! That fellow." His lip curled under his mustache. *"Hijo,* don't worry yourself about this ignorant faker. You are a graduate of a big university, a real doctor. Why, it's beneath your dignity to associate with such a man. He's only a poor, toothless, old creature anyway. Now, in Rojas, they have a real devil of a *curandero.*"

"All the same, he didn't have to leave. I was going off anyway."

"Pues! That is his strength. You see, he wants to frighten us with the idea that now we will have no one to look after us in Santa Morena, neither him, nor you. The man only fools himself." Don Socrates got up from the hammock. "As far as the trip to Rojas is concerned, we ought to be ready to travel the day after tomorrow or so."

"Good," I said in dry voice, figuring on a week or ten days at most, in line with the usual hurry-up-and-wait schedule making.

"Along with the *carreton* containing your supplies, I shall send my *mozo,* the one who has been helping you. He knows your equipment, what things must have special handling. The *carreton* will go on ahead, and then I and probably two of my sons will accompany you to Rojas. I have some business I can attend to at the same time, and I will introduce you to *amigos* on whom you can rely there. I shall also speak to the 'authorities' on your behalf," he added with a smile.

You had to like this man! In spite of his disappointment in me, he insisted on being just as helpful as possible.

"You've been very kind," I said warmly, "and I greatly appreciate it. I don't know how to thank you, so I won't try, but I do need your advice. It's about a personal matter."

"Hijo, ask me anything."

"Sometimes it's difficult for a newcomer to know how to behave. I'm only a guest, so to speak, in Santa Morena right now, but it is not only the *curandero* who does not like *gringos.* Other people, as well, have dropped unmistakable hints."

"Ah, those fools! They don't count, doctor. I am older than you are, so I can speak at liberty. A man cannot help making enemies. While he must work hard to make and hold friends, enemies make themselves, and he does

56

not have to work hard to hold their antagonism. Take yourself, for example. That miserable quack has persuaded some fools here to be your enemies. Naturally, the *curandero* fears your coming, so he incites his followers.

"Doctor, any community has people who are jealous and quarrelsome by nature. If you take the greatest pains to avoid their hostility, they will still manage to find some grounds for their pent-up hatred. And I tell you this because there are more of the quarrelsome kind in Rojas than in Santa Morena!"

"I think I know what you mean, Don Socrates," I said thoughtfully.

"Of course you do, doctor, but I must add one thing. You are alone, and that is not good. Alone one is prey to oneself as well as others. There are enemies within as well as without." He paused and, with his right thumb and index finger, carefully molded the ends of his mustache. "To live right, you should buy a house, take a wife, and raise a family."

*   *   *

It was only after Don Socrates had left that I remembered he had spoken of having two of his sons accompany us to Rojas. I didn't know how many sons the patriarch had, but certainly one of these two could be the sick one—the one recovering from syphilis in the shed in my patio. Yes, Don Socrates was a good man, but better yet he was all too human. I hadn't counted on being in Santa Morena long enough to complete the treatment of the two young men and—here I was.

There was plenty of time to administer the entire series of salvarsan treatments, check on my patients, and dismiss them from their makeshift isolation ward. It was early evening of the day after this that Don Socrates strolled into my house, greeted me, and took his ease in my hammock. He deftly brought up the question of my fee, in regard to his son, and gracefully accepted my plea not to press for a bill. It was the least I could do under the circumstances, I felt, and it would be an insult to take his money, especially after all he had done for me. So that was settled. Then Don Socrates brought up the subject of the prevailing cattle prices on the Bolivian border, and there was a soft knocking at the door that caught him in mid-sentence.

"*Entra!*" I called, getting to my feet.

I opened the door and was amazed to see two girls standing there. They seemed almost as confused as I was, then Don Socrates rushed by me.

"Ah, but I forgot," he exclaimed. "I was going to meet them outside, but I went ahead and talked to you." Now he stood between them and introduced the girls formally. "Doctor, my daughter Rosita. She and her mother have come back from the *estancia* expressly to have the honor of making your acquaintance. And this is Carlotta, my godchild, whom I believe you met at the airstrip."

"*Qué honor,* señoritas," I said, bowing slightly as the girls folded the parasols they were carrying, bent their heads in gracious greeting, and went in after Don Socrates. "I am delighted."

Among the men it was the custom on introduction to shake hands, embrace, and shake hands again. I wanted to be polite with these two girls and, particularly with Don Socrates watching, to express warm greetings. I tried a casual handshake with Rosita, then, encouraged by her response, I touched her left shoulder with my right hand. The gesture must have been reasonably correct, for she smiled her appreciation. I followed it with a final handshake, and repeated the whole business with Carlotta. This done, I said what I knew was proper on the occasion of an introduction to a *muchacha.*

"*Encantado!*" I smiled at both young women. "Charmed."

Don Socrates, secure in wisdom and old age, did not have to make do with taps on the shoulder. Although he must have seen them only minutes ago, he gave both Rosita and Carlotta a fond, warm embrace.

"How have you been, *muchachas?*" he said heartily. Then, beaming at Carlotta, he told me again that she was his godchild.

It seemed to me that Santa Morena swarmed with godchildren of Don Socrates, many of them having been pointed out to me by Pierre and others. It must be quite an honor, I thought, and Señorita Carlotta apparently enjoyed being so designated. She glowed all over, and gave me a full and fiery look, her eyes shining with promise under straight, thin brows. She had softened her brown complexion with a liberal application of face powder, and there was no doubt that she was pretty—much prettier than Rosita, and also bolder and more flirtatious. I remembered how warmly she had looked at me at the airstrip, and she did the same here, her eyes speaking volumes compared to the shy, well-behaved Rosita.

The lengthy introductions completed, father and daughter exchanged glances, and Rosita now addressed an invitation to me, requesting my presence at a ball that was to take place in her home that evening in my honor.

"My señora is preparing a little *fiesta* for you tonight, doctor," said Don Socrates, echoing her. "We want to welcome you officially to our pueblo."

58

An official welcome just as I was about to leave? How odd. I was flattered and surprised, but I must have looked a little doubtful at first, otherwise Don Socrates would not have so promptly thrown his weight behind his daughter's invitation. (Or perhaps that was another custom here, a sort of guaranteed invitation.) He went on to explain that everything was prepared for the *baile,* that it would be a colorful and enjoyable *fiesta*-dance, and that I must come. I knew I would, but I bowed gravely and ceremoniously accepted the invitation with the elaborate acknowledgment which, in time, I came to recognize as a ritual.

The *muchachas* had accomplished their mission. For a little while longer we exchanged pleasantries, and then the girls showed their polite but unmistakable intention of leaving. We shook hands, touched shoulders, and shook hands again, and I began to feel that the amenities had consumed most of our visit. I was sure Don Socrates would go through the embracing routine either with me or the girls, but instead he got up, bestowed a royal *"Hasta luego!"* on me, and filed out after the *muchachas,* who glided off under their open parasols with studied grace.

* * *

Relaxed, warmly inclined toward Santa Morena and its people, I lay down in the hammock, dozed, woke up, and then hovered somewhere between sleeping and waking. Black evening shadows filtered through the mud walls and the thatch, filling the corners of the room and spreading outward like a threat and, unconsciously, my thoughts darkened with them. I couldn't say whether or not I liked Santa Morena and the jungle; it was too early to tell, and it didn't matter either way since I was committed in word and bond for two years. Like a tourist flung into a new *milieu,* my impressions were still on the surface and totally superficial. The isolation, the primitive life, the crude housing, the awful food, Don Socrates, Pierre—all these things drifted together in and out of focus, bathed in a glaring miasma compounded of terrible heat and sweat that all but suffocated me, as the black shadows of the past lay in the background to engulf me.

It was dark when I came to myself, aroused by some sort of commotion from across the plaza. The noise came to my ears at first like the dots and dashes of a code, then I made out the first tentative tuning up of musical instruments. Flute notes now emerged clearly from this blur of sound, sketching lines of soft gold in the darkness around me, now a little less terrifying in my half-dream state. Then a drum exploded with a violence that drowned out everything else, and the hammock quivered under my weight. I was shaken, overcome with fright. *Run for your life!* cried one impulse. *Fight for it!* screamed another, while I lay paralyzed, except for my hands and feet, which had begun to shake uncontrollably.

The dissonant drumbeats became muffled and settled down to an easy rhythm. The hammock no longer shook, only its fringes twitched like human hair in fright. Drumbeats. A jail somewhere in the outskirts of Vienna. Its *Kommandant* liked to call himself humane, and he believed in discipline. He had a drum and used it constantly. I could hear it now, its beats coinciding with those of the drum in the dark streets of Santa Morena. It was BOOM get up; BOOM sit down; BOOM march; BOOM, BOOM, BOOM, BOOM, one, two, three, four. The jail was a battered schoolhouse. Meals were doled out in what had once been the gymnasium. BOOM, BOOM, BOOM. The *Kommandant* was humane. Once he ordered the three hundred odd men and women prisoners to get up and down—BOOM, BOOM—sixty-seven times. I did it—and counted —but some of the older people fainted, and the *Kommandant* ordered some of the others to carry them to their pallets. "You see, pigs of Jews, that I am a humane man!" he shouted. And the prisoners could not get over his kindness.

BOOM, BOOM, BOOM. It was the fault of the shadows. I was safe in Santa Morena and the terror was two oceans away—but still in my bones. I had a curiously empty feeling in the pit of my stomach, a yawning emptiness overlain with worry and fear. Oh, God, if only I knew specifically what to fear—danger, sickness, death—but there was no way of foretelling, and nothing could terrify me as prison once had.

Stop it! I said to myself. The past is dead. From down the street the flute sang light, lilting tunes, and my hammock began to swing again. All the time the drum went on beating. One, two, three, four, five, six. Pause. One, two, three, four, five, six. Pause. An altogether different drum, not so loud, not so insistent, but gay, friendly. There was no terror in its six-beat. On the contrary, its regular simplicity was soothing and reassuring. Just as Greta had been during the bad times.

Sweet Greta, the pretty young secretary who had remained loyal when my elegant women friends—how snobbishly proud I had been of their friendship!—had shunned me. They went out of my life with a charming sniff of contempt for the New Order, but they were afraid and their eyes burned with fear. Losing what I had prized, however fatuous and foolish, I had clutched Greta, whose unfaltering love had at last gained its objective.

Her lips were as sweetly tart as a fresh plum. Her every sigh had spelled soul. If I had betrayed my better self with those sophisticated sluts, then I had betrayed love—and myself again—with Greta. I returned her love with sex—meaningless and forgotten a minute after consummation. Poor, slender Greta with the eyes of a lost deer and the selfless devotion that could only boomerang on her heart. She had deserved better then, deserved better now than a shaky memory touched by insincere remorse . . . They were cruel times; they made me cruel; Greta was made an object for cruelty and—

Daguero's barking brought me wide awake in the darkness. He stood there, ears up, tail erect, barking his head off at the knocking.

"Doctor! Oh, doctor!" Don Socrates stood at the door, holding a small kerosene lantern as I blinked and rubbed my eyes. "There was no light in your house, and we looked for you everywhere. The *baile*—didn't you hear the *drumbomba* and *flauta?*"

"Oh, I'm terribly sorry, Don Socrates. I've been asleep and I do sleep heavily. Please forgive me."

"Are you all right?" he said, coming closer. "You are shaking all over."

"Just a little chill. It's much cooler now." I got up. "I'll change as quickly as I can and go right over to your house. Please convey my apologies to the señora."

"Oh, come as you are, doctor. I have a lamp to light your way."

The *fiesta* was in full swing by the time I got there, still sleepy-eyed, dazed, and flustered. Since I was guest of honor, I felt ashamed at my tardiness, but no one seemed to notice and everyone was having such a good time that the party would have been just as successful without me. I was glad of that, and there was no need to apologize. The crowd was in the *sala,* the main room of the house, gathered in the fitful glare of a gasoline lantern dangling from a lasso tied to a beam under the hollow ceiling. Don Socrates pointed out the lamp's proud owner, Don Antonio, who lounged against the wall, never taking his popping eyes from his treasure, and wincing nervously every time one of the tall men in the room bumped his head against the gently swaying lamp.

Under the garish light the women's silk and sateen dresses shimmered and glittered. The men wore the clean white or blue suits and dark neckties they saved for special occasions, and I was the only one dressed informally. I felt unbearably hot and ridiculously out of place in my khaki and high boots. I should never have let Don Socrates talk me into coming as I was, but I had only myself to blame. A party was being given for me, and I came close to sleeping through it. That was good manners, wasn't it?

As Don Socrates turned to greet a guest, the *alcalde* of Santa Morena bounced up to me with a large glass, half filled with what he identified as *aguardiente*. The short, fat dignitary made a little speech, most of it lost in his asthmatic wheezing and the general hubbub, then he raised the glass to his streaming, tobacco-stained mustache, exposing blood-red gums and the pitiful ruins of teeth. He took a good gulp of the yellow stuff, smacked his lips and then, to my dismay, held out the glass to me. I dared not refuse; I was being honored, and custom demanded that in Santa Morena I do as the Santa Morenians did.

Wondering how many people had already sipped from the same sticky glass, I wished him good health and drank as indicated. The raw liquor not only singed my mouth, but burned all the way down, and then started a bonfire in my belly. He looked at me for some sign of appreciation, and I gave him the same stunned smile that a put-upon teacher manages to summon up when parents demand that he or she praise their stupid, offensive child. The mayor now looked well satisfied, took the glass from my limp hand, and panted off to favor more lucky persons with the same noisome treat.

I looked around wildly for some water to extinguish the blaze in my belly, but as soon as the *alcalde* left my side, other men took his place and held out their glasses to me. There was nothing for it then, and it would have to be a case of fighting fire with fire. Soon my mouth, throat, and belly were scorched, and my head was spinning. This stuff packed a straight alcohol kick. I'd be reeling drunk if I had to share a drink with every man eager to do honor to the *gringo* doctor.

Fortunately, it was time for the music to begin. The Indio drummer and his partner who played the flute swung into action, and the young men, who had clustered around the table where the *aguardiente* was dispensed, rushed off with the first notes. They hurried to the stools along the walls and took their preference of the *muchachas* sitting there waiting. A few older men lingered to share a toast with me, and I took the opportunity to follow the lead of their juniors and to escape into Carlotta's arms. Her eyes had been on me since my tardy arrival, hot, black eyes burning in a white-powdered face, and I had known I would have to dance with her sooner or later. I couldn't help wondering now what she'd say if I told her the truth: that I had chosen her as my partner to get away from unsanitary glasses filled with stomach-turning *aguardiente*. But I had the feeling that these fiery *muchachas* had little sense of humor—or if they had any, it would tend to be on the grim side.

62

As it was, I was in no shape for anything tricky. Fortunately the dance step was a simple thing, straight steps to the one-two-three-four of the drum, and a turn to the five-six beats, followed by a counterstep in the pause. The *muchacha* danced well. Carlotta moved easily and gracefully; it was pleasant to dance with her, and I would have enjoyed myself thoroughly except for my dizziness from the liquor and the heat of the close-packed *sala*.

My throat still had a burning-rubber taste, my stomach had a shipboard uneasiness, and my awkward movements did not coincide with Carlotta's. Another thing, I was holding her, embracing her much too tightly. To cover my poor dance co-ordination, I began to talk to her, but my Spanish turned inexplicably clumsy and I seemed to be tripping over my tongue as well as my feet. Carlotta suffered it all tolerantly, smiling and smiling and smiling. She was very close to me, but she seemed far away. So did everyone we passed on our merry way, and all of them were smiling, smiling, smiling, too. It was all for me. I was guest of honor here. Yesterday I was a pariah; today a celebrity; and tomorrow—?

Suddenly I awoke to my surroundings. Carlotta had stopped dancing, I had bumped into her, and blood was burning in my cheeks. Why, the music had stopped, too—perhaps some minutes ago!—and the *muchachas* had already been taken back to their seats along the wall. The young men were back at the refreshment table, refilling their glasses, and talking animatedly together. Only I, Martin Fischer, the *gringo* doctor, stood alone in the middle of the *sala,* my arms around Carlotta, while mothers and fathers looked on, raising their eyebrows and throwing knowing looks at each other.

Carlotta had more poise than I did. She laughed gaily, as if the joke were somehow on her, and she carried off my *gaffe* beautifully. The evening seemed to blend and flow and spin smoothly after that. I had more *aguardiente,* and it came to seem neither as strong nor as vile-tasting as at the beginning. My tongue loosened, and I felt as if I were speaking Spanish like a native. Because everyone I talked to nodded and smiled politely, as is the Spanish way, I blithely assumed that I was understood as one of them. I only half listened to the replies given me. The general elation and hilarity made conversation unimportant anyhow, and I thought it an exciting truth that, given wine, pretty women, and music, a party was a party anywhere. I also had the feeling that I was swaying somewhere above the floor, but it couldn't matter so much, for others seemed to be doing the same thing.

I danced with Carlotta a second, third, and fourth time. She was Lisa, Greta, and every lovely girl I had desired, her body burned against mine, and I grew fonder of her with every dance. I could say anything to this darling—perhaps, if I'd gotten the message right, *do* anything.

"Do me the favor of meeting me after the dance," I whispered in her ear.

"*Con mucho gusto,*" she said with a radiant smile.

Why, there was nothing to it! She wanted what I wanted—or was it the other way around?

"Good! Suppose you meet me at the corner of the plaza closest to my house." It was just the place for a rendezvous, with a large tree to protect us from inquisitive eyes, then a hop, skip, and a jump to my door, then the privacy of the house, and then—the familiar delights so lamentably become unfamiliar delights. "Is that all right?"

"*Con mucho gusto,*" she said again, without hesitation.

I let out my breath. The victory seemed won. Let the music play on, let the *aguardiente* flow. I had the answer, and Carlotta was all the women I had ever loved—or desired. And what was the difference anyway?

Midnight was the witching hour. The ball came to a sudden end and, in a matter of minutes, Don Socrates' *sala* was empty. The automatic gasoline lantern shed its light on the bare dirt floor which, in the glare, looked like a deserted stage after the audience has filed out and the last echo of applause has faded away. Carefully and tenderly, Don Antonio took down his precious light, unfastened it, and screwed the flame down lower and lower until darkness fell over the room and the ghostly night air of the village streamed in the open door.

I tried to thank Don Socrates, but my host threw his arms into the air exuberantly, as if he might be embracing the entire room, and retired after his señora, an attractive woman of about fifty, and his children. The last guest to arrive, I was also the last to leave, and I started across the room as if dutifully going through the motions of a dream. At the door I tripped over some people and came close to pitching on my face. The musicians were sprawled across the entrance by their instruments, exhaling clouds of alcohol with each snore. I leaned across one of them and tapped his drum. It gave out a hollow sound that greatly pleased me, and I tapped it again and giggled at the delightfully doleful boom.

I was not myself at all. (Or was I really myself now?) All my self-restraint was gone. I walked slowly toward the appointed rendezvous, hot with anticipation at the thought of my first love affair in the tropics. Spanish girls were supposed to be passionate, according to the stories. Well, I could

64

be passionate, too, couldn't I? I was mellow with *aguardiente,* burning with a quick, warm glow. I'd have to give the girl time to get home though; then she'd have to wait until her mother put out the lights and went to bed before setting out from wherever she lived for our agreed-upon meeting place. Twenty minutes ought to do it, then we would see what happened, although from personal telepathy and alchemy both of us seemed to agree that a little romance would be a fitting conclusion to a fine day.

I was strolling leisurely in the direction of our rendezvous, my thoughts on love and passion, the *aguardiente* now burning hotly in my loins rather than all over, as I sensed some people approaching from the other side of the plaza. I moved quickly into the dark shadows of the big tree, edging about the massive trunk as far as the barbed wire enclosure and hoping to keep out of sight as they came nearer. I thought I was successful, and they had almost passed by when a sweet voice called out to me.

"*Qué tal,* doctor. Would you not like to join us on a promenade around the plaza? It is so pleasantly cool now."

It was Carlotta, gracious and friendly as ever, even though she was flanked by both her mother and younger brother. Not at all what I had expected, the fact that she was escorted-guarded-chaperoned was enough to awaken me to a cold shower of reality. I was numb with embarrassment as I mumbled that I would be delighted to walk with them. Helpless as a marionette, I circled the plaza twice with mother, brother, and daughter, my only contribution to the politely correct conversation an occasional "*sí*" or "*no.*" When the señora and her children turned to go home, I murmured a curt *buenas noches* and slunk off.

I was so let down that, once in my own house, I didn't bother to light the lamp or use my flashlight to undress. Not even Daguero's wagging tail or friendly whimpers made me feel any better. My loins, so certain of pleasure and release a few minutes earlier, now began to ache, but I felt that I was more angry at myself than disappointed in Carlotta, who had breathlessly led me on to—nothing. A good, responsible doctor had no business drinking so much anyway. Furthermore, a man in my official position should never involve himself with someone like Carlotta, whose boldness—even if it had proved a fraud tonight—appeared to be the complete antithesis of everything I had heard about proper girls from good families in Latin America.

I threw myself on my cot, not even bothering to yank the mosquito netting into place. In a sense the whole episode had its laughable side, although I was in no mood to appreciate that just then. Fatigue battled with the slap at my ego and my crushed and frustrated desire, and I sleepily began to rationalize away my disappointment. It hadn't been Carlotta I wanted anyway, only an *aguardiente* dream that had made her Lisa, Greta, and all the others. Besides, it was poison to tangle with Carlotta's family. I ought to know better than to get mixed up with *El Chileno's* relatives.

*　　*　　*

I awakened as the sun reached like a soothing hand through the door I had neglected to shut. Considering all I had had to drink, I felt better than I had any right to feel. I had only the faintest trace of a headache, I was rested, and I could look back on my aborted affair with Carlotta with the detached spirit of a heavy loser the day *after* the big race at the track. Daguero was sitting on his behind, watching me closely as I yawned and stretched. I was grateful for his company, held out a hand, and he came close to lick it in good morning, and be petted.

From across the plaza came the murmur of voices mingled with the soft clumpings of the cows that grazed in the village streets and in front of my house, and from way back came the sound of hammering, where the pueblo's only tinsmith had his workshop. It was peaceful and serene and picturesque as the opening footage in a movie travelog about a "romantic and exotic" country. It was late, but I had no desire to get up. Then I heard footsteps outside and merry singing.

"*Quere me un poco mas, abri tu corazon* . . . Love me a little more, open your heart."

A moment later Arnaldo, the slickly handsome son of a wealthy man, swung into the house, cut off his song, and gave me a big, beaming smile.

"Good morning, doctor! How have you arisen?" Then he burst into song again. "*La vida es linda cuando el amor lo anima, cuando el amor lo brinda* . . . Life is beautiful when love abounds, when love is the thing . . ." He broke off with a smile and repeated even more cheerfully, "Well, doctor, how have you arisen, eh? But you haven't arisen yet, have you?"

He laughed, and I sat up. Then he hauled himself up on a table and all but sat on my writing pad.

"*Hágame el favor,* doctor, and sell me a box of those magic sulfa pills, eh? Like a good friend that you are."

"Sulfa pills!" I exclaimed, jumping out of bed. Arnaldo was one of the few white patients I had treated yesterday afternoon—and for what I had come to regard as "the usual reasons." I walked across the room. "Why do

66

you need more? You told me yesterday that you had just recovered from a gonorrhea infection, and Don Socrates told me that your father got you several boxes of them when he was in La Paz several weeks ago."

"*Sí, sí*, but I have it again," he said with a smile. Then he added smugly, "Don't worry about the cost. I have two cows that will pay for them."

"The payment has nothing to do with it, Arnaldo," I said, shaking my head at his casual way with what could be a serious infection. "You're a young fellow, just nineteen as you've told me. Well, how many infections do you think your body can stand? Keep on like this, and I warn you a time will come when no drug will have any effect. It would be better to give the *muchacha* some pills so she would be cured and wouldn't infect you over and over again."

"But, doctor, it is not the same *muchacha* as it was the last time." He laughed. "In fact, I don't know which one it was. Anyway, it was all that liquor last night that started it."

"Oh, well, you're incorrigible! But how do you fellows get all the girls, anyway?" The question came out before I realized what I was saying but, now that it had, I told myself it was pure curiosity that prompted it and not envy. "And what do you say to them? Why, only last night at the party, while I was making conversation, I said to one of the *muchachas,* 'You are very pretty.' And she replied, '*Gracias,* but I am very ugly.' I was doing my best, and I felt just as if I'd been slapped down."

Arnaldo roared at this. "Ah, it is because you are a foreigner. The girls feel they have to impress you, put on airs, show off their good upbringing and education. That was just an expression of modesty, and I'm sure the *muchacha* liked your compliment. And that was just the time and place for it, but you have to follow up. During a dance, you can even snatch a quick kiss and no one will notice. Of course, there's not much privacy at such an affair, only a little opportunity to talk and make arrangements for later on."

"Arrangements?" I thought of my tragi-comic rendezvous with Carlotta. "All right, where do you go for privacy?"

"Here in Santa Morena—in Rojas, too, as well as elsewhere in our province, there is really only *one* place." Arnaldo's voice took on a pompous and slightly patronizing gravity as he filled the *gringo* doctor in on the social niceties involved in a boy and girl getting together. "The only place is beneath a girl's *mosquitero.*"

I couldn't help looking shocked, and Arnaldo laughed boisterously.

"Do not look so alarmed, doctor. There is a system everywhere and here,

67

to speak seriously, one has to go to the *muchacha's* house at night *por visitar*. If a man is lucky, there are not many people around, the family is out of the way, and he sits with her in front of the house. He gives her sweet talk that becomes even sweeter as the darkness falls. And then, doctor, what joy, eh?" He rolled his eyes and smacked his lips.

"It's not hard to see how you get so many infections," I said dryly.

"True, true. But all delights have their price, and your magic sulfa pills make them less than half price." He smiled at the conceit and went on with his lecture, our age difference coming close to reversing the traditional roles of experienced father and innocent son. "To go on, sometimes a *caballero* goes there at midnight and serenades the *muchacha*. It is well, though, to choose a night when the father is away from the pueblo. Then, after a few weeks during which you have gained her confidence and affection, she will tell you which one is her bed."

"Her bed?" I repeated the words without getting at the meaning. "Then there are usually several in one bedroom."

"Certainly," said Arnaldo impatiently. "You have to know exactly where to find her."

"Oh! You mean, Arnaldo, that you have to go into the room where *all* the beds are and locate hers?" He nodded, looking pleased that I wasn't as dull as I seemed. "But what if you make a mistake? Or, say, the father or mother becomes suspicious and looks inside the daughter's *mosquitero?* Or if somebody wakes up and hears you?"

The young man gave a fatalistic shrug. "It happens, but you needn't worry about anyone looking under the *mosquitero*. No mother or father would do that. It's like an unwritten law out here. Not that there aren't enough stories about men being caught while they sneaked in or out of their *muchacha's* room. For instance, there was that *gringo* a few years ago who—"

"*Basta!*" I exclaimed. "I've heard enough."

Again Arnaldo threw back his head and shook with laughter.

"It's not that serious, doctor, or as difficult as it seems. A man always finds the opportunity, and the fathers are often away about their business for long stretches at a time. And a good thing, too, if you ask me, otherwise what would the poor girls do, eh?"

"But all this creeping about in the night. I don't see—Arnaldo, why don't the girls meet the boys outside somewhere or go to the boys' homes? Lots of you young fellows have your own places."

I was really thinking of myself and Carlotta as I spoke. I knew that and didn't care; my ego was still a little bruised. Arnaldo hunched forward on his perch, resting the palms of his hands on the table.

"Doctor, no *muchacha* who wishes to remain in good standing in the community will ever come to a man's house unless she is married to him. Nor will she take a walk alone with him. These things are never done, and it is a grave offense even to suggest them." He looked at me, and I managed to remain innocent and interested. "We may not be as sophisticated as the Europeans, but we have our own code, our own standards of behavior. And a girl's reputation here is as important as it is anywhere else in the world. She must look out for herself. Guard it!"

He spoke seriously and with conviction, but his topsy-turvy reasoning was too much for my simple right-and-wrong European mind. Under the *mosquitero,* it was fine and no offense; but a lonely walk was *verboten* and a capital offense. But since you could get caught in both circumstances, I failed to see the fine, subtle difference involved. In any case, I felt pleased now about last night after all. Carlotta's peculiar behavior was explained— in fact, I had put her on the spot and she had reacted in the only way possible—and, best of all, my ego was restored.

"And now, doctor, how about my pills?" I tossed him the box and he juggled them, grinning at me. "I think you should pay me, you know. That information I've given you is worth a fortune in itself."

"Get out of here, Arnaldo!" I shouted in mock anger.

*   *   *

The day was not very different from the previous one. I was hot, sweaty, and busy most of the time with a few stolen minutes spent playing with Daguero. I was more aware, however, that most of my patients continued to be Indios, with only a few white Bolivians coming to see me. It soured me a little, and the bitter part of my mind sneered that it was only justice for a member of Europe's inferior race to treat those of South America's inferior race, but there was much more to it, I knew, than this.

From time to time I took many of my meals at Don Socrates' house and, at the table that night, I took the liberty of bringing up the matter. He quietly acknowledged that it appeared to be so, pointedly refrained from comment, and I was not reassured. Something was going on. The *curandero's* poisonous seed was rapidly bearing fruit.

For the first time, the son I had had under treatment joined us at his father's table. He was quiet, well behaved, constantly deferred to his father, and he certainly belied the reputation Pierre had given him as a rampaging man-about-town. Don Socrates' wife was a dignified woman, darkly self-contained, capable, intelligent, and discreet. The whole family impressed me as solid, worthy people, and I felt I was lucky to be associated with them.

After dinner Don Socrates said something vague about going to visit a friend who was alone. He asked me to accompany him. It seemed to me he was asking only out of politeness and, while disinclined, I felt I had to accompany him. Never having been there before, I must admit I was startled, as it turned out that the "friend" was at Carlotta's house. I looked at Don Socrates, as I recognized Carlotta, and his lips twitched in a faint smile. What a man! I thought. Not only does he know which way the wind is blowing, but first he makes it blow.

Carlotta smiled warmly at me, then hastened to help her mother place four chairs in a semicircle in the *sala*. Then we all sat down and talked pleasantly enough about nothing in particular. I wanted to ask about *El Chileno,* but he was never mentioned and I thought it best to keep quiet. (They probably were keeping silent to spare my feelings, which were supposed to be hurt since the man had not heeded my advice, and this amused me because *El Chileno* had been much too sick a man to pay much heed to anything except drawing his next breath.) A few minutes later Don Socrates' *sirvienta* poked her nose into the doorway. He asked her a question, she murmured some reply that seemed to call for action, then off he went after her, apologizing for the briefness of his visit.

More casual talk among the three survivors, then a few minutes later Carlotta's mother arose, made her apologies, and retired to a back room. Somehow I was now alone with Carlotta. I hadn't planned it, I was hardly prepared for this matchmaking gambit, and once again I had the disturbing sensation of having been skillfully manipulated without realizing what was being done to me. But this time I didn't care. I knew that nobody could force me into any serious attachment; for everything else the matchmakers would have to bear the responsibility.

With her black hair more simply arranged than at the *baile,* her face no longer clouded and disguised by the heavy white powder, which was probably the accepted fashion for a big evening, Carlotta seemed no more than a charming young girl, who could have been sixteen, rather than twenty. We had the chance to look straight at each other without interruption and, embarrassed as I was by the abrupt desertion of our elders, her big dark eyes, overflowing with warmth and friendliness, quickly put me at ease. We chatted amiably about Santa Morena, my medical work, my puppy Daguero, and it all went smooth as butter.

Then, because I still wanted to know what had happened to *El Chileno,* I thought I could approach the matter obliquely.

"Have you heard from your father?" I said offhandedly. "When is he returning?"

The question had a curious effect on Carlotta. Her eyes became coquettish, her smile broadened.

"He will be away for some time yet, doctor."

She said it just like that, but her meaning was unmistakable. Without half trying I had gained vital information, and I thought back to Arnaldo's saying ". . . the fathers are often away about their business for long stretches at a time."

After this our conversation turned intimate. We discussed things we liked and didn't like, what mattered most to us, and flirted with love, honor, the meaning of life, and other abstractions.

"I want to show you something," she said suddenly. "Come." She looked me in the eye, took my hand, and led me to the open door of an adjoining room, where I made out several beds, *mosquiteros* enshrouding them, and pointed to one particular one. "That is where I sleep," she whispered.

I think I was more scared than shocked. What went on in this girl's mind? I knew hers was a good family, otherwise they wouldn't have Don Socrates' friendship and esteem. And Arnaldo had spoken of a few weeks of courtship. We had had none at all, and here Carlotta had me plunging cold under her *mosquitero.* It was startling, and refreshing, too, this direct approach of hers. European girls wanted the same thing and pretended not to; they made such a *thing* of the preliminaries, much more than of the real thing. All the same, I was a victim of my own background, the slow, easy stroll into the bedroom.

"Carlotta," I said hesitantly, pretending to pick at a sliver in my hand so I wouldn't have to look at her intense face. "Carlotta, there's something you have to understand. Where I come from, uh, men and women usually do not become, uh, lovers until they have known each other for some time—until they are sure they care for each other."

"But I care for you, doctor."

I looked up now and saw that she had not grasped my meaning—or that it was beyond her.

"Every part of the world has its own customs," I continued hurriedly, thankful that the dim light covered the blush I felt prickling my face. "And I am not yet used to your customs. I will be soon, of course, and—well, Carlotta, you are a very pretty girl and a very sweet one. I like you. I want to be your friend."

"So do I, doctor," she said in a vibrant voice. "I want to be yours."

I needed time to think, and this made a good exit line. We had established communications, we were thinking alike, our objective was similar, and we would go on from there.

"Remember me to your mother," I said, starting for the door.

She smiled, tolerant, amused, a woman of the world humoring a callow schoolboy. "Let us be friends then, doctor," she said softly, and with that she was again the charming young child I had noted earlier.

*　　*　　*

The next morning young Arnaldo again dropped by my office. Looking at me searchingly, he asked the usual, "How have you arisen?" I told him well, asked him the same question, and got the same answer.

"Don't tell me you want another box of magic pills?" I asked jokingly.

"Not exactly," he said, smiling to himself. "But tell me, how is the *niña* Carlotta?"

"Oh, I saw her last night," I said, purposely casual. "It improves my Spanish, you know."

"*Sí,*" my mentor observed readily. "A language is learned best that way."

5

I Join the "Mosquiteers"; Pierre Treats a Rattlesnake Bite; He Changes His Story; Pierre's Illness and Don Socrates' Explanation

Don Socrates had told me matter-of-factly that it would take two days to prepare for the trip to Rojas, the capital. As I had anticipated, they *mañana*-ed themselves to a week . . . then another week . . . The delay was interminable and, at first, annoying. Now my office, such as it was, was again a forlornly bare room with no examining table, nothing I could write on, not even a chair. The boxes and packing cases were jammed full of supplies, their lids leaned close by, ready to be nailed down at a moment's notice, and everything hung suspended in time. No one seemed to mind, however; the confusion, endless postponement, and on-again-off-again alert status bothered only me.

Daguero ambled about excitedly, sniffing, barking, scratching. The black dog had responded to good care and affection—how he had grown in the short time I had had him!—and he had grown genuinely attached to me. Pets roamed at will around here, but I was a European and my dog—for so I thought of him now—was going to be well brought up, disciplined, and affectionate. My informal training of Daguero was a source of amusement, but I didn't care. I wanted him house-trained and obedient, not just another heedless wild one. My patients had continued to be Indios, but they had dwindled off, and I had plenty of time to give to the dog.

Actually I didn't too much mind waiting for Don Socrates to leave. Carlotta obligingly kept all my evenings—and the greater part of my nights—pleasantly occupied. Put that way it sounds cold-blooded, but if Carlotta was eager and hot-blooded, my feelings were mixed. I had to shut out the overpowering desire for Lisa in Paris, and I couldn't do it. I yearned and ached for her; I still missed her, still wanted her badly. I was thus hardly in the mood for love with another woman—and surely not the serious marriage kind for which Carlotta so obviously yearned. Then there were my own scruples and background, my uneasiness over the village proprieties, the desire not to get involved, the fervent wish not to offend when I was so new here. Oh, there were a thousand things, and yet . . . and yet . . .

When there is a delightful game to be played and one partner is so willing, why deny her—why deny both of ourselves the exquisite pleasures of the sport? Carlotta was a lovely, desirable woman in a shabby village in a godforsaken country; she had made her intentions clear from the day we had met. I was a man, lonely, restless, and a stranger, still haunted by the broken memories of my Paris love. So why shouldn't I sneak under her *mosquitero* as she wished? Why shouldn't I join the "mosquiteers" with an "all for one and one for all"? Just so long as I didn't have to fight any duels or defend myself against some outraged father.

I worried too much. Having been shown where to go by Carlotta herself, the strategy of approach was as simple as Arnaldo had outlined. All the same, the first time I went to her house late at night I would have felt easier if there had been some sort of all-clear signal in the window. Tiptoeing close, carrying my shoes, I thought of Paul Revere in old Boston and the church tower showing one if by land, two if by sea. I could only trust the warm promise in Carlotta's eyes earlier, the insistent pressure of her hot hand on mine, and her silken whisper that her father was still away. The door opened as if it had been greased, and the moonlight was just bright enough for me to find the passage Carlotta had indicated. This door was partly open. It moved the rest of the way without a sound, and I paused on the threshold.

My heart began to beat violently. I wanted to laugh aloud, then I wanted to run. The right room, yes, but which bed? I had forgotten! I saw three or four of them covered with big, ghostly *mosquiteros,* looking like indistinct crafts under full sail. I took a deep breath, held it, heard my own heart beating, then the gentle sighs, murmurs, and snores of the sleepers beyond. Folly, I told myself, sheer folly. Fine for someone like Arnaldo or the other "mosquiteers" who knew the local customs, but a foreigner like me—with horror I remembered the *gringo* who had been caught in a girl's room, the one Arnaldo had started to tell me about. Then I stiffened as one of the sleepers snorted and there was a rustling sound as she—surely not he!—turned over. What was I doing here?

74

I stood unmoving until everything was still again. Much as I wanted to now, I hated the thought of running away. Enough of that. I was a *mosquitero* cavalier, wasn't I? A self-styled, dashing "mosquiteer" like D'Artagnan, Porthos, and Aramis. It was a time to be bold, not to cringe. The idea gave me heart. I laughed to myself and suddenly felt carefree. Paris was far behind in the shadows of time.

Which bed though, I wondered impatiently now, which bed? But to get a sign, it was up to me to give one and meet Carlotta halfway. Surely she must be expecting me. I took a few tentative steps forward, the shoes I was carrying bumped into something, and there was a tiny thump, terribly loud to me in that pregnant semidarkness. I stopped dead and heard a rustling. A hand was moving, a disembodied hand was beckoning from a slit in one of the *mosquiteros*. It had to be Carlotta. If not—the devil with it! I was D'Artagnan. A sudden spray of moonlight suddenly illuminated the bed. The hand gestured liquidly in its sheen, seeming to draw me irresistibly toward the bed as if by a powerful silver strand. The hand opened the *mosquitero* more widely just as the moonlight ebbed. If the opening had seemed inviting before, now it was black and cavernous. *À toi, D'Artagnan,* I urged myself, and took the plunge.

"I thought you would never come, doctor," Carlotta whispered.

"Neither did I," I said truthfully.

She had called me doctor, and it seemed quite proper to go on with, "Well, shall we proceed with the examination?" To stifle the laughter welling up in me, I kissed Carlotta hurriedly on the lips, aware of a quick intake of breath, a gratified flash of her eyes, and a tremulous smile. I kissed her again lingeringly, and she responded. I felt her tremble all over, then myself. That for Paris! One of the sleepers moved as I was about to speak, and Carlotta put a fragrant hand over my mouth.

"What if they wake up?" I asked after a time.

"They won't," she said. "We will be very quiet."

I had placed my shoes at the end of the bed and was stretched out in awkward, clothes-encumbered full length next to her. We were walled and shut in by the transparent intimacy of the mosquito tent, and I felt like a fly trapped in a spider's web. All Carlotta had to do was grab me and cry out. I could see it all. The alarm, family outrage, and she had caught herself a husband. It often happened just that way in Europe, but thank God, if I could believe Arnaldo, things were managed differently in Santa Morena. Removing my clothes in such close quarters was as much a matter of gymnastics and doubling up as in an upper berth on a railroad train.

I was so anxious to be done with it that I wasn't aware of Carlotta's loving assistance until afterward.

She was experienced in love, too, and I was thankful. I was no D'Artagnan, I knew, not that night or any other since the terror had begun in Vienna. Although our time was limited, we did not hurry the preliminaries. Just before we joined I felt that I had forgotten something, but I couldn't remember what. There were sighs and quickened breathing, but no groans, bed-shaking, or thrashing about. We both knew what to do, and we did it. We seemed to fit together nicely, and we were good to each other. Afterward, we lay at peace in each other's arms, and I think I would have slept there the rest of the night if Carlotta hadn't warned me that it was time to go.

"Why do I always have to go?" I grumbled sleepily. "Go, go, always go."

"The day will come when you won't, Martin," she whispered in sudden passion. "It can be so."

Her words jogged me wide awake immediately. I began fumbling wildly for my clothes. I was a fool to come here like this and especially not to take any precautions—that was it!—*me*, a doctor. What was I thinking of?

"Hold me once more, dearest one," Carlotta pleaded. "The time together is so short."

I held her, and the feeling of power and recklessness came over me again. If she had no thought of the consequences, why should I? It was all part of the local custom, since she had neither inquired about or asked any precaution, nor, I reminded myself, was any available. I had included everything else in my medical supplies. So I was with Carlotta ten minutes longer—ecstatic for her, if I was any judge, and for me—? I felt weak and drained as I dressed, ashamed of myself since I had no love for this beautiful young woman, and thoughts of Paris began to intrude darkly. I dropped a shoe, and Carlotta shushed me.

"Put them on outside, Martin. And come tomorrow night. I will look for you, my lover."

Rather than answer, I kissed her quickly and slunk out into the drab, empty night.

*   *   *

If my nights were taken care of and gave me some measure of peace, my days were not, and the delay, the heat, and the hours with next to nothing to do but play with Daguero made me increasingly restless and irritable. I had noticed the chip-on-my-shoulder attitude and my mounting irascibility, but I couldn't contain myself. Insignificant little things made

76

me lose my temper. I kicked Daguero when he made a mess in the house or forgot what I had painstakingly taught him. I snapped at the Indios who stopped by for treatment and, worse, in my thoughts quarreled with Pierre, Don Socrates, and everyone over some imaginary slight or comment, raged at them in my mind, and then came out of it to learn, as I knew all along, that there was no basis for my anger, hatred, or combative attitude.

I realized that my bad case of nerves was caused by my ambivalent feelings over the projected trip to Rojas. I hated the delay and yet I welcomed it. An indescribable urge drove me on to leave Santa Morena with its airstrip and umbilical cord to civilization, the big cities, and the outside. Since I was miles from anywhere, I wanted to plunge still farther into the interior and the unknown. At the same time, I had to admit to myself that I dreaded leaving Santa Morena and the safety of the known, that I *had* to see the plane arrive once more before I left. In all the weeks I had been there, it had not come even once. I felt irrevocably lost and abandoned.

As the weeks passed, and we still hadn't left, I fretted and fretted. Then early one morning, with Daguero at my heels, I went to see the operator of Santa Morena's radio station. A dark, conscientious young man, he lived and worked in a clean, simple bungalow as functional, but much better organized than my own so-called office. He welcomed me considerately, but I had no time for small talk. I had questions burning on my mind, and it was all I could do to keep my temper as he talked around them.

"Doctor," he said, pointing to a neat row of dry cells on a wooden bench along the bamboo wall, "these are my batteries. In our damp climate they easily exhaust themselves. Twice each year the *avion* exchanges them for charged ones. But if I can't make them last long enough, there is no way for me to send or receive a message."

"But the plane *is* coming soon then?" I repeated irritably.

The operator gave me a patient smile, revealing a row of gold teeth as neat as his row of cells. "It is coming, yes. Every afternoon fifteen minutes are given to me for communications between Santa Morena and La Paz, and also between here and the small town at the Brazilian border where our *estancieros* drive their cattle for sale. Now from La Paz they say that several complications have held up the *avion*."

I sighed. "All right, when are they coming then?"

"*Quién sabe?*" He smiled. "Perhaps *mañana*."

I could no longer hold myself in. A muscle twitched above my eye and I burst out with, "How the devil can you be so patient? What if this was an emergency, a matter of life or death?"

The dark young man grew serious, gave a faint shrug of his shoulders. "Doctor, *cuando llega la hora*—when the hour strikes for any of us—a plane would hardly help, eh?" Now he smiled again and I felt abashed. "You must be expecting a cargo, a message, letters of some importance."

"No," I said, suddenly sober, "I am not expecting anything." Nothing except perhaps letters from the Ministry of Health, from Karl and Herbert, my fellow refugee friends who had come with me to La Paz, or—dare I hope?—from Paris. "No," I repeated softly, my voice a contrast to my earlier rude outburst, "I am not expecting anything at all. It's just that—I don't know."

He was a good man doing his job, and I was disgusted with myself. Why had I come here? What was I doing here? What had I hoped to do? If I could just see that plane coming in once, if I could just be sure that my exile wasn't permanent . . . My gaze drifted out through the window to the plains of the pampas where they seemed to stretch to infinity. Lost, I thought, forever lost, then my eyes were caught and held by a strange sight in the foreground. Two figures seemingly all legs and feet like herons.

"What—?" I began in bewilderment. "Who are they?"

The radio operator came to my side. "Those? Ah, they are *chimanes,* primitive Indios who live deep in the forests. You have not seen them before?"

"Never. Is that all they wear? Just a shirt?"

"Yes, doctor, only the long shirt you see and a straw hat. Of course, they do not live in the *pueblo,*" he went on in partial apology. "They are not like other Indios, but usually they carry bags of the things they make, which they exchange for necessities." He shaded his eyes. "These appear to be empty-handed. They come, they go." He shrugged and moved away from the window. "About the *avion.* When I hear news, I will tell you."

I thanked him and walked back to my house, not at all satisfied with the conversation. The same old *mañana* everywhere, every time. Would I ever get used to it? The dirt? Poverty? Ignorance? Insects? Heat? I rubbed my cheeks, and the stubble reminded me that I hadn't shaved. I didn't feel like it, but it was something to do. I brought out my razor and began to shave, contortioning my body to the whims of the light breeze playing with the small hand mirror I was using. It dangled down from one of the bamboo rods spiking the window frame, and I had to bob with it to keep from losing my reflection.

I had just nicked myself and was cursing the *avion,* the radio operator, and everyone and everything in Santa Morena as Pierre, typically, ran inside panting, his fat bulk heaving like jelly as he struggled for words.

78

"Doctor, a *chimane,* one of their best workers, has been bitten by a rattlesnake! Two messengers just arrived and told us. If we hurry—" He stopped to gulp for air. "If we hurry, we might have a chance to save him. Come quickly! I have a horse saddled for you."

A *chimane,* I thought. Interesting since the radio operator and I—but those must have been the messengers. I dried my face, put away my shaving things methodically, and began to assemble the snake-bite ampules and medical equipment I needed. I moved hurriedly, but not fast enough for Pierre, who was impatiently walking up and down.

"Never mind those things. I've got some *específico.* Here." He shoved a small bottle containing a brownish liquid at me. I uncorked it, smelled the stuff, and jerked my head back from the foul odor. Pierre grinned. "I know, but it's all right. You'll see. Come on."

Two hours later, I was glad that I had had breakfast before wandering down to speak to the radio operator. We had ridden miles and miles, and I was tired, saddle-sore, and drenched with sweat.

"Is it much farther, Pierre?" I asked.

"We are close to the woods now," he said confidently. "Only another short mile or so."

I knew this meant a good hour's ride farther and painfully rearranged my burning buttocks on the hard saddle. It was a relief that Pierre wouldn't stop talking. He spoke of the "civilized" *chimanes,* who lived in clearings in the virgin forest. They planted rice and *yuka,* a sweet, potato-like fruit, and brought their produce into the *pueblo* every so often to exchange for strips of linen, from which they made their long shirts, or for what they thought were beautiful colored pearls. They were just cheap bits of colored glass, said Pierre, imported from La Paz by the people of the village for just such a purpose. A Spanish woman would be too proud to wear such stuff, Pierre sniffed, but these *chimanes* . . .

"The 'civilized' ones live in what you might call the outskirts of the forests, but their wild cousins who go around naked and eat one another, live in the depths of the jungle." I looked at him from my horse. "You don't believe me, eh, doctor? Well, listen. Here in the province there is a very fine harbor village situated on the big river which ultimately flows into the Amazon. Small trading boats often come up that river from Brazil, and the people of Santa Morena would like to meet these boats and trade. But it is a long, arduous four days' ride. Oh, there is a short cut though. It goes right here through the forests and would save two and a half days out of the four. And you know why they don't take it?"

I shook my head, and he waved his free hand dramatically.

"Is it because of the savage boars? Is it because of the fierce *tigre?* No, *señor!* It is because of these wild Indios who are still cannibals and hunters of men."

I didn't know what to believe. He could be joking, but I doubted it. Boars, tigers, and now cannibals on top of everything else.

"These head-hunters," I said, trying to be casual, "do they often roam out of the jungle?"

"Ho! Ho!" Pierre laughed heartily, and I could have brained the fat slob. "They haven't eaten any white man for a long time. It is dark meat they like."

He was still laughing as we rode into a clearing in which stood a few miserable straw huts. In front of one on a straw mat lay a big, brown-skinned man, over whom hovered a gaping group of people. The man's face was bluish, his mouth bubbly with bloody foam, and he breathed stertorously. I noticed that his eyes were rolled back in his head and that his near-nude, heavily muscled body was covered with large hemorrhagic spots of the kind one often sees on corpses. I hadn't had too much experience with snake bites, at least nothing as deadly as the South American rattle-snake, but I knew this was a very sick man—a dying man. Too much time had elapsed since he was bitten. The poison was all through his system now, and no antidote would help. I had too few ampules as it was to go through the motions to no purpose. Still, I was a doctor.

"Hopeless after so long." I sighed as I prepared the ampules. "Absolutely hopeless now."

But Pierre wasn't even listening. He was taking out his vile *específico* or whatever he called it. Surrounded by the brown, primitively savage, long-shirted figures—it was imposible to tell which were men and which were women, they were so repulsively similar—he lifted his brown bottle high as if in supplication. Then he pulled a little spoon from his trousers' pocket and carefully poured the bilelike liquid into it. He raised the body of the unconscious man, uptilted the head, and forced the stinking stuff through his teeth.

The lips stayed back in the half-snarl into which they had been forced by Pierre's doctoring. Then they relaxed, and a little of the *específico* dribbled down the brown chin. I looked on skeptically, convinced that this, too, was a complete waste of time. Ridiculous nonsense like so much in this damn country, I sneered to myself, then I was angry. Who and what was I to feel so superior to these poor people? To Pierre, who at least was doing something? I swore never to find anything ridiculous in this country any more, then felt my eyes bug out. My God! Could it really be? The *chimane* was moving his lips. Now he seemed to breathe more regularly, the color of his skin became more alive, losing its fatal bluish cast.

Presently the man's eyes opened. He didn't move for a few breath-taking minutes, then his eyes flickered, he gave a little smile apparently in recognition of family and friends grouped around him, and I watched overwhelmed as life slowly came back into the body I had given up for dead.

"Good God, Pierre!" I said with a gasp. "What is that stuff? It ought to be written up everywhere and immediately introduced into the medical profession. Why, you've raised this man like Lazarus!"

Pierre beamed with pride and looked tenderly at his treasure. "They bring it along from Brazil when they come home from selling cattle. It's amazing stuff, isn't it? In a few minutes we shall give him another teaspoonful and he will be all right. It usually never fails."

It didn't this time either. Pierre gave him more, then examined the man's ankles until he found the pin-sized punctures made by the rattlesnake's fangs. Continuing the magic treatment, he dunked a little stick into the bottle, then smeared the brown liquid over the wound. The man was sound and smiling—everyone was smiling except me. The snake-bite ampules were in my hand, and I had to fight an impulse to fling them in the bushes. I noticed the other *chimanes* in the background now. They were clenching their fists and stamping out some kind of victory dance. A few came out of their huts with spears and pointed them at us. Pierre stood up suddenly, and I thought I saw a worried look on his broad face. Cannibals! I thought hysterically and felt weak in the knees. We would be the main course at a celebration banquet.

Sweat ran into my eyes. I wiped it away and saw now that Pierre was listening intently.

"The *avion!*" he exclaimed.

I can't explain what came over me at that instant. It was like an alarm bell to me, a ringing signal for which I had waited years and years. With one bound I was on my horse and prepared to gallop away. As I yanked the animal's head around, my eyes happened to light on the *chimane,* who was still stretched out on the ground. The sight brought me back with a sense of shock and shame. I felt the blood drain from my face as I reined in my horse, then I breathed deeply, my cheeks flushed, and I was aware of the burning redness of my features and the suffocating heat. I could not dismount. Pierre looked at me uncertainly.

"Let's go," he said. "The *chimane* really doesn't need us any more. That's all we could do for him, anyway. In a few days you will see him carrying bundles into the pueblo just like the others."

" 'We,' " I said scathingly. "I am the doctor and I did nothing."

"What does it matter?"

He wrapped his little brown bottle in an old torn shirt and stuffed it into his saddlebag. He patted the man he had raised from the dead on the back, murmured friendly words of encouragement to the other *chimanes,* then swung into the saddle with a series of grunts. In a short while we were out of the oppressive woods and out on the flat pampas. The thought of the plane still nagged me. Pierre must have imagined it back there. Surely the radio operator wouldn't lie to me.

"Are you sure about the *avion?*" I said anxiously.

"Quite. It's a little faint now, but I can still hear it."

Blinding blue sky above, small white clouds blotting out the horizon, the sweltering heat, the crazily buzzing of insects punctuated by the chirping of a million crickets—everything was just the same as a few hours before. I strained my ears for the sound of distant engines above the creaking of the saddle and the measured, muffled clop of hoofs. Nothing except the droning hum of a fly about my ears. But there was no fly, and desperation gripped me suddenly.

"For God's sake, let's hurry!" I exclaimed.

I dug my heels into my horse's flanks. The animal gave a lurch, then leaped ahead so frantically that I had to grab the saddle to keep my seat. Looking back, I saw that Pierre was keeping his animal reined in at a walk and I managed to restrain mine with difficulty. I was some distance ahead now and had to turn in the saddle to call to Pierre.

"Come on," I pleaded. "Let's hurry." But he did not urge his horse on. I was feverish with impatience, but I did note his expression, both sad and serious. What was the matter with this fellow? He must know what it meant to me—to reach the airstrip, just to see the plane poised there. Then why—oh, damn the man! "Don't you want to meet the *avion?*" I was almost sobbing, and I didn't care.

He plodded up to me on his horse, slowly, deliberately. "The plane means nothing to me," he explained, his voice strangely deep for a change. "Absolutely nothing."

His words, the way he looked, sobered me like a slap in the face. I was a fool, a babe in the wilderness. Pierre could treat a man dying from a rattlesnake bite, but there was no *específico* for what ailed him.

"I'm sorry," I murmured.

"Don't be, doctor. It is just that you are very fortunate. For you the *avion* means something—letters from your family or friends, perhaps a sweetheart left behind. For me there is nothing, so don't be angry if I didn't gallop with you. I would give anything to help, but it is senseless."

"I know. I just thought if we hurried—"

"You don't need to apologize. I understand, but no matter how much we hurried, it would still be too late. Only if they are delayed in Santa Morena with engine trouble or something, or, say, if the weather over the Cordillera is bad for the return trip, then you would have a chance. Besides, we are a long way out; the few minutes we might gain by going at a breakneck gallop would make our horses break down from heat and exhaustion. Listen," he said, clucking to his horse. "It is coming now."

We had gone a dismayingly short distance as the humming overtook us, the plane roared overhead and past. My eyes watering in the glare, I followed its effortless flight over the pampas before us. In a little while, the plane dived earthward and disappeared in the cloudy-blue haze. The humming was audible for a time, then it died away. My eyes misted over as I stared at the broad plains stretching before us—all that distance that had taken us hours and hours. Pierre was right, of course. We could never have made it, yet my eyes brimmed with tears of anger. Just this morning the radio operator had shrugged and said *mañana*. I bit my lips. They probably flew on an hour's notice. If I had stayed in Santa Morena, I could have met the plane. But no, Pierre had had to drag me off into the jungle when he didn't even need me.

"There will be another flight as always," he was saying. "Just don't go to Rojas with Don Socrates. Stay in Santa Morena and take the next plane back."

So he understood, eh? I felt a certain fury against him rising in me. My cheek muscles bulged and flattened, and my horse's head jerked as my grip on the reins tightened involuntarily.

"I am not going to take a plane back," I said positively, struggling to control myself. "It was just a question of meeting the *avion*, keeping contact." Lies, lies, I thought, and then in sudden terror I asked myself, what did I really want? A marvelous message that the world behind the Cordillera had changed. That the Nazis had vanished, that Vienna was as I remembered it, that the girl in Paris still loved and wanted me? None of these things could be, and I knew it. So why was I torturing myself? Laughter suddenly broke from my lips, loud and ugly. "Come to think of it, the plane means nothing to me either, Pierre. Not a single thing!"

"Maybe so," he said thoughtfully, "maybe so. But I don't believe you'll be able to stand it here for long."

"You're wrong!" I snapped. "I'll manage. You wait and see."

We had gone on a few miles without a word as the sound of engines reached us again. The plane passed overhead, climbing, and shot off in the direction of the Cordillera and La Paz. Pierre glanced at me, but this time I neither looked up nor felt anything. I had committed myself voluntarily; I had responsibilities to others as well as myself. And that had to be that.

The sun was at its highest now, and sweat was raining off both us and the horses. As a few skimpy trees came into view, the panting, stumbling horses headed instinctively for their meager shade. Their nostrils quivered as they pulled up near a little ditch filled with brackish water.

"We might as well give them a rest," said Pierre.

He got down, tied the reins around a tree trunk, and eased his bulk to the grass with a stammer of little sighs so explosive and staccato I first thought he was breaking wind. Pierre looked done in. His pouchy cheeks were gray and hanging down like flabby cups. His unusually large eyes were bloodshot and strained as he stared at the horizon's bluish line, where the light humming of engines was still faintly audible. Sighing, he rolled a *cigarillo* and tried to lick the edge of the thin paper. It did not stick after repeated attempts, the tobacco streamed out, and he crumpled the thing in his thick fingers.

"I used to feel the same way as you do," he said, still looking off to the horizon. "Of course, twenty years ago no airplane ever crossed the mountains—only adventurers on mules and supply trains. But the mail came in every six months and, when it did, my heart raced like crazy. I was sure a miracle would happen, that somehow she would come after me. Oh, I was still romantic then, a dreamer and an idealist. I felt she had to follow me, driven by her guilty conscience if by no other feeling."

He stopped, rolled another *cigarillo,* licked it successfully, and jammed it between his bulbous lips.

"She?" I said questioningly. "You were married then?"

It was as if Pierre hadn't heard me.

"Oh, how I painted the scene in glowing colors," he went on, mocking himself as he had been. "How she would come, throw herself tearfully into my arms, beg me to forgive and forget, plead to stay with me." He inhaled deeply, then blew out a wreath of bluish smoke. "How easily I would have forgiven and forgotten," he said earnestly. "Why, I would gladly have kissed the ground her feet walked on. I would have built her a house like Don Socrates', raised a large herd . . ." He threw his *cigarillo* into the dust. "But nothing, Martin, nothing.

"I even made excuses for her. I told myself it was hard for a woman to make such a trip. And I waited for a message. I would have been contented with a word, a thought, a simple apology admitting the wrong she'd done me. Then I tried to convince myself she did not know where I was, where I'd gone." He gave a wry little snort. "A lie, Martin, this was a lie, too. Sheer self-delusion. She could have found out, but why should she? Why should she?" He kicked at the ground, oblivious of the choking cloud of dust that rose around his great head. "I'll never understand it. If nothing else, the common memory of our child should have urged her on. It wasn't my fault."

His head fell into his hands, and I waited for him to go on without showing any impatience or curiosity. Insects buzzed about us, the heat made the pampas undulate like a heaving ocean before us, and, not far away, the horses shook their heads, stamped their feet, and switched their tails.

"It wasn't my fault," he repeated, his voice muffled as he spoke with his head down in his hands. "The disease wouldn't have hit me half so hard if I hadn't spent day and night on my feet watching over her and the child. I had no resistance, nothing left mentally or physically, but I was still a human being. I swear to you I would have stuck if anything happened to her. I meant it when I took her for better or worse, in sickness and in health. My God, Martin! Twenty years and I'm still trying to forget her. The bitch! Bitch! All women are bitches."

I was about to protest his bitter judgment, my mind reverting darkly to Lisa in Paris, then I thought better of it and waited for him to go on. But he had subsided, lying as inert as a collapsed balloon. Poor Pierre! So he had a wife and family and a broken heart. I didn't quite know whether to believe his story, after the first one he'd told about getting the little girl in trouble, but it made more sense. But what was this disease he had had? My medical curiosity demanded that I ask him. It was on my lips, and then I saw that Pierre was in no condition to answer personal questions. I pitied the man, wondering what had made him open his heart to me. Here, of all places, in the midst of the romantic pampas that were but parched fields, squatting beneath a sorry tree that contrasted sharply with the lush vegetation my mind had always associated with the jungle. I felt time and space falling away, and I was caught and held in a trance which almost made me forget my lead-heavy boots and the burning band of the sombrero around my forehead.

"You are young for a doctor," Pierre was saying. "Were you happy as a boy?"

The question took me by surprise. He was more composed now, sitting up and smoking another *cigarillo*.

"Yes. Yes, I was."

"My parents—" He cut himself off and began again. "Were you ever beaten as a boy?"

"Only once." How clearly it came back to me! "I had come home from school almost hysterical with excitement. I had won a fight with the class bully before the whole school. He had insulted me, knocked me down, and I had gotten up and whipped him. It was the greatest day of my life, but my mother wouldn't listen or try to understand. I was filthy with dirt, my face bruised, and my shirt torn. She saw not triumph and victory, but shame and disgrace. Think of it!"

It all came back so vividly as I spoke that I trembled all over.

"White and furious, almost snarling like an animal in her anger, she raised her hand and hit and hit and hit. She screamed—I can still hear her— 'I will make a gentleman out of you yet. My son isn't going to be a *gassenbub!* I want no street bums in my family!' It was so awful that sometimes it's hard to believe that it was my mother who stood there holding that ripped white collar in her shaking hand. Didn't she understand, Pierre, that courage was a lot more important to a little boy than an immaculate stiff collar? That bravery and fighting back were essential for survival in the world into which she bore me? She was a grownup, and grownups are never supposed to understand, but all the same . . ." My voice lowered to a whisper because it had come to me as a sudden self-revelation. "Now I don't think she loved me at all."

"Sure, she loved you. Sure, she did." Pierre was rubbing his face with his palms as if he had just awakened. "She was just wrapped in herself the way women are. A spanking doesn't hurt a boy."

"You're wrong, Pierre. That was no spanking. I don't remember the pain, but it still hurts. It'll always hurt."

The bright sun was suddenly blinding. I had to shut my eyes against its glare, and I felt dizzy. The world was turning upside down.

"That picture of that angelic little boy you have in your suitcase—is that you?"

"Well, it was taken of me," I admitted ruefully. "To make my mother

86

happy, I had to live up to it. I carry it with me so—so I can laugh at myself whenever I feel like laughing at myself. That's good for a man."

"We all carry pictures around, false pictures. You in your suitcase, I in my heart. And you know, Martin, you are still wearing that stiff white collar like the boy in the photograph." Pierre looked straight at me. "I can see it clearly around your neck."

The accusation made me jump. "That's not so!" I insisted.

But he paid no attention to me. "My wife hurt me, too. She kicked me out of her heart and life, but I keep returning to her like a dog licking the hand that has beaten him. Our loyalties don't change with geography, you know; they only get more intense with time."

"I'm no dog," I spat at him. "The past is dead forever."

"Perhaps, but I urge you to go back where you came from before it is too late. You might have a chance to get rid of the collar there, but never here in no man's land. I can tell."

Pierre turned on his heel and started for the horses. Rage and self-disgust choked me, and I could not answer him.

* * *

It was midafternoon by the time we got back to the *pueblo*. The day's heat had abated, but everybody still seemed asleep and Santa Morena deserted. Daguero received me boisterously at my house. I gave him a dish of food and prepared something for myself. I cleaned the dishes, washed up, and felt better. Pierre came in a while later, and things were surprisingly easy between us. I marveled that the scene at the pampas was as remote as if it had never happened.

"I bring news both good and bad," he crowed on arriving, his voice a high falsetto again. "I am told it was a sudden flight and the *avion* brought no mail. But it did bring Carlotta's father." He flashed me a malicious smile. "And you were right, doctor, *El Chileno* died a few hours after he reached La Paz."

"I am sorry to hear it," I said.

"Don't be," said Pierre. "One must never be sorry when one is right."

At supper in Don Socrates' house, I tried to find out more, but the old man didn't seem to know anything further or want to talk about it. When I said I wanted to pay my respect to Carlotta's father, Don Socrates did not approve and that was more than a veto. The old man probably had good reasons. For my part, I guessed her father had a bad conscience, and it would be painful for him to talk to me. But it was Carlotta I was worried about. What would I do at night now that he was back? I felt a strong need for her just then, and I wanted a word with her if we suddenly left for Rojas tomorrow or the next day.

I said good night to the old man and crossed the plaza on my way home to Daguero and dreary solitude. It had been a wearying, fruitless, if revealing day. After Pierre's outburst and then my own, I felt depressed and sorely in need of company. I could have stayed on at Don Socrates' for a few more hours, but the coincidence of Carlotta's father's homecoming and my own sudden—and almost eager—availability would have been too obvious an admission of our intimacy. Not that it made any great difference, I supposed, since there had been enough hints, smirks, and meaningful glances to assure me that our affair was an open secret. Tiny communities like Santa Morena demanded more pretense than the big towns, where gossip and who-was-going-with-whom could dilute and dissipate without much notice. Here, just about everything was everybody's business—and only distraction.

My house was lighted by a single, guttering native candle, which the old *mozo* caretaker had set on a stool in the doorway between the two rooms. The *mozo* was there, waiting for me, and he seemed mad about something —or maybe he always mumbled in that fashion. I thought I heard him mention Pierre's name, but I couldn't be sure. In any case, he didn't press me. I decided that it was the unremitting heat that left me so tired. Or perhaps it was going at it so hard with Carlotta, the lack of sleep, the running back and forth. I could smell her suddenly, hear her passionate murmuring as she throbbed under me—and I shivered for her body with a raw ache.

I yawned, lay down on the bed, and stared thoughtfully at the dark ceiling. I felt lightheaded, dissatisfied, empty. *Chimanes,* rattlesnake bites, magic in a stinking brown bottle, Pierre and his wife and child and misery —and my own damned chains to the past. My sense of reality was badly strained. I didn't know who or what I was, where I was, and what I was doing here. The perfect mood and just the night for drinking. To get drunk and not think or care any more. But I was too tired to get up. The suitcase with the whisky was so far away across the room, and I was dead. I lay there in the darkness, no time or place existed, and I didn't know whether I slept or waked . . .

A thunderous knocking at the door brought me upright with a wrench. My heart was beating furiously, and I held my spinning head tight in both hands. It was pitch dark, no candle showing. I must have fallen asleep. What the devil was it now? Another rattlesnake bite?

"Doctor! Doctor! Doctor!" The voice grew louder each time.

"Yes, what's the matter? Who is it?"

"It's me, Antonio, the notary public. Don Pierre is sick. *Hágame el favor*—come quickly, please!"

I forgot my aching head. Let's see. Boots tied, shirt buttoned. The emergency kit I always kept ready at hand, the flashlight. I was set.

"What's happened, Don Antonio? What's the matter with him?"

"They had a fight. It seems he drank. Hurry!"

I couldn't make much sense of the little he told me, but there was no point in asking more questions. The ground was wet with dew and the cool night air made me shiver. I wondered aloud what time it was, then realized Antonio had no watch, and it was too dark to read mine. I turned on the flashlight and noted with surprise that it was just after four. Strange. I had slept a long time.

It was a long, stumbling walk to the outskirts of the village, where the huts of the poorest Indios huddled right up to one of the poles of the *currichi*. I couldn't believe that Pierre, who had made me understand he owned a herd of cattle worth driving to Brazil, should live in such squalor. We must be going the wrong way. But Don Antonio hurried on to a grimy shack with a single dimly lighted window looking like a blunted eye.

Inside there was only one dirty, ugly room. Pierre lay on a cowhide. But he did not exactly lie on it. His enormous body was propped against a wooden trunk that stood alongside the dingy wall. His wet, sandy hair was glued in strands to his narrow forehead, and he slumped like a fallen giant. It took only a few seconds to take this in, and I thanked God for my excellent professional training. No matter how I felt, my response to sickness was instantaneous. Pierre's chest moved in fast, labored respiration, the skin on his wrist clammy, his pulse faint and rapid. His eyes could hardly be seen in the sagging folds of fat on his skin, and he did not flinch as I thrust the hypodermic, filled with caffeine and coramine, into the fatty tissue of his hamlike upper arm.

Looking up from my work, I saw three people watching me in the steady light of a small kerosene lamp set on the opposite wall. A woman flanked by two boys, their black eyes glittering with hostility and suspicion. They were undoubtedly Indios, looking so much alike I was certain the woman was the mother of the teen-aged boys. She was in late middle age, with a lean, worn face and now, as she sat down, keeping both arms stiffly at her sides, she shot me a look of sullen apology—or so it seemed. For then I was looking in front of her to the earthen floor where a shattered bottle of liquor, undeniably mine from the label, had stained the soil a dark cocoa. I sensed that she knew that I knew; that she feared I would accuse Pierre of stealing the bottle from my house.

I gave her a quick, reassuring smile, then turned back to my patient, who seemed to be coming around. His eyes showed a trace of iris, then he motioned weakly as he recognized me.

"My friend . . ." he mumbled, "fellow countryman . . . doctor."

He struggled for breath and gestured for me to come close. I pulled up a stool next to him, and Pierre began to whisper in German.

"*Teufel.* That woman—she's a devil. I must give her a beating I must—"

I tried to quiet him, but he had to speak. He panted heavily and his breath was offensive. So was he now, lying there like some monstrous toad, squat, obese, and repulsive.

"Listen to me," he begged. "All these years how I've longed to see my beloved Vienna again, to take my sweetheart to the Wiener Wald and the Heurigen, to waltz with her close in my arms. Ah, Strauss, the *Blue Danube* . . ."

Somehow he managed to croak out the melody in so grotesque a manner that my spine tingled in disgust. It was beyond melodrama, here and in such circumstances, and Hollywood at its worst couldn't have improved on it. A sedative might shut off this fountain of nausea. I fumbled in my kit, then noticed the mist clearing from Pierre's eyes.

"They did it to you, too, didn't they, Martin? They taught you five years of Greek and eight years of Latin, instead of something practical like Spanish or riding a mule. Oh, they gave you a diploma, but first they made you torture your soul with literature and philosophy, logic and psychology —and for what? When life destroys you, tears you into little pieces, and you want to forget everything—mostly yourself—our education makes it impossible. Even spiritual suicide because one is always so aware . . ."

He trailed off to get his breath, and pity and compassion seized me. How could I have despised this man, been sickened by him when—God help me!—he was so much like myself? In Vienna, in Paris, on the ship, even in Santa Morena, I had felt the same and yet this wreck of a man had expressed himself as I never could. This man who had fled the past and the present as I had.

"Pierre," I said softly, much as one might say "brother," and reached out to take his hand. But the feverish look had come back into Pierre's eyes and he was raving again.

"I remember a story about the Wild West of North America. I was only a boy, but I never forgot the grave with the cross at the foot of the hill.

You see, there was a green valley in the prairies and the small hill behind. The lonely grave was at the foot of the hill and at sunset it turned red-purple. All my life I have looked for the lonely grave with the cross, but I never found it. I wanted so much to find it, then, then—"

He hunched up a little, anxiety wrinkling his face like defects in a great rubber ball. "Now I am afraid of the sunsets, the evenings." His whisper was a hoarse whistle, and I had to bend close to hear him. "In the night, it came to me. I sobbed, I yelled. Nobody wanted to stay with me, only that woman, that black bitch. And she broke my bottle. Yes, she did it. Give me my whip, give it to me. Oh, why shouldn't I drink? Why? What else is there? My friend, oh, my fellow countryman, I am so happy you're here with me, so happy . . ."

His head fell forward and rolled to the side. He slept, and the watchers—the woman, the boys, and myself—sighed as one. There was a stir at the entrance. Don Socrates stood in the doorway, his *mozo* behind him. The woman remained seated and he gave her a furious glare, until she rose, hate and defiance in her eyes before she lowered her glance. Don Socrates looked at Pierre sleeping peacefully, then beckoned me outside. I bent over Pierre, picked up my kit, nodded at the Indian woman and her son, and followed him.

A pale half-moon crawled over the uncertain horizon as we walked slowly back to the center of the *pueblo*. I felt sleepy now and bewildered.

"*Pobre diablo,*" said Don Socrates in a murmur. "I hoped you would be spared this, doctor. He should not drink, but in the last few years it has become worse. I don't think he's had a drop since you got here—not till tonight, and I can't imagine where he got it." He paused significantly and I said nothing. "It's a disgrace, but no reason for that she-devil to raise her hand against him. I've given her the whip myself for that!"

"What's this about his going to Brazil?" I asked.

"Ah, just talk. He has no cattle, doctor, and who would trust Pierre with so much as a single cow, eh? *Pobre diablo!* He is so terribly afraid of the shadows and the nights. And no woman will live with him except that Indio savage, who has two sons herself."

"But, Don Socrates, he surprises me. Just now, before you came, he spoke in a way that struck me to the depth of my heart. I don't understand—there are many things I don't understand about Pierre."

"*Hijo,* ask Don Antonio! When Pierre is sober, he writes the best letters and draws up the shrewdest contracts. He is a fine lawyer."

"You mean he really is a lawyer. I thought it was his brother who—"

"Certainly he's a lawyer, and a good one. He had a brilliant future in his own country, but something happened and he had to leave. Before the war, when they still had a consul in La Paz, our congressman checked on Pierre. He comes from a very fine family, you know. As I understand it, he took the blame for something he didn't do, and then the guilty party let him down."

Here was yet a third story to account for Pierre's being in South America. It was puzzling, but not half so worrisome as the coldness rising in my heart.

"Don Socrates, tell me: do all the *gringos* who come here end up this way?"

The old man stopped in his tracks and eyed me scornfully.

"*Hijo,* don't you say any such thing! I am a *gringo* myself, for that matter, only that I have been in this hemisphere for forty years. I have my *paisanos* here, and we don't end up this way. It is in the person, in the nature of a man what becomes of him. Pierre has his streak of brilliance and for that we keep a place for him in our community. But he took to the *aguardiente;* he is using it to kill something in himself and one day it will kill him. No, doctor, life in the jungle is no different from any other part of the world. A man has to work and fight for his place among his fellow men."

Nothing else was said. At his door the old man bade me a simple *"Buenas noches,"* and I touched his arm in silent reply.

Back home, Daguero rose from his burlap bed to sniff at me. I patted him absently and thought about going back to bed. But I was no longer sleepy, and the space enclosed by the transparent mosquito netting was as empty as my heart. A little gray light entered between the slits of the window shutters. Early morning, bleak and barren. I shivered. A gray line at the top of the window, another at the bottom. And there was one of the big packing cases for the trip looking just like a coffin in the dimness. Now the light entering the slits seemed to form a cross on the coffin—the grave Pierre was looking for and had come to fear so much! My God, was I seeing things!

Panic hit me like a fist. One good pull and the mosquito net had been torn from my bed. Another few seconds and I had the shutters flung open. The weak, gray light of the time before dawn washed the darkness from the room, but it was as comfortless as tepid water on an icy day. All right now, I advised myself, all right. Take a deep breath, then relax. It's silly to

92

get frightened over nothing. These things couldn't be helped. Pierre is Pierre, you are you . . .

The plaza slept. There were no graves, no red and purple sunsets, just a grayish-white hillock close to that big tree. A cow that had sprawled there for the night. And those standing shadows, what were they? I squinted my eyes. Oh, horses. Why did horses sleep standing up? I wondered with idle intentness. Did they, too, always have to be ready to run at a moment's notice?

To hell with it! I needed a drink and never mind the reason. There didn't have to be one. Just say it was to brighten my outlook and make me sleepy. Just that and nothing more. I picked up my suitcase, but the lock didn't work. Pierre must have picked and broken it to steal that bottle. Damn him! No, no, pity him.

I fumbled in one of the supply boxes—the coffin of a few wild minutes back—and right on top I found a bottle. I popped the cork and drank it straight, a big gulp, then another, and another. Black, bitter, and strong, it turned my stomach before it settled, then magically dragged me down into a deep sleep.

6

Pierre Briefs Me; We Leave for Rojas; The Sick Indio and the False Priest

Fortunately, I had no patients or calls to make the next morning, and I was able to sleep late. As it was, I awoke with a vile headache in the heat of noon to get the news that we were finally starting out on the trip very early the next day. After waiting so long, I could hardly believe it was the real thing, but I wanted to get busy, went ahead with final preparations, and felt much better in the afternoon. Pierre came over then, behaving just as if nothing had happened the night before.

It was just as if he suffered from convenient amnesia. He looked and talked much as always, but occasionally I caught a look, a subtle undertone, that convinced me that he wasn't feeling as well as he pretended. Chronic alcoholics have hang-overs just like the rest of us and, although it was on the tip of my tongue to refer to his trouble, I thought it best to leave it up to Pierre, should he want to discuss it. But he obviously didn't, showing up again at dawn the next morning just as the *mozo* drove the *carreton* up to the front of the house, and obligingly helping load all the cargo without being asked. As the cart lurched off, he hurled some quick instructions at the Indio, who accepted them with downcast eyes.

"Remember now," he called, "if the doctor does not catch up with you at the river, be sure to wait for him at *El Cementerio*." We watched the vehicle rumble off, and Pierre added, "And you, Martin, check there and make sure your supplies are intact. And don't look so surprised at the name *El Cementerio*. Travelers always stop at the hut there. It's where the sick from the surrounding *estancias* gather to get a lift to a *pueblo*—to go to see the *curandero*—I mean *you* now, of course."

I had had my fill of *curanderos* and didn't particularly want to discuss

94

them. "I see," I said. "Anyway, that's still a grim name for a way station."

"I suppose." Pierre scratched the back of his head. "But once these people make up their minds to head for the *pueblo,* they're usually on their last legs. Some don't make it. First there was one grave, then another, then more and more. So now you have *El Cementerio.*"

The mules and horses wouldn't be setting out for a few hours, so we had plenty of time to talk. Pierre explained that hauling the *carretons* was hard work and the carts usually went on ahead, moving preferably at dawn or dusk, but never during the burning hours around noon. I had written a few letters to my friends in La Paz and was anxious to send them off before leaving. I got them out, and Pierre led the way to the neat little house in which Santa Morena's postmistress handled the mail. She was a shy, plain woman with an exceptionally white skin, and I courteously asked her to make sure my letters were dispatched on the next *avion.* I also requested that she forward my mail to Rojas through a reliable person.

The young woman stamped my letters and gave my request serious, brow-wrinkling consideration. As I waited for her reply, Pierre embarrassed me by stalking around the room and sniffing at everything like a dog. It seemed to me he was overacting the *gringo,* and I wondered what these people must think of foreigners.

"*Como no,*" said the woman at last, her slow speech somehow pointing up her extreme pallor. "We now have a reliable Indio who carries the mail on his saddle ox. Since I have been postmistress, we have only lost the bags twice."

"And how did that happen?" I prompted her, my professional instincts aroused by her complexion. Was the girl naturally so pale or was her skin tone a symptom of disease?

"*Pues,*" she said, smiling politely. "The first time the *mozo's* hat was found on the riverbank. The river was high, and it was assumed that the saddle ox drowned and that alligators killed the carrier. Of the second time, we know nothing."

I thanked her, she nodded, and we went outside.

"A nice *muchacha* and still to be had," said Pierre with a smirk. "You would never believe it, eh? You probably don't even know that she is Carlotta's sister."

I said I didn't and veiled my annoyance with him. I was surprised, however; there was no resemblance between them, and I had never met the postmistress at Carlotta's house. The thought of Carlotta made me uneasy. We had seen much of each other, enjoyed our passionate nights together

95

under her *mosquitero,* and then our trysts had ended with her father's return. Since that time I had not seen her, nor given her sign, and she must think I was avoiding meeting her. I felt guilty at what she must take as my selfish thoughtlessness, and it seemed a relief to be leaving Santa Morena and such problems. I supposed I ought to say good-by to Carlotta, but it was too late now.

Pierre stood by as the travelers gathered in the patio of Don Socrates' house. One of his sons adjusted the saddle on my horse, and I watched, suddenly wishing I had a camera with me. The colorful scene stirred my senses. The hustle and bustle, the snorting and pawing of the horses and mules, the men and women congregated expectantly in the patio. Don Socrates had thrown a ragged old cape over his shoulders, but a king could not have worn it with more poise. A wide felt sombrero covered his gray head. It was set at an angle and this, with the leather band dangling under his chin, gave his lined features a dashing, daring appearance. Solemnly he shook hands, embraced, then shook hands again with his wife and daughter. He did the same with the oldest *mozos* and *sirvientas.*

His two sons wore old trail clothes and jaunty hats like their father's. They, too, made a bold, dashing appearance as they embraced those staying behind and raised their arms to wave repeatedly at the crowd of male and female *criados* standing around the patio. I wore a wide-brimmed sombrero myself. Woven by a villager, it was made from white fibers supposedly able to resist the wildest rain torrents. But I had looked at myself in my shaving mirror and was sure it made me look ridiculous. I was a self-conscious *gringo* then.

There was no one for me to make my good-bys—except Pierre and he obviously was counting on a big farewell scene. His eyes brimmed with tears and his quivering bulk drooped pathetically. Because of his big belly I couldn't have embraced him if I'd wanted to, but a lump came into my throat as we shook hands warmly. Perhaps my feelings were a bit exaggerated, but I had said good-by so many times lately, and it had so often turned out to be a last good-by. Besides, Pierre had been a good, helpful friend and, whatever his faults, we had more in common than I liked to think about.

"*Adiós! Adiós!*"

Daguero was barking excitedly now. It was as big an adventure for him as for me. The men all waved in unison, trotting elegantly out of the patio. I had a last glimpse of Pierre blubbering sadly as I followed the others, but nowhere near as elegantly. There was a terrible howling and barking as the women and *mozos* held back the dogs. Only one of Don Socrates' brutes was being taken along as company for Daguero, and the rest protested volubly as we rode away.

Going along the street, the riders halted frequently to shake hands and exchange good wishes with friends and villagers. They also were given messages and commissions that it was the practice to give those traveling to the capital of the province or from village to village. I felt rather left out of things until we passed Carlotta's house. Her father was standing there smoking a *cigarillo* and looking very serious as we passed in review, as it were.

I felt a pang at the sight of him—for Carlotta's sake, I suppose—and, acting on the rashest of impulses, dismounted and approached him. He showed no surprise as we clasped hands, embraced, and clasped hands again. He wished me well, but made no mention of *El Chileno,* nor did he invite me into the house, although I was sure I could see dark eyes drilling me from a corner of the window. There was my good deed for the day, and I jumped on my horse feeling like a fool, and hurried on to join the other travelers.

On the outskirts of Santa Morena, I again passed the half-moon-shaped *currichi.* A feeble breeze rippled the surface of the brackish pool, and I looked at the water in disgust.

"This is our *currichi,* doctor!" Don Socrates announced proudly from his horse, then repeated what Pierre had told me the day I arrived. "Whoever has tasted of this water will always come back to it. See there." He pointed. "Those are purifying plants. They make the water clean and sweet."

He smacked his lips as he might over some delicacy and drove his mule ahead, the water splashing under its neat little hoofs. It could be so, since every region has its inexplicable wonders, but I had my doubts about the purifying effect of the cherished plants. I was almost sure that every child and most adults in the village harbored intestinal worms which undoubtedly came from the drinking water. So far as taste was concerned, Don Socrates was right; it *was* sweeter and more satisfying than filtered water. To them this mattered more than germs and, doctor or no, it would be impolite not to agree.

The grassland began beyond the *currichi,* flat and limitless and stretching out to the horizon. Don Socrates reined in next to me, making a dramatic arc with one arm.

"This is blessed soil you see here, doctor. The grass-rich pampas supply us with food and yield the products with which we buy clothes and pay for our necessities. Here," he went on, glowing with pride, his arm still sweeping the air, "our cattle graze and multiply. We do not even know about it until we see the calves at their mothers' sides. Then every year we round up stock and make the difficult drive to the Brazilian border. Oh, it is a terrible trip for man and beast, but every year we arrive with our cattle at the market, and people pay a premium . . ."

Don Socrates broke off, his body hunching forward in the saddle as if the mule's pace were suddenly too slow for him. I admired him greatly then, this man with the face of a patriarch, the enthusiasm of a child, and the faith of a disciple.

"Yes, blessed soil, doctor," he continued. "And we look at the pampas as our church. As we ride the endless, lonely hours, God speaks to us from his pulpit in the sky. The vastness of the pampas is the vastness of time— both penetrate our hearts. If life burdens a man, he has only to saddle a horse and ride out here where there is only the sky and the plains. On the pampas he will forget what oppressed him, he will be free of the little things that bind and enslave all men. He will feel like, like—" he searched for the right word, his eyes musing on the distance ahead—"like an umpire, high above the petty game of life."

This man had already surprised me in many ways, but I hadn't expected such a philosophy. The others were ahead, we were riding side by side and, although Don Socrates had stopped speaking, his words still hung challengingly in the air between us. My heartbeats ticked away seconds and minutes of time, my horse's hoofs ticked away yards and yards behind, while ahead the pampas stretched into eternity. Now that incomparable union of time and space, about which Don Socrates had spoken so movingly, seemed to take hold of me. I could feel it sorting the solid strands amid my chaotic emotions, disentangling them, choosing and discarding, then all in the same disembodied process presenting me with enlightened thoughts, clear pictures. Through my partial reverie I was aware of Don Socrates clearing his throat expectantly.

"I don't know about being an umpire," I remarked absent-mindedly. "Nor do I want to be above daily life. Because of my profession and background, I am compelled to be a member of the team playing the game, rather than an impartial spectator. But then some of us don't play too well and that again is because we're not sure we want to be on that team in that place."

"Sí, doctor," he said, a pleased smile kindling his weathered features. He looked on me fondly for a moment, lovingly as a father watching a son take his first stumbling steps after a serious illness. "You are right, but it is always difficult. I repeat this is blessed soil, but some of us still succumb to the urge for the busy, noisy ways and the narrow streets of the big cities. Some of us, doctor, and mostly when we are young. I yearned for them myself; I had to see where my desires led me." He smiled again, a secret, inner smile.

"And what happened?" I said, now fully alert.

"*Pues,* I am here." Again he waved an expressive arm at the pampas. "That is the answer."

The old man sank into silence, the faint smile still on his lips as he re-lived the past. I looked around for Daguero and saw him scurrying about with the other dog. They darted from side to side, yapping, playing, and jumping with catlike grace, then scooting off to disappear into the high grasses of the roadside. I could see it rippling under the movement of their bodies, then they exploded from the billowing greenness and took their places back of the horses, heads and tongues hanging, hot and subdued, resting a brief moment before sallying forth anew.

I watched them for a while, then my thoughts turned inward, running backward from Santa Morena to La Paz, the ship, Paris . . . When I looked up again, I saw I had fallen far behind the other riders. Don Socrates' two sons were only dots on the horizon, and I had the queer feeling of having been abandoned. Or had I abandoned them? "A lone man on horseback moved through the endless pampas." The sentence leaped into mind, harking me back to the daydreams of childhood. What had been a youthful fancy of the adventurous life was now a part of my daily experience—and nothing like the dream.

Blinking in the bright sunlight, my body moving loosely with the rhythmic movements of my tireless horse, I thought of the little house I had lived in with my mother, shield and protector. I remembered my own special room under the attic roof with its skylight through which I could watch the moon and the stars. How I read up there! How much I looked forward to Saturday afternoons, when half of the day and the whole of Sunday stretched ahead, free of school, and I could lie alone and read about the riders of the endless pampas. And here I was, and it was hardly romantic, only drab, bleak, and cruel.

I was homesick. I had a savage, overwhelming yearning for the happy time when this life was only a fancy, when I lived in a dear little room in a safe little house, when I was told what to do and not to do by the voice of loving authority. When I didn't have to take drugs to fall asleep! Look-

99

ing up, I saw the other riders so far ahead that it seemed I would never catch up to them. I cursed myself, cursed my thoughts, and kicked my horse to a gallop.

Unused to riding all day, I was so stiff, sore, and exhausted at night that I all but fell asleep as we ate supper. We camped out, and I was struck by the great contrast between the enervating heat of the days and the coldness of the nights. Sometimes just before drifting off, I thought of Pierre's lonely grave in the prairies, its cross shimmering in the purple-red rays of a sunset much like the one we had just seen on the pampas. A fantasy this and not like my mother's grave—poor Mother buried somewhere in one of Europe's vast graveyards . . .

* * *

As we went on and on and on over the grasslands, I became convinced there would be no end to them. But on the morning of the third day, after a long ride that had begun at sunrise, we pulled up by a river lined with vegetation.

"The River Yucoma, doctor," said Don Socrates, reining in next to me. He pointed ahead, then to the left and the right. "Those green lines of trees and bushes accompany the waters all the hundreds of miles to the Amazon." His bushy eyebrows contracted as he frowned, and he raised his eyes to some black birds circling over the river at one point. "Vultures," he said darkly. "They're just at the *puerto* where we cross."

He clucked at his mule, then gave the animal a crack with his whip, and the whole caravan broke into a gallop, the dogs barking in the lead. As we reached the crossing, I began to worry about my *mozo* and the supplies. Maybe he had made off with the lot. But no, there he was unloading cargo from a canoe on the other bank. Don Socrates shouted to him, asking about the vultures wheeling overhead.

The Indio straightened up and shaded his eyes. *"El caiman,"* he called across the river, his voice for once betraying emotion. "Over there behind the trees." He pointed proudly in the direction of the fallen enemy.

How quiet it was here, I thought. An idyllic peace enlivened only by the shrieks of a pair of low-flying parrots, the coquettish, whistling calls of small monkeys in the trees, and the playful splashes of beaver-like creatures frolicking along the riverbank. It was a lotus land, the sparkling, lazy water somehow redolent of a complacent leisure that made a mockery out of haste. Stay, they seemed to murmur, stay, tarry, stay. *Mañana* and *mañana* and *mañana.*

I followed Don Socrates, who had disappeared behind some large trees where my *mozo* had pointed. The foul, gorge-rising stench of the dead alligator reached me well before I saw the carcass of the huge animal, putrid and torn apart by vultures.

"Sometimes they travel overland from river to river to lake," said the old man when he saw me. He was keeping himself at a distance and his nose was twitching. "In the dry time, at least you can see them, but in the rainy season, when all this is nothing but black water for many miles, they are treacherous." He stared gloomily toward the river, as if envisioning the ravages of the flood period. *"El caiman* is liable to surprise you then." His hand shot up so unexpectedly I shrank back. "He is apt to pop up at your side as close as I am to you. He respects a horse though, so we make sure to be in the saddle as much as possible. We have to be careful with our dogs. These beasts go *loco* after dogs."

The *mozo* had paddled back to the *puerto* and beached the canoe. Now he was standing high and erect on the front of his *carreton,* almost leaning over the oxen as he frantically urged them toward the water. Shouting and swinging his whip wildly, he lashed the agitated animals down the embankment. At the water's edge they hesitated, their great heads jerking against the yoke in protest, but finally the whip and the hoarse entreaties of the driver prevailed, and they threw themselves into the river. Only their horns, their fearful, rolling eyes, and their noisily sucking nostrils were visible as they struggled toward the land on the other side. With a tremendous effort they toiled up the opposite bank, dragging the dripping, bucking cart behind them, and we all breathed in relief.

"That's hard work for the animals," said Don Socrates' older son.

Then he and brother uncinched the saddles on our horses and mules, removed them, and carried saddles and harness to the canoe. I helped drive the horses and mules into the river, and they went much more easily than the oxen, tired and sweaty as they were. They swam across effortlessly and climbed ashore shaking the yellow water from their bodies.

Don Socrates called his dog to him and turned to me. "Watch me, doctor, and do the same with yours. It is because of the alligators, as I told you."

The dog struggled limply, whining through his great teeth that could have torn two men of Don Socrates' size in pieces. With the help of his older son, the old man finished tying his dog's legs. Then they carried him to the canoe and lay him flat on the bottom. Daguero had watched the struggle closely, but he came when I called him. I grabbed his neck, and he put up a token struggle, snarling and snapping in pretended anger.

Then I looked into his eyes, he quieted to a whine, and I had not the slightest fear. I felt I could have eviscerated him and he would not have resisted.

The big canoe had a heavy load, and we all paddled against the deceptive current. It was a good thing I wasn't alone because I couldn't concentrate on my paddling. I kept thinking of these great dogs giving in so meekly to us, acknowledging weak man as their masters. They were as much our captives as Pierre was the captive of his wife and the bottle. But wasn't I some sort of captive, too? I asked myself. Didn't—?

"You must paddle harder, doctor," said Don Socrates kindly. "We are drifting a little."

"I'm sorry," I said and dug viciously at the water.

The animals were allowed to rest, their glistening coats drying as they grazed, and the dogs made the most of their freedom by racing about frenziedly. Then the supplies were loaded again and the *carreton* made for the straight road, the rasping squeak of its wheels fading away quickly. We had something to eat and then, refreshed, mounted our horses.

"We shall make a little detour," Don Socrates told me. "*El Cementerio* is only about a half mile from here. It stands on hilly ground, so it won't be drowned out in the rainy season."

He was about to add further explanation, but the narrowing path absorbed his attention as it drew his horse ahead of mine, and I was glad Pierre had told me about the place. We plodded on without speaking and soon a simple hut appeared ahead in a patch of partly cleared woodland.

"We'll stay here until the hot sun is lower in the sky," said Don Socrates, wiping the sweat from his forehead. "We will make better time then." He glanced ahead where two *carretons* had halted, the four teams of oxen grazing nearby, two and two paired by strong yokes, then his eyes shifted to the hut as a tall, young, blond-bearded man came out of the door. "The priest is here," Don Socrates cried to his sons.

If ever a man looked like a priest, this one did. I was just about to comment on his appearance as Don Socrates explained that the young man was the valet of *El Cura*. He added that he was mute, but could hear. I was glad I hadn't expressed my opinion. The young man welcomed us indifferently, and Don Socrates paid little attention to him. On entering the hut, I couldn't see anything after the glare outside, but after my eyes had accustomed themselves to the semidarkness, I made out a man lying on a cowhide. He was a big man, from the way his naked feet stuck out from the blanket, hammock, and heavy rubber *poncho* that covered him, and he was sick.

102

I couldn't see his face distinctly, but I could tell he was an Indio. His teeth were chattering audibly in chills and fever, his exposed feet shuddering and his body trembling and heaving badly beneath his coverings.

"*El Trimotor* has malaria," exclaimed one of Don Socrates' sons.

He subsided immediately as a stern look from Don Socrates reprimanded him for speaking out of turn in the presence of a revered figure. I was puzzled until, at the far end of the cowhide, I discerned a short, powerful, remarkable-looking man attending the sick Indio. He wore a dark cape with a long shirt underneath, reminding me of the *chimanes,* and he had well-scuffed sandals on his feet. His big head was topped with white curly hair, his nose was strong, his lips full, his chin square—but it was the black eyes and the peculiar white circle at the rim of the cornea that gave his countenance its real character. Without trying, he had a mighty, commanding appearance.

"Padre!" said Don Socrates, hurrying forward. The two men went through the routine of clasping hands, embracing, and clasping hands again. "My sons are here, too," he said with childlike pride. Then he drew himself up. "It gives me honor to introduce you to our new doctor."

I moved a few steps, and the priest walked toward me. I noticed he had an odd gait, as if resting on his heels a little longer than was necessary. We met and shook hands, a loose, impersonal, somewhat guarded handshake.

"This man here has a grave attack of malaria." The priest spoke with a youthful, metallic voice which surprised me, since I guessed him to be at least sixty. "The quinine liquid that cures the *paludismo* of our region does not help him. He brought the disease from Brazil. He was hired to go there and help with the cattle."

I welcomed the chance to be useful, to disassociate myself from others and do what I was trained to do. I stepped closer to the cowhide "bed." Hmm, chills. I recalled the words of a wise teacher that you didn't have to see chills; if they were real, as in malaria, you could hear them. And this man was rattling noisily. The body of *El Trimotor,* as Don Socrates' son had called him, was shaking the cowhide, shaking the ground itself in a miniature earthquake.

"He might have a tertian, as well as an every-day-fever malaria," I said, reaching for his pulse. "In combination they can be hard to control, but if we give him atabrine in pills, quinine and plasmochin in injections—it ought to help."

Normally, I would never diagnose and suggest a cure out of hand, that is, without a thorough examination, but things were different in Bolivia and the *mañana* spirit did not hold in medicine. Don Socrates and his sons looked impressed; the priest seemed to be considering what I had said, and malaria was, after all, malaria.

"Let's do it right away," I suggested. "Don Socrates says we'll be here for a few hours. We might see some effect then. I'm very curious myself."

Nobody said anything, and I went outside to get my emergency kit from my saddlebag. As I undid the straps, I was joined by the priest. In the merciless sunlight he was even more impressive with a benign, compassionate side to him that I had noticed inside. But his words startled me.

"Doctor," he began. "Before you treat this man—I must tell you he is poor and that he has nothing. When he gets well enough to work, I think he might be able to pay a little, but I cannot promise it."

Always the same, I thought angrily. Do they think I'm here to make money from beggars? I hid my irritation, but I could not refrain from asking ironically, if politely, "Why not ask me how much I'm going to charge to cure this man?"

He looked me straight in the eye. "Doctor, I'm going to ask you just that."

I made a face. "Padre," I said sharply, "I really don't know how or what to answer you. All I can say is that it never occurred to me to ask for anything. But now, now," I went on in a biting voice, "you've given me an idea."

His large, unusual eyes looked steadily into mine, and I felt nothing could dismay, shock, or surprise this extraordinary man. He must have seen, heard, and experienced everything among these people.

"I wish to be entirely frank, doctor. They say you asked an impossibly large sum back in Santa Morena to cure a man called *El Chileno*. And then, because he could not afford to pay, he had to go to La Paz, where he died."

For an instant I stood with my mouth open beyond speech. "I–I–I never —the people know that—it's a lie, padre!" I took a deep breath and sputtered on. "Pierre was there when this happened, and there were others, too. I'm sure Don Socrates knows the truth." My anger made me stutter. "Th–th–this is outrageous! I'd like to get my hands on those who spread such poison."

There was so much more that I wanted to say, but my anger rose and choked me. With tightly compressed lips and a flushed face, I snatched my syringes, ampules, and drugs, bypassed the staring priest, and hustled inside. *I mustn't pay any attention to these people and what they say,* I tried to convince myself as I stood over the sick man. Now I was trembling in every limb myself. *They can't help themselves any more than I can help myself*. All the while I was shaking out three yellow atabrine tablets into my palm and weighing them meaningfully, as if they were so many small bombs to be flung at my enemies. At my feet the sick man was reaching out pathetically for the precious tablets, but he was too weak to do anything more than flutter his hand beseechingly.

I supported his head and stuffed the pills between his shattering teeth, then picked up an old tin can filled with water and brought it to his bluish lips. I adjusted the syringe, filled it carefully, then swabbed his arm with cotton soaked in alcohol.

"This is going to hurt a little," I said gently, "but the injection will help." He cringed at the sight of the needle. I shot it in smoothly, but he winced and his big, muscular frame cramped with pain. "I know," I said smoothly, removing the needle and again swabbing his arm with the cotton. "Quinine is as unpleasant in a hypodermic as it is bitter in the mouth as a powder." He nodded weakly, and I smiled. "But you're going to be all right."

I patted his shoulder, covered him carefully, and went outside with my kit. Don Socrates and the priest were near the horses in deep conversation, and I was sure they were talking about me. I looked away and concentrated on replacing my kit in the saddlebag. As I finished, the priest came up to me.

"I wish to thank you, doctor, and I hope you have not taken offense. What I told you about *El Chileno* did not come to me from Santa Morena, but in a roundabout way from San Marequo, a village six days away from here. It is in another province and the *avion* stops there once a week going to Brazil."

"Then it must be *El Chileno's* brother who spread the news—this story. That accounts for his strange actions lately." The priest lowered his head almost imperceptibly, but remained silent. I was still bitter, however, and felt I had to justify myself. "I wish though, padre, that people would make sure of things and not repeat lies and slander without proof."

"Son," said the priest, all the metallic quality gone from his voice, "son, I have just learned that when *El Chileno's* brother asked about the fee, you gave no specific answer. How could he know what you meant? People out here are not used to looking behind what a man says, searching for meanings. And, believe me, they have had some bad experiences with strangers from the big cities and the other side of the oceans."

I raised my eyes defiantly. I knew what was coming and resented the inference, but the priest continued before I could interrupt.

"Wars and troubled times have forced people to leave Europe. Here in this section we have received the broken in spirit as well as the broken in health—also the desperate and unscrupulous who wish to get rich quickly, who do not shrink from exploiting innocent people to achieve their purpose."

Another European-hater, I thought bitterly, another persecutor of refugees and men without a country. Maybe I ought to pin him down, ask him in which category he placed me, but I said nothing. The priest soon excused himself and went inside, and I joined Don Socrates and his sons. The general embarrassment convinced me I had been the subject of discussion and now, to break the uncomfortable silence, I asked one of the young men why he had called my malaria patient *El Trimotor*.

The youth scowled, scratched the back of his head, and Don Socrates undertook the reply. "Well, you see, doctor, that fellow has had a trembling right arm ever since he was a *chico*. Whenever he tried to use it for any purpose, the arm began shaking harder and harder—just like the three motors of the Junkers *avion* before it lifts itself into the air."

It was as apt a description as I had ever heard for a neurological condition, and I told Don Socrates that it was better than in the medical books. He and his sons were pleased, but Don Socrates wanted to make it plain that no disrespect was intended in its use. We sat in the shade and talked for a while, and the time passed pleasantly. I noticed that the priest's helper, or valet as Don Socrates had called him, was busy back of the hut and soon delightful cooking odors filled the air. The term valet amused me because out here, in the jungle, pampas, and wasteland, nothing could be more incongruous than a true manservant helping his master dress, make his toilet, etc. There were no fine distinctions here, however, and I gathered that valet carried a different meaning than at home.

By whatever name, I appreciated the man as he passed with a platter of roast chicken that made my mouth water. The priest graciously asked us to share the feast, and we joined him at a simple low table. The chicken was delicious and quickly consumed. The priest made a fine, dignified host, and I was struck by his intelligent and penetrating comments on climate and weather, crops and cattle, and the spiritual and medical needs of his people. It was not talk for the sake of talk, and we all listened attentively. You had to respect this man, whatever your beliefs.

By midafternoon it was time to go. Don Socrates gave the word, and the riders rounded up horses and mules. I checked my patient and thought him better. The fever was down, the chills were less frequent. I saw the priest watching me thoughtfully, and I went out to my horse. I gave him a small bottle of atabrine tablets, ampules, and a syringe, and instructions on when and how to give medication. He listened impassively, nodding to show he understood, and I didn't have to repeat a word. Then he looked at the sick man and turned to me with gratitude in his fine eyes.

"He is sleeping now for the first time in days. I think he will be cured."

"I hope so, padre." Then, although I admired the man greatly, I felt I had to needle him for his earlier remarks. "Tell me, do you think you will ever learn to like Europeans just a little?"

The dark, white-rimmed eyes looked full at me with a most benign expression. "I am sure I will like them. I am from Spain, you know. From Barcelona. We have had our wars and troubled times, too. It is the same everywhere now." He sighed. "But now I must thank you again."

* * *

A heaviness settled over us as we started out. Either we were thoughtful or no one felt he had anything important to say after hearing the priest, but we rode for hours without speaking. I was close to dozing in the saddle as Don Socrates rode up next to me. Clearly, he had something on his mind.

"Doctor," he said casually, "please forgive my *compadre*, Carlotta's father. He probably wanted to save face because you were right. It is difficult sometimes to accept the blame one has earned."

I made a deprecatory gesture. I no longer cared, and I certainly did not want to touch on my own guilty feelings concerning Carlotta.

"This priest—is he the one from Rojas?"

Don Socrates hesitated. "He is the *cura* from all over," he said lightly. "But about Carlotta's father now, you must understand why—"

For once I was persistent. "What do you mean, 'from all over'?" I asked, interrupting him.

Again Don Socrates hesitated, looked off in the distance, gave himself a sort of mental push, and told me the whole story. The priest was—well, he had not been sent out here by a higher authority or church. He represented no one but himself.

"He just came one day. There was a bad flood, a lot of land was under water, and people were starving, dying of yellow fever, malaria, and attacks by alligators. And he arrived and took over. He helped us, gave us medical treatment, fed us, prayed for us, and worked in the building that had been put up for a priest, although one had never been assigned. So he stayed on as the priest—our priest, everybody's priest. But he is always on the go and that is why I say he is the *cura* from all over."

"That's interesting," I said, "but perhaps he is not a priest at all."

"Once in a while some insolent *hombre* says so, but only when he is drunk. No matter. You will see all of Rojas is changed when he comes to the capital a day or two before Easter. The padre gives us all new life—a new life of the spirit."

"What do you think, Don Socrates?"

"Ah, what I think is not so important as what I feel and see. Who is to say what a man is and what he is not? Only God, I think. But what a man does, what he says, how he acts—that is something else. Do you agree?"

"Yes," I said strongly.

That he was a false priest, an impostor, a masquerader did not matter to these people. Pierre was right in saying that here a diploma and official credits were not necessary—and justly so, I thought. A high official of the church could not have left a more lasting impression on me than the padre. I had no doubt that he was a great, good, and selfless man. Don Socrates had trotted ahead to join his sons, and I reflected on his words. Out here a man was, of necessity, no more and no less than—what he was. Titles, honors, special designations counted for nothing. His words, actions, and behavior spoke for him.

To get down to cases then, just where did that leave me? Close to nowhere, I thought with a smile. Out here, compared to the padre, to Don Socrates, to many others, I was a foreigner, a stranger, a little man of little account. It was a good thing to know for sure, and I felt a warm glow of self-realization as I settled back in the saddle. If I won the battle with myself, I could easily win any and all of the others. I was *not* Pierre; I was Martin.

"We have not much farther, doctor," Don Socrates called to me.

"It's all right," I said cheerfully. "I'm not tired, and it is so beautiful on the pampas."

The old man beamed.

7

*I Am Welcomed in Rojas; I Find a House; I Address a
Protest Meeting Against the Doctor; Daguero
and I Acquire Assistants*

"We should reach the capital in an hour," said Don Socrates. "It is not far
to Rojas now."

Although I knew it would be more than an hour, I hoped he was right.
It had been a long trip for an inexperienced rider. I had become fairly
accustomed to the grind, but I was stiff and sore to the bone. I wanted to
rest, to stop and get off my horse, to be on my feet again. We were passing
through a stretch of fertile lowlands, where herds of cattle grazed peacefully. They dotted the broad, green meadowland in clumps, looking up
to stare at us curiously, then lowering their heads to crop grass again.

"This land and the cattle on it belong to the *estancia* of my *amigo,
compadre* Don Arnulfo," Don Socrates explained. "There is something I
have to tell you about him."

"He is sick then?"

"*Sí.* That is, he has been stricken by a strange paralysis of the face. If you
could do something for the man, help him in some way, we would all be
grateful. You see, he is one of the most educated men in Rojas and one
of its finest citizens."

"I'll do my best."

"Good. You can live with him until you find yourself a suitable *casa.*
And all the cattle you receive for *curaciones,* I am sure he will let you keep
on his *estancia.* When you have your own, you can transfer to it all the
stock you keep on Don Arnulfo's and my land."

The idea of being a cowman and rancher no longer appalled me. Owning
an *estancia* and raising cattle might be fun. It would be something to do
and, oddly, that appealed more to me than just mere profit.

"*Oiga,* Don Socrates," I suddenly called to him. "Whatever happened to the cattle you got for that *curación?*"

"*Ai, hijo!*" He shook his head disapprovingly. "Didn't I tell you that you are the owner of two five-year-old oxen and six young cows? They will stay on my land until you decide to dispose of them."

"Well, well," I said, amused at the idea of ownership in this vast, strange land. "I must learn more about cattle, but I know a little already." I pointed at some grazing animals. "You see that cow with the black spots? I'll bet that's a two-year-old. Am I right, eh?"

"*Sí,* doctor." Don Socrates smiled as he shaded his eyes. "You are right, but we must be careful. Right behind these cows a bull usually lurks and these hot-blooded beasts have no patience with us riders. They just put their heads down and charge. I've known careless men who have been killed that way."

I noticed the bulls now, stamping, snorting, and pawing the ground back of the cows. It seemed that very little would set them off. Even the dogs sensed that. They kept close to us as we veered off and moved away across the lowlands. Rojas, too, had its *currichi* and it wasn't long before we trotted through the pool and approached the tiny provincial capital. An impressive, elegant entrance was expected of us, and now the others spurred their horses and we galloped through the streets setting heads to turning.

Dogs came sniffing and barking, children ran hooting and shouting, and people who stood or slumped before their doors put on smiles and waved an enthusiastic welcome.

"*Qué tal,* Don Socrates!" they called out.

The old man bowed and acknowledged their greetings like visiting royalty. They seemed to be his subjects, and he the kind and gracious king. I was only surprised they hadn't rushed out bearing gifts to kiss his hand.

Other than being obviously larger, Rojas was not much different from Santa Morena. The houses were bigger and some even had street names painted on their calcimined walls; the streets showed more trampled earth and less grass as proof of the traffic they bore, but I imagined that in the rainy season they would make for an identical sea of mud. There was the usual plaza, and the church, standing above every other building, was the most impressive structure in Rojas. We kept going until Don Socrates reined in by a large corner house. He turned to me, and I rode to his side.

"Here, doctor, we have the hotel, restaurant, and gambling house all rolled into one. Before we go to Don Arnulfo's *casa,* we shall visit under this roof for a few hours. We must do so that no one may become offended lest you show preference." He cleared his throat and lowered his voice. "The people are very sensitive in Rojas. These things count for much with them."

I said I would gladly do as he wished just as a fat little man bounced out to greet Don Socrates and his party. He was very effusive with so shrewd a face and manner that craftiness seemed to exude from every pore.

Don Socrates introduced him with more than his usual show of poised dignity. "This is Don Bonaparte, doctor, the owner of this establishment, which is the best of its kind in Rojas."

The man's name seemed a joke until I noticed the napoleonic grandeur with which he directed us inside and ordered two *mozos* to push the tables against the walls, then to place all available chairs and stools in a semicircle, as in an amphitheater, so that all the visitors would face the guests of honor. Then a *sirvienta* brought in a big tray filled with steaming cups of distilled coffee. I sipped mine gratefully and looked around the room, which seemed to be filled with people all talking at once.

Just as in Santa Morena, news spread rapidly in the capital, where the arrival of strange horsemen on the few small streets was like an invasion. I was just getting back to normal after hard riding, just about regaining my ability to stretch my legs and bend my knees as people swarmed around me. After I had duly performed the embraces and handshakes the same as the rest of my party, we all sat down again. Then someone else came in and most of the men stood again. I hadn't gotten to my feet as the newcomer approached me, a bald, stocky man with an evident flair for the dramatic.

"Doctor!" he boomed. "What a pleasure to see you at last!"

He gave me a particularly hearty embrace. I guessed he was an important man and looked questioningly over his shoulder at Don Socrates.

"Doctor," he said matter-of-factly, "I want you to meet the subprefect."

Very soon the *alcalde* came in, very excited as the bearer of good news. By good luck there was a house for rent, exactly what the doctor needed for an *officina,* with even a wooden floor in the *sala*. I understood that it had been a schoolhouse, but no reason was advanced for its sudden availability. I was pleased and dying to get settled. Still, I could not rush away to look at it, and I was too hemmed in to move. I was forced to remain seated, staring at the guests taking up formation in one row after another, the late-comers finding only standing room in the back and around the door.

Don Bonaparte seemed to have mobilized an army of *mozos* and *sirvientas,* and now they darted about serving coffee and *chicha*. With no women guests present, it was a little like a big stag party with the inevitable discussions first about local affairs, then national, then international. They talked about La Paz, they talked about Paris, and one could not have imagined a less cosmopolitan group. I was drawn to one man in the first row. He had a deep, resonant, pleasing voice, spoke authoritatively on every subject, and I surmised him another leading citizen of Rojas. He had a thin-lipped mouth, revealing an upper bridge with a decided gap between it and the gum. With the idle mind of the typical stranger at the party, it struck me that this gap, yes, was just large enough for a fly to slip through easily.

There were plenty buzzing around us, and I thought he might already have gulped one in. I watched, fascinated, forgetting the commotion around me as I waited for the fly to emerge. Several hypnotic minutes passed before the absurdity of the idea penetrated my consciousness, but the reverie relaxed me. I went back to answering questions politely, then supplying information. Most of the cross-examining was done by the man with the gap. He had a high forehead, but the back of his head sloped sharply to his nape so that he looked top-heavy. He seemed sincere, and I thought it a pity he was so ugly.

I was beginning to feel dazed by the time Don Socrates had concluded the amenities had been observed. It was suggested that he show me the house I was to rent, and one by one the citizens filed past me. With each one I shook hands, embraced, and shook hands again, and all warmly assured the new health officer of their good services. All in all, it was like a simple, friendly reception, and I felt heartened.

The house was in fairly good condition and quite an improvement on the one I had in Santa Morena. The *sala* with the wooden floor would do nicely as the office, there was a small waiting room, and another larger room for me to live and sleep in. It would do, and I told Don Socrates I would move in immediately. He advised me to wait until the carts arrived with my things and urged me to accompany him to Don Arnulfo's house. I liked Don Arnulfo right away. About fifty, he had a bald head, a gray mustache under a beaklike nose, and a warm personality. His twitching features struck me immediately; I knew he suffered from facial palsy. After we were introduced, he watched my reaction closely.

"Will my face always be crooked?" he asked in a sad, scratchy voice. "Am I doomed to carry this thing with me always, doctor?"

"Not necessarily," I said, perhaps too optimistically. "I think you will get better and I will give you some medicine as soon as the *carreton* arrives. I hope that in several weeks you will be much improved. It's too bad," I added rashly, "that you cannot be given electrical treatments. That would hasten your cure."

He sighed, and I wished I'd kept my mouth shut. We had a pleasant evening, and Don Arnulfo kindly asked me to stay to eat. The *carreton* reached Rojas late that night, and I was in a fever to get all my supplies unpacked. I had been strongly welcomed, a home had been found for me, and I had a mission. It was good to be wanted and needed. I worked until late, flopped on my bed, and was soon asleep as happy and peaceful as I had been in a long time. I was up early and hurriedly made more preparations, anticipating a rush of patients as I had had in Santa Morena. Not a one materialized. In fact, to my astonishment, not a single person showed up all morning.

They're shy, I told myself. Shy and afraid, and they're waiting for one of them to take the initiative. When that happens, there'll be a flood. By noon nobody had come to the doctor's office. I walked over to Don Arnulfo's house for lunch, striding through the streets with a confidence I did not feel. It all seemed like a betrayal somehow, and I couldn't understand it. The fact that Don Socrates was missing from the luncheon table also seemed significant.

I walked back through the baking streets with what I assumed was an air of nonchalance. Then I spent the next few hours biting my nails and cursing Rojas and its two-faced inhabitants. I told myself that you can't make patients, can't make people sick when they aren't sick—but I didn't believe a word of it. It was the middle of the afternoon, the sun seeming to melt the walls of the house, as Don Socrates stamped in. He looked disgusted, looked about him dispiritedly, and threw his arms about him as if searching for the right words to say. He said nothing, however, and I thought I ought to take this particular bull by the horns.

"It's a funny thing, Don Socrates. I haven't had a patient all day, not one. I thought it would be like Santa Morena. A deluge of the sick . . ."

"*Hijo*," he said in an ugly voice. "In my *pueblo* they knew you would stay for only a short time. So they did not want to miss you. Here it is different; they know you have come for good, so they are taking their time about coming."

"The good old law of supply and demand, eh?" I looked at him. "Do you believe that, what you've just told me?"

"*Hijo*, doctor. The best for you is to listen to what I say: You pack up again and come back with me. You have the right to make your headquarters at any place in the province. That was the understanding."

113

So, as I had suspected, something had gone definitely sour. It had been too good to be true, the reception last night, the big speeches, the embraces —all a sham. I might have known it. I walked across to the window, and I stared out without seeing anything. I felt the heat clamp down on my skull suddenly, and I grasped the bamboo window bars so hard that my nails dug little crescents into them.

"All right, Don Socrates," I said harshly. "What happened? Tell me the truth."

He mouthed a curse and cleared his throat. *"Por Dios, hijo,* I am ashamed to speak about it. That devil, Doctor Malvenido, left the *pueblo* this morning as a protest against you. He thinks he can take care of the people's health without anybody else's help. Some of his followers are raising the devils from hell." He took a deep breath. *"Hijo,* they are holding their own meeting to protest against you."

Damn it! Damn them! My first impulse, as usual, was to run. Run as fast and as far away from trouble as I possibly could. I always had, hadn't I? And I wasn't staying where I wasn't wanted; not for a minute after that masquerade of a welcome yesterday. Then the impulse to run—it was already making my body tremble—changed to white-hot anger which was suddenly directed, not at these peculiar people, nor myself, but at Herbert, my fellow refugee friend. Herbert, who was now in La Paz and probably sitting in an office with an electric light, or a movie across the lighted street, or in a coffee house conversing with friends. Wasn't it Herbert who always talked of following the line of least resistance and leaving others to fight the common battle? (And wasn't that just what all we refugees had done in leaving our tortured homeland, wiping the dust of Europe from our tired, blistered feet, and going across the seas in search of a sweet freedom, a new hope—an empty dream without reality?)

Herbert and his stupid catch phrases! This protest meeting against me— now here was a fine line of least resistance! How would Herbert, the strong, the logical, the perfect exponent of he–who–fights–and–runs–away–lives– to–fight–another–day face up to this battle here in Rojas? I was being challenged, by God! The flung gauntlet had caught me full in the face, and I throbbed with the pain of it.

"Hijo," Don Socrates was pleading, "do me the favor then. Pack up quickly and come back with me."

I looked at him as if he were mad. How could he know that this was the end of the road for me? This time my back was truly to the wall; I had made no provision for retreat. I had no place to go, no place to hide. Besides, I had run away so many times in the last few years, and nothing had ever been settled that way. It had made me no happier. Over and over I'd quit, given up, hoping for a better chance, promising myself that next time I would *really* start fresh. And I hadn't, hadn't, hadn't.

Slowly I turned to face Don Socrates, who still paced in distress and flung his arms about inarticulately.

"No, señor. Even if I wanted to go back to Santa Morena, the people would think they had me for good, that I would be there permanently. In that case, the followers of the *curandero* in Santa Morena would surely protest, and where would I go from there?"

Don Socrates stared and blinked, started to say something, then shifted his gaze to the window.

"Where did this Malvenido go?" I asked, surprised at the belligerence in my voice. "He is here in Rojas?"

"No. He owns an *estancia* about two miles to the east."

Damn! "And where are they holding this, uh, meeting?"

"At the gambling house." Don Socrates spoke scornfully. "This idiot, this ignoramus with the big mouth, Arturo—he is the one who started it all. And to think that only yesterday he came to embrace you! What a hypocrite," he spat.

If the only door in a place were slammed on you, what was to stop a man from pushing it open again? My jaw stiffened as I made up my mind.

"I'm going to that meeting, Don Socrates. I would appreciate your coming with me for moral support."

He looked embarrassed, much more embarrased than the situation warranted, I felt.

"*Hijo,* you don't want to talk with these characters, doctor. Why, it would be beneath your dignity."

Dignity, eh? What dignity? The word had already long lost any meaning for me in the endless struggle for identity and survival. Only the proud and secure who walked on the clouds could afford to be aloof and dignified. Seeing my decision was irrevocable, Don Socrates waited for me to proceed, but first I had to batten down my emotions. I was thinking of what I would say, how my hearers would accept my words, how they would react. And I was afraid. Why was it that in such damnable showdown situations versus vicious storm troopers, bullying consular officials, and weasels like Arturo, when a man was most in need of his strength and a clear head, his body chose to betray him? Was I truly so gutless a coward? I wondered, my heart hammering, my knees trembling, and my belly filled with ice water.

I had set out like a man with a purpose, Don Socrates keeping pace with me, and now we were near the plaza. I heard a deep, resonant voice making a speech, a voice I immediately recognized as that of the ugly man whose bridgework showed a gap that would let a fly in and out.

"Is that Don Arturo speaking?" I asked.

Don Socrates nodded heavily. We moved closer, then stopped to listen.

". . . *Por Dios,* it is all as I told you and worse—much worse. My friends, I am told that this man wanted such an outrageous fee for his services to *El Chileno* that his family had to put him on a plane and take him to La Paz. And there he died because they could not afford a *gringo* doctor. Neither can we because . . ."

Again that miserable, lying story, even more distorted than before. I clenched my fists as the voice went on smoothly about the hardships men faced making the trip to Brazil to sell cattle.

"Our government should spend its money building a road to La Paz through the mountains. Then we could drive cattle to our own capital, and the excellencies there could stop paying in gold for the cattle they import from Argentina at five times the price we get for our animals in Brazil. Instead, what do they do, these criminal officials? You see for your-selves: they send us a *gringo,* and a *judio* at that, to drive our own Doctor Malvenido out of town—Doctor Malvenido, a good man and, I assure you, a true healer who only last year saved my own child from certain death. In all Rojas no man has done more for the people than . . ."

Don Arturo stopped in midsentence as I appeared in the doorway, pro-pelled by my anger and looking much calmer, I'm sure, than I felt. About thirty citizens were gathered in the same *sala* on the same chairs and stools, set in the same formation, as on the afternoon they had welcomed their new doctor. Some of them had the grace to show acute embarrassment at the sight of me, but not Don Arturo. He was unabashed, undeterred, and prepared to go on. These Arturos were the same the world over, I re-flected. Put a black uniform on them, and you had your storm trooper. I had seen their ugly faces, looked into their snaky eyes, listened to their venomous voices too often not to recognize the type. I had to take a stand quickly; it was put up or shut up in Rojas.

"*Caballeros!*"

Damn my trembling voice, but at least I had their attention.

"*Caballeros!*" Ah, that was better. "I would have appreciated being in-vited to address this gathering of good people so that you might hear the other side of the argument. That would have been more in the spirit of Bo-livian friendship and fair play, of the assurances and embraces with which your esteemed speaker here—" I nodded to Don Arturo—"favored me only yesterday. May I tell you that I did not come to this province on my own? I was sent here. I came. And I am going to stay. No one has driven *Doctor* Malvenido away."

I underscored the title doctor without being obviously sarcastic, then paused.

"On the contrary, I would have considered it a privilege to meet him in order to discuss the health problems of the province. But I am glad to be here and look forward to serving all of you." I looked about the silent room and ended abruptly. *"Gracias, caballeros!"*

Looking neither to right nor left, I hurried out of the room and outside. I kept on walking fast till I reached the corner of the plaza, then slowed my pace. I was breathing hard and annoyed that I had forgotten to clear up the matter of *El Chileno's* brother and his big lie. Too late to go back now. It had been a short speech—probably a fiasco—but this time, at least, I had tried to fight back as best I could. I mopped my forehead with a handkerchief. The sun was setting and its golden-purplish rays touched the thatched roof of the former schoolhouse, which was to be my home and office. A gentle hand touched my arm. Don Socrates.

"Doctor, you have my respects," he said sincerely.

"Gracias, señor." We plodded on without speaking, and I was the first to look up as we approached my house. "I think I am headed for trouble, Don Socrates. Those people there—"

A group of people stood by my door with what I took to be a hostile intent. Malvenido had organized this demonstration, I thought. He had told them to drive me out of town, to use any means possible—perhaps even to break in and destroy my equipment.

"Maybe—no, doctor, it is not what you think. These are the sick, the patients you have been waiting for. They are Indios, old, fat, broken down, and with ailing children. They have already heard of your answer to the protest meeting." He smiled broadly. "And they are no longer afraid, because you are no longer afraid either."

It was the boom time in Santa Morena all over again. Don Socrates came in to assist and for the next few hours we were like an understaffed hospital facing the inroads of the lame, the halt, and the blind. And they kept coming with worms, diseased wounds, festering sores, infected teeth crying for immediate extraction, malaria, throat trouble, and I don't know what else. I took care of the easy cases first, putting off the more difficult ones until the crowd had thinned. I felt relieved, happy, and vindicated.

It was overwhelming, particularly since the protest meeting was still in progress, and I felt like cheering. There was much more to this than met the eye, however, and I had a feeling that Don Socrates was somehow responsible. He had spread the word, encouraged them, forced them to come to me, something. And they had waited for a sign and the right moment— the moment when I finally took my stand. Yes, Don Socrates was really wonderful. I wanted to tell him and thank the old man. He looked so pleased with himself, bustling about like an aged scoutmaster. As I looked my gratitude at him, a shadow crossed his face. My patients had mostly gone now, and the new arrival was a man of importance. Ah, yes, the subprefect, and he evidently expected to be received with the respect due his office.

"*Caballeros!*"

He flung the greeting, then pushed forward a young man dressed in a neatly pressed linen suit. The young man's eyes fluttered nervously as he removed his black felt hat. He had blond hair, and his fair complexion was in striking contrast to the dark skin and hair of the Spaniards in the room. Spying Don Socrates, the youth hailed him enthusiastically.

"*Buenas tardes, tío!*"

Tío meant uncle, and I guessed that Don Socrates had just met another of his many, far-flung relatives. The intricacy of his family relationships was apparently only matched by their number. The subprefect raised his shaggy eyebrows and introduced the young man to me.

"This is Rudolfo Gonzales, doctor, and I wish that you would do me the favor of examining him. His eyes have given him trouble since he came back from his year of military service."

"Do young men have to do military service here?" I said, surprised. "I thought that was only in Europe."

"Here, too," said Don Socrates in explanation. "Every *joven* in our country must give one year of service to the military when he reaches nineteen. They make them work hard, and this one seems to have come back with bad eyes."

The young man's boots were nicely polished, and he wore the black tie that most men wore only for the important *fiestas* and high holidays. Examining him, I noted that his eyelids had stopped fluttering in the comparatively somber light of the room, and that his sensitive, slightly inflamed, light blue eyes were looking at everything with quick, lively interest. He was a prepossessing, self-possessed youth, compared to most I had seen, and I did not take long to come up with a reasonable diagnosis.

118

"The sun is very bright in this country," I told him. "So bright that it can damage the eyes. You see, fair-complexioned people like yourself haven't enough pigment in their skin or in their eyes to protect them from the burning rays. I would say you had been exposed to the sun quite a bit."

"*Como no?*" Rudolfo agreed quietly.

"Too much, too much, if I know the military." Don Socrates spoke bitterly. I knew how much he had suffered from the loss of his eldest son in the Chaco War. Anything concerning the army angered him, and even the subprefect held his tongue when Don Socrates now cursed the generals. "They make the *jovenes* work in the noontime sun and on projects that are not military at all. I have great fear when I think that my youngest son has to go soon. It is not right to take the young and ruin them."

I had no eye charts with which to test Rudolfo's eyes. Perhaps he just suffered from the glare. If I could find some makeshift until—I rummaged around in my suitcase and came up with a pair of sunglasses, which I handed to him.

"Here you are, Don Rudolfo. Take these as a gift from a friend of Don Socrates and of the Señor Subprefect. The glasses came from Paris."

Flushing like a schoolboy, he took the glasses and put them on.

"*Ai,* doctor. *Muchas gracias.*"

To test the effect on his eyes, he opened the door and peered out at the dim evening light. As he did so, a sleek brown dog pushed his nose into the crack and then, as dogs will, forced his way into the room. Ignoring all of us, he bounded straight for the corner where Daguero was lying, long forgotten in the confusion of my impromptu clinic. Daguero leaped to his feet and braced himself for battle, the hair along his spine rising ferociously on end, his fangs bared. He gave a deep growl, the strange dog answered nearly on top of him, then they growled together, and thunder seemed to reverberate in the room.

"Hordimales!" snapped Rudolfo.

"Daguero!" I cried.

It had all happened in an instant and, as we dived for our animals, it appeared too late. Muzzle to bared muzzle, they were poised for combat and circling warily, snarling and whining. Then, unexpectedly, one tail wagged, then another, the snarling stopped, their back hair went down, and they moved about speculatively sniffing, smelling, investigating, making tentative overtures.

"Get out!" Rudolfo ordered his pet. "Go." He looked embarrassed.

The animal turned plaintively, sniffed Daguero again, seemed to gesture invitingly with his head, and started for the door. Daguero followed and, with the pride of ownership, I decided he was much the younger of the two.

"What was that you called your dog?" I said.

"He is bad," said Rudolfo, "a real wild one." But from his tone I could tell he didn't mean it. "His name is Hordimales."

We began to talk about our dogs, dogs in general, and our ideas about training them. We were in what was to be my bedroom and the subprefect, without so much as a by-your-leave, was leaning back in the hammock that had been put up for me. Neither he nor Don Socrates had paid much attention to the dog incident.

"Doctor," the official now broke in importantly. "I'm sure you need help in your house and with your work. In my opinion, this *joven* is just the right assistant for you."

The suggestion caught Don Socrates by surprise, from the look on his face, but he extended his arm in one of his gracious, lordly gestures. "Yes indeed, doctor. I can only recommend him highly. He is honest, dependable, and a good worker."

Rudolfo looked elsewhere, seeming to stand apart from the conversation, and I didn't know what to say. It had been apparent to me that relations between Don Socrates and the subprefect were not particularly cordial; they could hardly have planned this then, but it did not diminish the embarrassment of the situation. I'd never given any thought to having an assistant. If I had, I doubt whether I would have chosen Rudolfo. He struck me as much too young, frivolous, and probably irresponsible. It would be better not to say anything, however, and I pretended to consider the matter.

The subprefect took my silence as near-acceptance of his suggestion and applied a clincher. "In the military service Rudolfo was a medic. He gave all kinds of needles. And I do know there is no one in the *pueblo* who knows better how to give injections to horses."

So this was the criterion, I thought with bitter amusement. Well, well. Rudolfo still wouldn't look my way, Don Socrates' lips were pursed thoughtfully, and the subprefect wore a pleased expression. Here was a *fait accompli,* and I saw no other course open except to accept it. Besides, I told myself wryly, his dog and my dog liked each other.

"*Bueno,* Rudolfo," I said amiably, "since you have such excellent recommendations and want the position, you shall be my assistant and learn to be a doctor for humans."

Again the crimson schoolboy flush mantled his cheeks, and he thanked me volubly. We made small talk a while longer, then it was time to eat and I went along with Don Socrates and the subprefect, leaving my new assistant behind.

*   *   *

Coming back that night through the damp, dark streets, I warmed to the welcoming light waiting inside my house. It was good to be cared for, to have a friendly assistant on my side and on my team. Rudolfo was still straightening things around, happily, as a child with a new toy, and he greeted me pleasantly. Much of what he was doing was finicky and unnecessary, but he was enjoying himself, the barren rooms did seem much more homelike, and it all made a fitting end to what had been a memorable day.

I would always remember those Indios waiting on my doorstep as I returned, shaky and sweaty, from addressing that protest meeting. Their trust, their congratulations, the friendliness shining in their black eyes would always stay with me. Rudolfo asked some question about storing the medical supplies, and I answered automatically. Yes, we would manage nicely together more because of his personality than any medical knowledge. It was good to have someone to talk to in the house.

Not that I particularly wanted to talk just then. My house, my possessions spread out neatly as if they belonged there, filled me with a sense of peace. I stood by the door looking out, and Daguero came close to share the night with me. I fingered his collar affectionately and stroked his smooth coat. Crickets were chirping in full-throated chorus and I marveled at their chatter. They always sang in Bolivia, I had learned, but never so distinctly as here— or maybe it was just because for once I was at peace and attuned to the night. I had a fleeting notion of sending for a battery radio so I could keep in touch with the world, but I dismissed it immediately. A radio would only shatter the peace of this life and disturb my equanimity with painful reminders of what I had left behind.

I grew aware of a shimmering radiance at the end of the street, and the moon seemed to rise so close that I could touch it. It moved unbelievably fast, leaving a trail of strong silvery light as it climbed the sky. It was a wonderful, calm, clean sort of beauty and somehow tremendously reassuring—the serene loveliness that follows after a storm. I sighed and looked at a group of palm trees silhouetted against the silvery radiance. There were five, no, six, straight, slender trunks, and one bent in the middle reminding me, not of an old man surrounded by young men but a stooped young man surrounded by straight young men.

The fronds topping the trees were sharply outlined against the molten moonlight, a jagged black against fiery silver, powerful young blades dipping and swaying like great daggers in the night breeze. Then something else came into the picture, and my eyes fastened on what seemed the head and body of a monstrous cobra, a bulky silhouette moving in long gangling strides.

"My God!" I exclaimed. "What's that?"

Rudolfo joined me quickly at the door, looking in the direction that I pointed. He laughed softly.

"That, doctor, is a tame ostrich that has a nest there between the palms. There used to be two, but one was killed . . . I forget how and when, though."

The long neck and head undulated like a cobra again, the big body and ungainly legs moved into the light, then out again to disappear in the black shadows close to the ground.

"What a sight," I mused. "But, Rudolfo, an ostrich—I thought ostriches were found only in Africa."

"I think you are right. That is really a rhea, I believe, but we always call them ostriches."

So be it then. He waited for me to say something more, but speech was superfluous, and I cared little about correctly identifying the great bird. The moon shone brilliantly, the crickets sang, and the palm fronds rustled in the cool night air. What a night and what a night! People had a harsh life in Rojas, and this was one of the compensations, although I doubted if any citizen were looking at it and, if he were, looking at it with my eyes. I longed for my friends in La Paz so I could show it to them. It was just the thing for a pessimist like Karl and his sensitive wife Maria. Even the worry-gnawed Herbert would profit from the sight.

It was, I told myself, a tranquil beauty of hope, and I longed for all my friends so they could share it with me. This was the place to convalesce from Europe and its trials. Tonight, I knew, I would sleep like a baby, and I put off the delicious moment of going to bed to stare on and on at the moon still climbing in the sky, still spreading its radiance not only over Rojas but all the world.

8

"Dr. Malvenido Says . . ."; I Battle the Ghost of the Curandero; I Get an Emergency Call; I Gamble with Death

As I should have expected, both my optimism and fresh hopes were in the nature of moonshine. The fault, of course, was in myself, but it was easier to find it in Rojas. I appreciated Rudolfo's good nature and had to admit that, within certain limits, he was an asset. But he was still a young man with the reputation of a gay blade. After working hours he liked to mingle with the young men of the *pueblo* and his eyes were always alert for feminine company.

At the beginning his interest and energy were contagious, but we had settled into a routine by the end of his first week as my assistant, and it was clear that his initial enthusiasm was lagging. This was just a job now, and he did not care to remain in the *officina* at night. He would adjust the wick of the kerosene lamp, worry a bit with himself about whether he was doing the right thing, then hastily curb his doubts with a *"Buenas noches"* to me, and hurry off to meet his friends.

I couldn't really blame him. It wasn't Rudolfo's fault that I was lonely and had no liking for gambling, card playing, or after-hours small talk with the people of Rojas. I could share only elementary needs with these people, who were so different from myself, but, regrettably, I had yet to find a local girl under whose *mosquitero* I could have found comfort. No doubt Carlotta was pining for me in Santa Morena and, crudely, I had to admit that all I missed in her was the sensual anesthesia we sought and shared in the darkness of her room. Rudolfo would probably gladly introduce me to some girls in Rojas, but he was younger than myself; I was his employer and a doctor, and I could not have put myself in his hands with a clear conscience. As for Don Socrates, he was convinced that my heart belonged to Carlotta.

So I stayed home at night, with only Daguero to pass the lonely hours and, from his accusing looks, even he chafed at the confinement when he could be out roaming the streets with his free and easy friend Hordimales.

I tried to read the few books I had brought with me, wrote letters, and halfheartedly jotted entries in the journal I told myself I was keeping. Then I'd stop, walk around my *officina,* and look at the shelves Rudolfo had so proudly designed to display our medical stores. It had the air of a small drugstore and, for my assistant, this was all to the good; the more medicines he had for sale, Rudolfo explained seriously, the better the doctor. The young man had proved handy with a hypodermic needle. To date, he had usually managed to shoot Salvarsan directly into the vein. And, no doubt about it, we used more Salvarsan than anything else.

Most of the poor Indios suffered from enormous ulcers on their legs. Neglected sores, they had become infected, continued to fester, and struck down both men and women. The prevalence of liver diseases could be blamed on infestations of worms, as well as germs, plus too much *aguardiente,* the cheap, fiery, stomach-corroding liquor that most villagers distilled themselves from *caña* (sugar cane) and consumed on all occasions. Considering the numbers and kinds of illnesses and diseases I came across, it was always a wonder to me that I never found a single case of high blood pressure or stomach ulcers.

"I'm really amazed," I had told Rudolfo once. "They're very common in the big cities with all their hurry and competition. There's none of that here."

"*Como no,*" said my assistant, as he always did to such pronouncements.

The only one likely to get a stomach ulcer was myself, and it would not have been caused by the local food alone. Along with everyone else, meat was my staple diet, with little variety. Meat for breakfast, meat for lunch, meat for supper. It was mostly pork and beef, with now and then a chicken thrown into the pot, but however prepared, to me, it was usually unpalatable compared to what I had been accustomed in Europe. There were soups, too, but they reeked of rancid fat just like the homemade candles, and at first I almost gagged getting them down. Bananas, or *plantanos,* were served daily, either fried, boiled, or mashed with pieces of meat. There were eggs, too, but fortunately cooked to my taste. Milk and butter, however, were rarely available. Milk was for babies, sometimes for the sick, and from the look of some of the cows who stayed in the pueblo, I would have hesitated before drinking it raw. Butter was too much trouble. Some *estancieros* made it in their own dairies from time to time, but there was no ice, no way of keeping it refrigerated, and it spoiled quickly. It had to be churned daily, there was rarely the inclination for such a laborious task, so it was seldom performed. Who needed butter?

As health officer, my biggest frustration concerned the introduction of even the most simple kind of sanitary measures. These people had their own ways of doing things, and they weren't going to be changed by anyone, particularly a *gringo* doctor. There were flies everywhere, all the time, and over everything. There was no garbage, in the big-city sense, to be disposed of, and food wastes were simply thrown into the street or a corner to rot until devoured by dogs and pigs. The community drinking cup was common even when those sharing it had some festering disease or oozing sore on the face, mouth, or hands. It was an insult not to share a drink from a glass at a party. It was impossible to refuse and, on trips, I found that one had to eat from a common pot with a man whose nose might be eaten up by leishmaniasis and dripping into the stew. It was bad enough undiluted, but with this added touch . . . Ugh!

All the food was prepared over an open fire and wood smoke was part of the taste. I had noticed in this connection that most Bolivian women I had seen had brownish, leathery skin on their legs, from the knees down. It was a rippled mahogany, unattractive to the point of being repellent, and undoubtedly due to being exposed to open fires over long periods of time, a form of erythema ab igne. As to drink, there was little choice. We often had oranges, but rather than squeezing them and drinking the juice, they were cut open and expressed directly into the open mouth. There was an insipid corn drink called *chicha,* currichi water disguised with some sweetish flavor to take away the brackish taste, distilled coffee, and, as a rare delicacy, beer. *Aguardiente* was always at hand, but cherry soda was hoarded like a treasure. It came in from Brazil at long intervals and was extremely expensive and invariably flat.

While a few of the more prosperous people had rudimentary indoor latrines, most of them used outhouses set in the open fields and swarming with flies. Some were not even covered, being no more than holes or trenches bridged by several poles strong enough to hold a squatting man. There were no ways of decontaminating these filthy pestholes, no chemicals were available, and I saw no point of attempting severe reform when I had no means to effect the sanitation measures called for. So far as my own needs were concerned, I was careful to avoid giving total local offense as I had in Santa Morena. It had occurred shortly after my arrival, and I had no idea that I was being talked about until Pierre had explained the reason.

In the patio back of my house at Santa Morena I had noticed a small, empty hut. It was a shabby little place, no one had explained what it was for, and I had then assumed it to be my own personal outhouse. I had availed myself of the place several times, and I had been mystified at the almost magical disappearance of my stools until I went out once, and came on a species of long red ants with voracious fangs bearing the disgusting deposit triumphantly away. All that remained to betray me then were the soiled pieces of newspaper I had used to clean myself.

At least, so Pierre rather gleefully explained it. Paper does not exist in Bolivian villages, and the few newspapers that reach there are cherished and read till they fall to shreds. But I had brought plenty of old ones in my packing cases, and the remnants had been found in the empty shack by the Indio woman who occasionally cooked and cleaned for me. Because, although there was no way of my knowing, this was *the* kitchen of the house and I had shocked all of Santa Morena by using it as a latrine.

"You should have told me," I scolded Pierre. "Now these barbarians will consider me worse than a barbarian."

He laughed. "I accept the blame, but it is funny. The old woman who cooks for you played detective after seeing those dirty bits of paper. You see, out here they use leaves, bits of grass, or what have you. They cannot conceive of using paper for such a purpose."

"My God! And I am to be a health officer."

"You will see much worse, doctor," Pierre had said.

But there were other things to trouble me besides my stomach and the problems of sanitation. It was mostly the Indios who came to my office for examination and treatment, but some of the white citizens had come, too, although they preferred to buy medicines as if I were running a drugstore. They liked to treat themselves with what I prescribed, but from a word here, a hint there, I gathered that the majority of them drove out to the *estancia* of the *curandero* Malvenido for consultation. In their position as esteemed, intelligent white men, one would have expected them to take the lead in helping introduce modern medical practices into their province. But they stayed far behind their Indios, continuing to immerse themselves in the sheep dip of quackery and superstition.

In the few instances that a prominent citizen had come to my office, the examination would inevitably take place in the malevolent shadow of the *curandero*. Dr. Malvenido had said this, Dr. Malvenido had said that, Dr. Malvenido had said the other thing. If I did not agree with the quack, if I found a flagrant error in diagnosis and treatment, there was a quick

126

reluctance to accept what I knew to be my own superior medical opinion. I was reputable, qualified, and Dr. Malvenido was not—he wasn't anything! It was infuriating, but there seemed to be nothing I could do about it. Not a damn thing.

Take the old man who came to see me, not two days ago, probably as a last resort. He had syphilitic ulcers on his arm, and Dr. Malvenido, like the *curandero* in Santa Morena with the two sick lads (whom I had attended on my arrival), had burned some off only, in the nature of things, to have others take their place. Patiently, I explained that he needed antisyphilitic treatment to clear his blood of the microscopic organism causing the infection. He scowled, and I tried to explain about germs and the rest. But he left sullenly, refusing to meet my eyes, and muttering that he would come back *mañana* for treatment. As I expected, he never returned, and Rudolfo said he had gone back to Dr. Malvenido for more cauterization.

Then the next day Don Hector's wife came in, from all signs in the terminal stages of tuberculosis. Malvenido knew the old lady was dying— it took no skill as a diagnostician to be sure of that—and he didn't want to go on treating a hopeless case. So she came to the new doctor who could also do nothing for her. Of course, she would die soon, and then people could say that I had killed her, that so long as she had stayed under the care of their *curandero* she had lived. Oh, he was a devilishly clever fellow, but to have refused her, for me to have begged off her case, would have been a betrayal of my appointment as health officer. As a doctor and a man, I couldn't have anyway. These were human beings in distress, and I soon found myself becoming fond of this elderly couple, who bore their poverty and dire trouble with such touching dignity.

I liked them, I admired them, I wanted to help and couldn't—and all along I had the uneasy feeling that that damn *curandero* was only waiting for the poor woman to die, so he could point out to his followers what happened to those who patronized the *gringo* doctor. I could almost hear him gloating, and I wanted to kill the man with my bare hands, slowly though so he could die just as excruciatingly as Don Hector's wife.

I became incensed just thinking of the man who had brought in his ten-year-old nephew with a grotesquely swollen right cheek. The boy looked as if he had a deformed jaw. He was sobbing, in pain, and afraid.

"Doctor," said the man casually, "his tooth was extracted yesterday, but a piece of the root remained. Be so kind as to remove it, eh?"

After soothing and quieting the boy, I managed to get his mouth open. A fine "piece" it was; another perfect example of Dr. Malvenido's bungling.

The crown of the tooth had broken off, and the whole root still lay embedded in the red and swollen gum, which was terribly tender to the touch. There was no way of applying dental forceps to the edges of the roots without cutting away the gum, and this would amount to a small surgical operation. Further, because of the inflammation, local anesthesia probably would be ineffective and might cause an abscess later. The alternative was to pick and probe delicately, hurting the boy as little as possible. A tricky business, I thought as I set to work, but if I were lucky enough to remove the root, at least my reputation should improve.

I sat the boy as comfortably as possible, so that the maximum light would be on his mouth. Then, distracting him as much as I could, I sought to clear away the gum tissue. The little boy was brave, and I blessed him for his trust and patience. It took a painstaking half hour to ease the decayed root from its unyielding socket, a neat, competent job if I had to say so myself—and I was no expert dentist. Wiping the sweat off my brow, I felt proud of my handiwork as I held up the bloody root to the boy and joked with him. There was blood on his face, he looked a little battered, but still he smiled with me. Just then the boy's mother—for so Rudolfo identified her—burst into my office, stared hard at the uncle, and took her son into her fat arms.

"So long it took," she said, tears streaming down her face. "Dr. Malvenido said it was only a little piece and he had no time."

It was like the proverbial red rag to a bull. Nothing she could have said could have thrown me into such a rage. I flung the piece of root on the floor.

"Then I should have let your precious son keep that 'little piece' in his jaw!" I said furiously, glaring at her.

The woman drew back, her fat arms pulling her now sobbing son protectively to her. Hurt and insulted, she looked at me as if all the terrible things she had heard about the *gringo* doctor had been proved to be true.

"*Claro!*" she said, cuddling the boy. "Doctor Malvenido said that if you refused to take it out, you probably couldn't do it at all."

I was so angry that I turned my back on her and walked into the next room. I heard her leave, the boy wailing, the uncle arguing, the mother sputtering, then Rudolfo joined me.

"You must not let this upset you, doctor. These people are like this now, but it will not always be this way."

"You're damn right it won't!" I said threateningly.

I was still boiling mad as I told the story at Don Arnulfo's supper table later on. I spat out the details without bothering to see how they registered on my hearers.

"You know," I went on, after I had finished, "I've had just about enough of this fellow Malvenido. I am going to see him and give him a piece of my mind. I'm not standing for any more of this!"

"*Pero,* doctor," said Don Socrates mildly. "Easy now. It's only your European temper getting the better of you. It's beneath your dignity to argue with an ignorant quack. Let him talk."

Dignity again! What did I care for dignity?

"But don't you see, Don Socrates? This man can't lose. He is always in the right and I am always wrong. Sure, everybody knows he's a quack. But if he does something good, they all think he's wonderful. And what do you think people are going to say when Don Hector's wife dies of tuberculosis? I am allowed no bad luck, no margin for error—every case is the ultimate test of my ability."

"*Hijo,*" said Don Socrates calmly, "he is an ignorant faker and that is all."

He had no conception of my position, but I took the flicker in his eyes as a warning. I was on trial with him, too, and probably not even he would give the new doctor a second chance once he was wrong, once he made a fateful mistake. With all his faults, I felt certain that Pierre would understand, but he was far away in Santa Morena and harsh judgment had been passed on him long ago.

I went back to my house exasperated, ignoring Daguero as he frisked about me. It was already dark, and Rudolfo had lighted the kerosene lamp. He was sitting on one of the wooden boxes and rolling a *cigarillo.* He lighted it, stared thoughtfully at the ash, and seemed to know that I was still angry and upset. He pulled down the rim of his black felt hat until it almost touched the sunglasses that he never discarded, rain or shine, day or night, and puffed hard on his *cigarillo.*

"Doctor," he said, sighing deeply, "will you go to the coffeehouse tonight?"

"*Quién sabe?*" I said, turning to the window. I had no desire to join the coffeehouse gossipmongers, but I was touched by his concern for me and his indirect invitation. "It looks like rain, doesn't it?" I added, not wanting to let the conversation die.

But Rudolfo had nothing further to say. He grunted, finished his *cigarillo,* then slipped out into the darkness. I lay on the hammock brooding darkly in the shadows filling the small room, not even looking up at the scurrying patter that came from overhead. I knew they were rats; I had observed them during the hours of the afternoon *siesta,* hurrying along the rafters under the thatched roof, threading and lunging their way as confidently as tight-rope walkers up and down, back and forth. I dozed fitfully, my mind returning over and over to worry the subject of Dr. Malvenido. Just the name for the son-of-bitch when you remembered such words as malediction, malevolence, malefactor, malfeasance, malign, malignance, malice—and how applicable!

Far from working itself out through patience, understanding, and co-operation, as I had rather wishfully counted on, this conflict with the *curanderos* was becoming steadily worse. The officials in La Paz had all made it sound so easy. "Instruct them," they had advised me. "Let them help you in your work after they have learned the accepted procedures. Your job is to make the people in our backward provinces aware of modern medicine and what it can do for them." My God! How pathetically little these officials knew about their own country. One of my legs was over the side, I dug an angry heel into the dirt floor, and the hammock swung violently under me.

Nothing had worked out, I was in mortal combat with the *curanderos* (modern medicine versus primitive medicine men), and this business of having to be always one-hundred-per-cent right in therapy and diagnosis—in order to prove my clear superiority—would drive me crazy. It couldn't be done in any field, much less in the medical one, and my whole Bolivian venture seemed hopeless. Worse than being a fool, I was naive and unrealistic if I expected a great surge of converts to the one and only true principles of modern medicine, health, sanitation, and all the rest. To hell with it!

I peeled myself violently from the swaying hammock, almost falling and staggering the few steps to the coarse mud wall of the room. A cold wind blew in through the bamboo window bars. It was gusty and, dark as it was, I could just make out low clouds scudding by. I put on my poncho and sombrero, grabbed my flashlight, and restrained the impetuous Daguero as he slyly attempted to beat me out the door. Rain greeted me as soon as I started for the coffeehouse, not just normal rain, but heavy, cascading sheets of water. As with everything in Bolivia, especially in nature or the weather, I felt it was exaggerated for my benefit and I was annoyed. I could hardly see in the murky darkness, buffeted by sheets of rain, but I had a good sense of direction. The beam of light from hotel-coffee- and gambling-house door was like a friendly beacon, shimmering with the promise of warm hospitality.

No one looked my way as I came in, blinded and dripping. The men took their cards with the utmost seriousness, and I could feel a palpable tension streaming from the gaming tables. It came from the curses of the losers after a hand and from the almost surly, purring contentment of the winners. Between these buzzed the post-mortems of the kibitzers, who were in the majority, until their loud, partisan analyses were hushed by the gamblers feverishly awaiting the next deal. I tried not to make comparisons with the coffeehouses I had known in Europe, but they kept intruding themselves. The room was bare, squalid, poorly furnished and equipped, hardly evocative of any spirit of camaraderie. Thousands of insects dashed themselves against the lamp chimneys, dead bodies littering the pools of light like a mound of ash, while others took their place in the assault, only to fall in their turn, to be replaced by still more, and so on and on.

The room swarmed with clouds of *cigarillo* smoke, potent enough it seemed to asphyxiate any insect, and giving the interior a dim, billowing unreality. Through this miasma, the younger men of the *pueblo* milled back and forth, mostly silent and self-absorbed, but continually throwing nervous glances at the door as if dreading the fateful call to a dentist's chair of horrors. More likely, however, they were passing the time as best they could before setting forth in the pursuit of love, biting their nails as they awaited the word, the signal that marked the hour of assignation.

I exchanged a quiet word here and there with an onlooker, a young man preparing to go on the prowl, or a gambler who happened to look up between hands. Their reaction could be termed neither friendly nor unfriendly as such, but certainly the respect that these men had showed to their new *gringo* doctor as a newcomer, at least in the first few days after his arrival, was gone. The attraction of novelty had faded and perhaps, in a way, this was a good thing. I could take it as evidence that I was accepted or belonged or, failing that, part of a more or less familiar landscape. But I was inclined to think it was deeper than that—a carry-over of Malvenido's contempt for me. Even though they might not share the *curandero's* feelings, as his followers they could not help reflecting his attitude.

Thinking of Malvenido stirred me to impotent anger. To think of their faith in and loyalty to a wretched quack who even went so far as to inject gasoline intravenously as part of his cure, as somebody had told me! The card playing, the talk, the comings and goings distracted me only briefly.

131

Then the gnawing restlessness returned, the frustration of a man who did not like what he was doing (when he knew in his heart that he ought to be fighting his enemies, the Nazis, somehow, somewhere), but did not know of anything better to do. *If only I had something in common with these people, someone to talk to with similar interests and background—at least another Pierre with something other than the most primitive instincts and motives. And if that made me an intellectual snob, who cared?*

I wandered to the door and stared out bleakly at the now almost horizontal sheets of rain. I squinted toward my house through the torrent, straining my eyes as I saw two torches flashing on and off in front of my door. One flashlight could have meant Rudolfo; two, I felt sure, meant trouble of some kind. A night like this was made to order for emergency calls. Who would venture into the driving wind and rain just to buy aspirin? It had to be that I was wanted and, unlike a doting Dr. Kildare-type of Hollywood medico who would have responded pantingly to the call, I waited expectantly until the beams turned in the direction of the coffeehouse, heavy steps sloshed through the mud, and two men loomed out of the darkness. One was Rudolfo.

"Ah, doctor, what good luck to find you here!" He came inside out of the rain, followed by a pale young man of about twenty-five, with an untrimmed mustache and dark rims under still darker eyes. "This is Fernando Nunez," said Rudolfo, introducing us. "His father has sent him to you."

"D–d–doctor," the young man's voice tripped in his anxiety, "the pleasure is mine. I am Fernando Nunez, at your service." The amenities done with, he blinked water from his worried eyes, then rubbed them wearily. "My father urgently implores you to come quickly to our house in the *campo*. It is only two hours to the east." He paused and I knew the explanation was coming. "My sister—she is hemorrhaging terribly."

"Is she married?" I asked calmly. He nodded. "Is she perhaps pregnant then?"

"Why, yes, of course." He was tired and confused. "She has given birth to a child."

"And is the child all right?" I had to get as much information as I could before it came out in a hysterical, unintelligible torrent.

"*Sí,*" said Fernando. "Quite all right. It is sucking nicely."

I frowned at this. "What do you mean—sucking nicely? Babies don't usually suck well so soon after they are born."

"But the baby was born yesterday in the morning!"

He was annoyed and impatient, anxious to be off after so long a trip, but I had to know all the details. So I soothed and prompted him, and finally he settled down to a more coherent recital of events. It appeared that the afterbirth had not been discharged. The matron or midwife had worked hard, done her best. She had given extracts of all the helpful plants she knew, but none of them did any good; it had still not come out.

"I see," I said.

"And then—then last night Doctor Malvenido finally came."

"Oh, yes," I said.

The name alone made me flush, but I forced myself to remain casual because several men, attracted by the excitement at the door, had come to join us out of curiosity.

"Yes," said Fernando, "the *curandero.*"

He explained that Dr. Malvenido had worked throughout the night and most of the next day. But all his efforts to expel the afterbirth were unavailing, and he had taken the father aside and told him that only one remedy remained. And that was? I prompted.

"To go to the carpenter and order the coffin."

The hangers-on all nodded understandingly. I gave a little start, then as they sympathized with him and mentioned similar cases, Rudolfo, noticing my bafflement, explained the coffin business. It was a belief handed down from generation to generation—and often proved right, too—that, in just such cases as this hemorrhaging young woman, the patient would not die once the coffin was ordered. It was an effective last resort.

"So you ordered the coffin?" I asked.

"But then my father sent me to fetch you!" Fernando burst out.

As if to underscore the high point of the unfolding drama, one of the onlookers gave a sharp, tin-whistle intake of breath. Quite fitting, it seemed to me, because this was the long-awaited moment for my grand gesture of refusal, for stating implacably that if Dr. Malvenido was sought to take care of the patient from the first, then let him remain in charge to the last. But Fernando's eyes hurt to look at, I knew what I would do, but first I had to be cruel.

"And did you order the coffin?" I persisted.

Fernando lowered his eyelids and, rather than replying, blurted that it was a particularly trying situation because his older sister was lost in just the same way a few years ago. And her husband, then a widower and needing a mother for his newborn child, had married the younger sister. Now, facing the loss of his second wife, he was almost out of his senses. Everyone nodded at this.

"When was the baby born, did you say?" I asked again, to make sure.

"Yesterday in the morning." Fernando licked his lips, his fuzzy mustache twitching. "My father begs the doctor to forget that they called in the *curandero* first. But the *curandero* is an old friend, and my father says the doctor will know how these things are."

"*Querido, amigo,*" I said acidly. "That does not affect me. I am just afraid that it will be too late. Besides, I cannot get my horse from the pampas at this time of night. There would be no good in—"

"Señor Nunez has sent horses for you and me," Rudolfo broke in.

He seemed intensely concerned with the affair, all hot and eager to be off and away. It was a challenge, I was sure to lose, and yet . . .

"Does Malvenido know that you came to me?" I asked. Fernando lowered his head, and I did not press for an answer. It hardly mattered anyway. "I hope I don't have to meet the son-of-a-bitch," I murmured to myself. "I'd probably kill him if—" But they were waiting for an answer. I looked at Fernando's imploring eyes. "Let's go then. Come on!"

❋   ❋   ❋

Back in the *sala* of my house, I used my flashlight as I hurriedly dumped supplies on a table. Let's see. Ampules of hemostatic drugs like ergotrate for controlling hemorrhage, uterine constrictors like pituitrin, heart medicines such as coramine, cardiazol, and camphor oil. I cut several yards of gauze bandage from the big bolt I had, and into two clean towels bundled such instruments as scissors, hemostatic clamps, hypodermic and stitching needles, and rubber catheters. Taking no chances, I also jammed in the obstetrical forceps. I bolstered my big leather saddlebags with clean cloths, put the drugs and instruments inside, and added two pieces of lysol soap. What else? I looked around, jabbing the darkness of my *officina* with the flashlight beam, then plunged two glass ampules, containing catgut sutures, into the breast pocket of my khaki shirt. Anything I'd forgotten?

"Rudolfo, get a big piece of cotton from the supply room and wrap it around two syringes and an ether ampule." He went into the next room, and I reminded him to bring some files to clip the necks of the ampules. I put one in my change pocket in case he forgot. "I wonder about hot water," I mused aloud. "Maybe we ought to bring—"

"We have plenty of big pots and two basins," Fernando interrupted worriedly from the door. "There will be no trouble in getting hot water, doctor. I will see you get all you need from the open fire."

The dogs were eager to accompany us, but they would only be in the

134

way. I grabbed Daguero and held him until Rudolfo had collared Hordi-males. We pushed them inside, locked up, and started off on horseback, hoping we hadn't forgotten something essential. The rain had lessened, but it was still coming down steadily. My *poncho* protected me, but some water still managed to seep onto the saddle and make it slippery. We rode in silence in the rain, Fernando leading, Rudolfo in the middle, and myself last. I had no idea where we were going in the blackness, but my horse followed docilely without being urged.

I didn't like the sound of this case, not a bit of it. The girl had been hemorrhaging for two days; she must have lost a lot of blood and, from what Fernando had said, the entire afterbirth had probably been retained. In such cases, manual removal was indicated, but the textbook stated flatly that deep anesthesia, absolute sterility, and immediate attention were im-perative prerequisites for such manipulation. And now thirty-six hours had gone by—Christ!—and they expected me to save her. If the delay were fatal, and I had no cause to believe otherwise, that damned *curandero* would talk himself out of any blame. Not that he had accepted any re-sponsibility in the first place; Dr. Malvenido would never do that, and hadn't he suggested that the father order a coffin?

As my horse plodded on behind Rudolfo and Fernando, anger began to boil in me again. I damned the quacks and those who believed in them; I damned myself and my position, which made me a party to superstition and murder; I even damned my profession, which gave us no means of retaliation, no way of exposing these fakers. The pampas we crossed, the jungle we traversed were a forbidding black and gray blotted out with rain and mist. Rudolfo and Fernando were moving shadows I could hardly make out, huge and grotesque, then small, cubed, and transparent as apparitions. The obstetrical forceps sticking out of my saddlebag added another jarring, macabre note. It looked, it felt—it must be a bad dream. This simply could not be happening to me. Better if the girl were dead before I got there. Better if—I swallowed hard. Wishful thinking was dangerous and self-defeating; anger much more healthy. I would be better off cursing the malevolent Malvenido and concentrating on the medical problems ahead.

It seemed as if half the night had passed, but we had ridden hard in the rain and darkness for about two hours when a dog barked, and a dark house appeared to rise out of the sodden mists before us. One weak light shone at a window, otherwise it was black and still like a house of the dead. The thought made me shudder, and I told myself to stop dreaming, attend to business, be a doctor, etc., etc. Fernando rode up to the house and so did

Rudolfo and I. The fence poles had been lowered, we proceeded into the patio, and dismounted. Fernando motioned me inside, and I told Rudolfo to unbuckle my saddlebags and bring them in.

Fernando led me into a room where a small lamp hung on the post, close to two beds. The only other light came from a pair of flickering candles. The pink *mosquitero*—the only gay note in a predominantly somber room—hanging over one of the beds had been pulled open and to the side like a curtain. A naked young woman with a waxy-yellow face lay on the bed. The wings of her nostrils fluttered faintly, and her breathing was rapid, shallow, and weak. I looked at the tableau she made—my worst fears confirmed—and a sound made me turn.

The pole supporting the roof of the small house reached high up in the middle of the room. From a peg driven into this supporting pole, a hammock hung across half the width of the room to another peg in the wall, like a loose, dangling spoke in a wheel. The hammock jerked now as the young husband, for so Fernando identified him, staggered to his feet, looking like a ghost in the dim, guttering light. He had been keeping a long vigil, fallen asleep, and now everything came back to him as he lurched toward us.

"Doctor," he implored me, taking my hands. "Doctor, *salve-me-la! Salve-me-la!*"

I muttered the same soothing, reassuring things most doctors use in such situations, wondering again at the rash courage many people had in antici-pating marvels and miracles from a doctor who, after all, was only another human being like themselves. I wanted him out of the way, and his outcry must have aroused the girl's parents, for soon they came in, calmed him, and took him off my hands. Though she had tears in her eyes and was obvi-ously grief-stricken, I was struck by the mother's poise. She had seen and borne much suffering in her life; she would see much more before she died and, from the look of her, would always be equal to it. One could learn from this woman, I felt. In a corner, two Indio women squatting on their heels caught my eye. One, who had recently had a child of her own, was serving as wet nurse to the newborn infant, the mother informed me. The other was the matron or midwife. And there, on the second bed under the *mosquitero,* was the child sleeping. I looked around, but saw no sign of the *curandero.*

Rudolfo told me that there was water boiling over an open fire burning in the back room. I threw my instruments into the pot, then steeled myself to examine the sick young woman. She was too weak and ill to protest at

136

my manipulations. Bloodstained pieces of cloth carrying an unmistakable estrous odor lay on the bedding, and I noticed that her abdomen was raw and bruised from the clumsy efforts of those who had sought to express the afterbirth. I bent forward. The placenta was entirely inside, only the cord sticking out, and now alarmingly dry. The situation was serious, if not fatal. I took the girl's parents into the next room, explained what had happened, what I hoped to do, and what the chances of recovery were. They looked blankly at me, and I thought they hadn't understood.

"The afterbirth has to be removed. I can do it, but the risk is considerable."

They looked at each other, then Señor Nunez said simply as amen, "Doctor, she is in your hands."

If he had said, "Do your best," or "We'll take the risk," I would have felt easier. His confidence was a burden, a dead weight on my shoulders as I prepared for my task. I rolled up my khaki sleeves as high as I could, and called to Rudolfo that I was ready. He poured hot water into a basin set on a stool, and I began to scrub vigorously, all the while watching the patient and giving instructions to Rudolfo and the Indio matron, who willingly offered to help us. Everyone stared at me as if I were a magician and scrubbing up was part of the mysterious incantations preceding casting my spell. Flickering candlelight threw dancing, distorted shadows over the whole scene, the basin water sloshed and splashed, and overhead the rain thudded against the thin roof. I scrubbed hard with the lysol soap, shutting out of my mind everything except what I was going to do.

It had been cold and windy outside. I was sweating, the room was hot and sticky, and then a gust of wind seeped through like a breath of ice. I glanced quickly at the front door; it had been closed before, and now it was wide open. Someone moaned painfully, then suppressed the moan. I saw it was not the patient, then jerked my head around. Dr. Malvenido stood in the middle of the room near the main supporting post. He looked like a gargoyle, a white-haired, quavering King Lear somewhere between madness, despair, and majesty—a quack and a murderer, but somehow an implacable, wiry figure of such strength and will power that it was impossible to ridicule or despise him. Rather it was fear, he aroused, this man, and I saw it in the others and, unbelievably, felt it in myself.

He wore a sleeveless fur jacket, leather trousers with the bottoms tucked into moccasins, and his bony hands rested on a knobby-headed cane, whose sharp metal tip dug into the soil of the floor. There he was, the *curandero* of Rojas in all his power and malevolence. My arms went on with their scrubbing motions automatically as I studied him, and it seemed to me

137

that the chill pervading that little room did not altogether come from the outside. I hated the man, but then I was biased, although the fierce, little black eyes showed nothing objective in their evaluation of me either. To him, I was the quack and usurper, and he bristled all over at my effrontery.

He had dense white hair covering most of his forehead, leaving only a thin strip of skin open above bushy black eyebrows. He had a long sharp nose and, beneath it, his mouth set in a thin line like an unstitched cut that has healed badly. His skin was pale, his face clean-shaven—and glowing menacingly. Slowly, Malvenido raised his arm and pointed a bony finger at the father of the girl.

"Your son has not ordered the coffin!" he accused, his voice like the rattle of bones on metal. "Do you want your daughter to die then?"

Fires of anger burned high in his eyes, and Señor Nunez bent his head before the blaze. Very slowly, as if he were being manipulated by strings like a puppet, the *curandero* turned on me. His eyes were like needles pricking me all over, and I started nervously although my hands, from long practice, kept right on kneading in the hot soapy water.

"If the *gringo* touches your daughter," he thundered, "she will surely die!"

My hands had come up out of the water and now, soap-covered, they remained suspended in midair. Against my will, I looked from Dr. Malvenido to Señor Nunez with hypnotic fascination. We were all holding our breaths, and the crackling of the open fire in the next room was the only sound that could be heard. Señor Nunez kept his head down.

"Tell him to go!" Malvenido raged. "Tell him, I say!"

The father remained silent, refusing to look up, and the *curandero* held up his arm threateningly as if to hurl a thunderbolt that would strike us all dead as we deserved, for defying him. Then a scene came back to me from an operating room in Vienna, as an older doctor had cursed the younger doctor for using a new technique, cursed and insulted him, and the younger doctor had silently continued to do what he wanted to do. The devil take the authorities in La Paz, and unity, amity, and co-operation.

"You go," I snapped. "Go on, get out! I've got work to do."

He did not move or change expression. "She will die," he chanted. "If the *gringo* touches her, she will die."

"If she does, her blood will be on your hands, your heart, and your soul. Now, go!"

He blinked, the others blinked, and he was gone. I didn't see him go. One moment he was standing by the center post, the next he had vanished.

138

I took a deep breath and began to scrub my hands again. I had defied the gods and still lived; it remained to see whether I could do as much for my patient. I recalled that in school we had learned from Plato that every man had an inner demon which at times delighted in advising him what *not* to do. This, the teacher had explained, had the same meaning for the Greeks as the psychologist's "inhibitions" of today. I had not thought of demons since I had left school and Greek far behind. It was probably Malvenido's appearance that brought them back with such clarity. All overblown stuff and nonsense, as he was, but just then I felt a peculiar fluttering in my belly. And my own demon of doubt arose joyfully from somewhere in the region of my diaphragm—the place the ancient Greeks called *phrenes*, the seat of the emotions. Anchored there firmly, the demon started to grow.

Everyone in the room, except the busy Rudolfo and the helpful midwife, stood tensely in a corner of the room as I sloshed my hands over and over in the soapy foam. Now my full-grown demon whispered in a clear, heckling voice, laughing to himself.

"Why are you scrubbing? The girl is already badly infected. She has lost too much blood and will only die under your hands. And do you think you are really better and know more than Malvenido? How cheap to insult and revile him like a third-rate Hollywood actor! He is of and by the people and you are a stranger in a strange land and will always be so. And the girl will die, and Malvenido will be doubly revenged."

I pushed my chin forward and kept on scrubbing more violently, but the insistent voice droned on in my ears.

"Oh, you are for it, doctor, as the English put it. She will die while you have your nice, sterile hands in her body. Yes, she will die with a whimper, and tomorrow the people of Rojas will say the *gringo* doctor has killed a young woman. Then the *curandero*, whom you insulted with your cheap melodrama, will lead them. They will carry sticks and stones in their hands. They will say the *gringo* doctor asked Señor Nunez to let him cure his daughter just to show that he was better than their good *curandero*, and that he killed her—killed her—and now they will kill him. Kill him!"

"Rudolfo!" I bellowed so loudly to silence my demon that everybody looked up, frightened and uneasy. In fact, I startled myself. "Rudolfo," I went on, more softly, "fill the syringes, will you? One with ergotrate and one with coramine." He prepared them as I finished scrubbing. "Good work," I said. "That's fine. Now break open the ether ampule. But wait a minute first, eh?"

In as crisply pleasant and authoritative voice as I could manage, I explained that we were going to give the young woman an anesthetic so she would feel no pain. I added that because the ether was flammable, that they would have to extinguish all the lights, and that I would have to do all the work only by flashlight. But after I had completed my instructions and explanations and resumed scrubbing to be certain my hands were free of contamination, the horrible voice came back to bedevil me.

"You're a fool, Martin, and you'll deserve it if they kill you. Why do you get yourself into such trouble? Why ask for it, make yourself deliberately vulnerable? Be sensible and say it's too late. That they have waited too long before calling you. That will be a lesson to the people *and* the *curandero*. Stop in time and save your reputation—and your precious neck."

Gritting my teeth, I stopped scrubbing and asked Rudolfo to pour alcohol over my hands. The damned voice was like an old woman; it wouldn't stop for a minute and had to put a final, clinching argument.

"You can't win, Martin. Just use your head, man. If you manage to get the placenta out and save the woman's life—and you won't, mind you— they will say that that is only to be expected of a professional man. You know too well you have nothing to gain. You can only lose! It's for your own good, Martin. Listen! Listen to me."

I heard nothing further. Either the voice was silent, it had been silenced, or I had silenced it, but like Dr. Malvenido, it had gone. I turned now to the miserable woman who had been placed crosswise on the bed. Rudolfo was standing at its head, and he had put a clean towel over her eyes and a band of gauze over her nose and mouth. I gave the signal for the lamp and candles to be extinguished, and waited for them to be truly out as the matron focused the flashlight beams on the young woman's middle. I gave another order and Rudolfo, as I had taught him, snapped the neck of the ampule, and began to pour ether on the gauze drop by drop.

Our Indio helper, fortunately, was rock steady, and Rudolfo had washed and cleaned her as well as possible. The pot holding the instruments was at my side as I sat on a low stool by the bed. The boiling water had cooled, and I reached in for the scissors. Unhesitatingly, I made a large cut below. There was only scant bleeding and the blood was black. Two small hemostats took care of that. Then I started the real work, as I had done it often before. The cord was dead and cold and I felt ahead along it . . .

I shut my eyes, and I was no longer in a broken-down shanty in the Bolivian jungles with a wild-eyed *curandero* swearing revenge in the darkness outside, as he sharpened his knife to plunge it into my back. No, I was in the immaculately antiseptic, white-walled operating room of the maternity hospital in which I had interned after graduation. I had done this operation here, under supervision, for the first time, and afterward by myself many times over. Now my hand met resistance and my fingers, working methodically under painful strain and constriction, firmly and carefully overcame it. My hand went ahead, tunneling, burrowing, and entering the hot, moist, clinging aperture until it found the fleshy edge it was searching for. It loosened what it had sought and found, kept on loosening it, getting the soft spongy mass balled in front of the palm . . . Before I withdrew the hand and the mass in it, I opened my eyes.

No white walls, no nurses, no overhead lights. Just the feeble beam of a flashlight, a tight-packed room sickeningly hot and close. I shook my head dazedly.

"Rudolfo, stop the ether. Give her both syringes."

He obeyed, neither nimbly, nor dextrously, but with earnest dispatch. I grunted appreciation, then examined my patient as the matron raised the flashlight. Her face was a little flushed. I doubted whether she had gotten much ether. She was anesthetized, rather, by sheer exhaustion and shock. I washed my hands and dried them, then with one hand I took the young woman's pulse while, with the other, I massaged the uterus through the abdomen. Her pulse was jumpy and irregular now. That was bad. I was about to give Rudolfo further instructions as the woman's face became visibly ashen and she began to gasp.

"*Por Dios, se muere!*" exclaimed the matron, the flashlight beam bouncing around the room, then back to the ash-gray face.

The husband, who had been quiet up to now, groaned, buried his face in his hands, and turned to the wall in an it's-all-over gesture. Mother and father knelt, folded their hands, and gazed upward as their lips moved in fervent prayer.

"Just shock!" I said, biting off the words. Damn it! She needed a blood transfusion badly, but I had no microscope and there was no means of typing for finding suitable blood within a radius of two hundred miles or more. Means! I thought. There wasn't even time. "Rudolfo!" I yelled, while all the time the woman's gasps grew fainter. "Give her more coramine and cardiazol quick!"

Just then something—my demon or I don't know what—impelled me to turn around. By the center ridgepole, two fierce eyes seemed to blaze at me through the obscurity, not in triumph but in fanatic righteousness. Was my imagination playing tricks? It couldn't be Malvenido. I had kicked him out. Blind, unreasoning fear gripped my heart. In desperation I grabbed the alcohol bottle and poured the liquid on the cold, clammy arms and chest of the dying—I had to admit it—young woman. Always an observant pupil, Rudolfo poured out more and immediately began to rub her legs. One of the stoic Indio women—I couldn't tell which—had lighted a candle and she watched us briefly. She held it high—it was the other woman, I noted—and now the matron dropped her flashlight, splashed alcohol into her palms and frantically rubbed the young woman's thighs.

All the time we frantically massaged her skin and muscles, hoping to restore some circulation to the inert tissues, the woman's breathing became shallower. No doubt about it, she was going, and I intensified my efforts and urged the others to do the same. As we pushed and mauled, rubbed and slapped, the husband sobbed and struck his head against the wall, and the mother, still on her knees, fingered her rosary. If only . . . if only . . . Cold sweat broke out on my forehead. I shut my eyes because I did not want to look at my patient, nor did I want to face my inner demon, who had assumed white hair and fierce eyes in a pale, fanatic face. He seemed to crane his neck and weigh down my back, struggling to reach my ear and bleat, "I told you so . . . I told you so . . ."

"Oh, God! God!" A furious prayer was born in my heart as my aching arms labored on. "This is no time to abandon me. You give life and you take it away as you desire, but this is not the time for this young woman to die. I have done my job, not for glory, nor for money, and you know it. Help her, help them, help me. Now it is your turn, and it is very urgent."

The tenor of my prayer was admittedly neither humble, nor polite, but I did not curse either. I put the issue square up to the Power so much greater than mine—and I meant it. Oh, God, how I meant it! And, as I massaged away and looked at Rudolfo sweating next to me, the midwife working with us, the other Indio woman holding the candle like a torch, the parents kneeling and praying, and the husband moaning and beating his head, I meant it—as I never had anything in my life—not for me, but for *them*.

A few minutes, with none of us stopping the body massage, and the woman still breathing. More minutes passing and the same. Perhaps it was only wishful thinking, but I was convinced that she was breathing more deeply and regularly. We kept on massaging until the smell of sweat in the confined room had obliterated ether, wood smoke, and the other drugs I had used. Now a sigh came from the young woman and she seemed to stir.

The husband cut short his sobbing and lamentations, and shyly came closer to the bed. He held his hands before his eyes, as if he feared the

142

dreadful sight of his wife in death, and, when he saw that she still lived, he lowered his hands and hope flashed in his eyes. He rushed forward excitedly and began rubbing his wife's legs with tender, eager hands, relieving the exhausted midwife who shuffled over to the hammock. We massaged on, slopping alcohol on the young woman's body until the bottle was almost empty.

I took her pulse. It was still very fast, but much more regular and fairly strong. Best of all, the deadly ash-gray had gone from her face. I motioned to Rudolfo to stop for a while. He wiped the sweat streaming off his hair and eyebrows and, for the first time, I noticed he had removed his sunglasses, although he was still wearing his black felt hat. His eyes looked red and inflamed, but they still managed to shine with accomplishment. He was a good boy, and I looked my gratitude at him. Sometimes willingness and dogged dependability were more valuable than skill alone.

"Give her more camphor oil now," I said.

Rudolfo did his best to draw the viscous medicine into the syringe, but his hands, tired and weak from massaging, were trembling so that he had to put them down for the moment. He smiled at me sheepishly and I smiled back. My fingers were numb, too, frozen in position and curved like claws. Now we massaged our own arms, restoring circulation and resting tired muscles, and my gaze shifted to the center ridgepole where, not long before, I had had the hallucination of burning eyes accusing me. There was nothing there, of course; and I told myself that there had never been anything.

Rudolfo had more control now, filled the syringe, and handed it to me. The sick woman groaned as the needle penetrated her flesh, and I knew I ought to hurry because my job was not yet finished. Quickly I broke open the vial that held the catgut sutures, moved close to the candles, and concentrated on threading the largest cutting needle I had with me. My eyes twitched and stung with fatigue, but I did it the first time. I went to my patient, and the old mother focused the flashlight beam on the incision that I had made at the beginning of the operation. Without giving the girl additional anesthesia, I approximated the surfaces of the cut, swiftly applied a dozen deep stitches, and tied them securely as she groaned again.

Gesturing to Rudolfo, with his help I carefully straightened the nude young body on the bed. She didn't move and, against her smooth, slack skin, I could make out the mad beating of her heart, faithfully trying to make the best use it could of the diminished blood supply still in her circulation. She was a sick young woman, but she was alive, the worst seemed overcome, and I felt that for now she was out of danger.

I stretched my aching back and washed my hands. I heard a scratching sound, identified it as a metal-tipped cane digging at the earthen floor, and looked up quickly. A bent, fur-clad back limped toward the door, moccasins shuffling over the dirt. The door opened, I had a brief glimpse of pouring rain, then the figure went out, the door was shut, and the driving, wet curtain cut off. Strange, I thought. Had he been there all the time after I had ordered him out? I was too tired to care and, anyway, it didn't matter. I could summon up no emotion against the man.

The parents came on tiptoe to their daughter's bed, tears in their eyes as they shook their heads unbelievingly. The father lighted the kerosene lamp, then another candle. As we stood there, the young woman's respiration became much deeper and quieter. Now she opened her eyes and moved her lips feverishly, but she was too weak to talk. Tears fell like the rain from her parents' eyes as they marveled at her recovery, and the midwife hastened to bring her a cup of water. She gulped it eagerly, and the father and mother gave a simultaneous sigh of relief.

I glanced again at the other bed, only a few feet away, where the newborn baby slept under the faded pink mosquito net. The infant was on its back, both fists doubled up beside his tiny ears, all unaware of the violent storm through which his mother had just passed. How serene, I thought, then, as often before, I mused at the thin, delicate thread separating life from death. Then I lay down on the hammock and knew nothing.

When I awoke with a start, cramped and uneasy, I saw from my wrist watch that I had slept barely an hour. It was dawn, pallid and gray, and the rain was not falling so fast. The lamp and the candles still burned, dimmer than ever in the fuzzy light of early morning. I didn't see the others, but Rudolfo was slumped asleep in a chair. Suddenly worried, I rushed to the side of my patient. She was still terribly pale, but her pulse and respiration were good, and her eyes had gained luster. The matron came in with some water and told me she had given her a glass of milk earlier. "Good," I said, then watched the Indio woman give her the water and urged her to drink as much as she could. A little later I gave her another camphor oil injection. This time she protested the needle, and it made me smile to hear her. A complaining patient, in this instance, was a good sign.

As soon as it was full daylight, I sent Rudolfo through the rain to Rojas for more medicines. He didn't get back until early afternoon, bringing our horses as well, and I passed the time sitting with my patient, dozing, exchanging a few words with her parents and husband, and eating what they brought me. The young woman showed no signs of developing a fever or a new infection. She had a strong, lithe body, and her strength was returning bit by bit as it manufactured more blood. Her features glowed with happiness as her baby was brought to her. She drank more milk and *caldo de gallina,* and remained smiling and alert.

We stayed until early evening. I gave instructions to the matron, who listened quietly, blinked dark, expressive Indio eyes, and said, *"Sí, sí."* I looked again at the patient, then had a word with Señor Nunez and his wife, both of whom were deeply grateful. It was difficult for them to express what they felt, but I didn't mind, for their misty eyes and shining faces more than said it for them. I looked for the husband, but he lay on a cowhide on the floor snoring. The parents wanted to wake him, but I insisted that they let him sleep. Fernando embraced us.

It was still drizzling as we started for Rojas in the fading light. Rudolfo led the way, full of talk, and apparently not half so tired as I was. On the way, he told me that the young woman's husband was his cousin. I smiled to myself; relationships out here were so closely knit and intricate.

"I talked to him this morning. He promised me two cows for what you did for his wife."

Again I suppressed a smile. It would be a long time before I became accustomed to such payment for medical service.

"That's fine," I said. "Soon I'll have a herd."

"Then with your permission, doctor, I will go back tomorrow and get the cattle. It is wise to cash in on such promises while gratitude is still alive." I looked at him and he added, "People forget in spite of themselves. In a few months, when his wife is sound and well, it will not seem so much. He will believe that she was not very sick at all and that you did little." He shrugged. "It is the nature of people."

"I suppose. Tell me, Rudolfo, do you think I was wise to order the *curandero* out of the house?"

"You were very angry and so was he. And it was not right for him to say she would die if you touched her. That is because he is jealous of you and his own position. But he came back into the house, doctor. I didn't see him, but I think he was there all the time."

We came into Rojas well after dark. The main street was awash with mud from the rain, and the horses slithered in the ooze. The *pueblo* had its usual deserted, abandoned look, but the beam of light still haloed the gambling house as we passed, and the noise from within was as loud and lively as ever. We were about to ride on, as an impulse seized me, and I pulled up my horse. It didn't matter that I was exhausted.

"Let us have a glass of *chicha*, Rudolfo. There is nothing in my house for thirst."

He agreed with pleasure. We dismounted, went inside, and the clinking, chattering, and conviviality hushed immediately. Even the card players, usually wrapped up in the tensions of their game, glanced up with embarrassment to peer at me shyly. Nobody said a word, and the quiet of the room was unnerving. They wanted to act as if nothing were different from usual, but they couldn't manage it and their self-consciousness became a sticky, palpable thing. In fact, it transmitted itself to me and I felt naked and vulnerable. And yet I knew I had no reason to feel so.

Rudolfo had ordered for us. Now I took the glass from the woman who offered her tray and gulped the *chicha* down nervously. Then I gave my assistant a friendly slap, bade the room at large a hushed *"Buenas noches,"* and went out again. The woman followed me outside hurriedly, and I turned.

"Doctor Malvenido has come back to the *pueblo*," she said in a penetrating whisper. "He has asked the subprefect to introduce him to you!"

"Introduce him!" I snorted. "We've met—and I'll never forget him."

I did not mount again, but led my horse down the muddy street. I felt as if I were swaying above the earth with no contact with the muck through which I plodded. Those minutes of silence in the coffeehouse—I couldn't get over them. It was a tribute, something unbelievably beautiful, sudden and unexpected. Happiness ignited and glowed in my heart.

But why this special show of respect? Was it because I had beaten death or their inviolate *curandero*? I should have ignored the faker, but I had gone on to humiliate him publicly. Had I, after all, gained anything in this so-called victory? *Easy, easy,* I told myself warningly. *There is no reason for such exuberance. A manual removal of a retained placenta is nothing so very extraordinary. Merely routine hospital procedure.*

Dreamy weariness overcame me as I entered the house, staggering at the boisterous welcome of Daguero and Hordimales. I hadn't the strength to undress and walk to my bed. I stood by the hammock and collapsed gently into it, fully dressed. Ah, this was good! And perhaps things would be better from now on. The *curandero* had been put in his place; now, surely, he would co-operate. But one thing *was* certain—and nothing mattered quite so much: a woman's life had been saved, an infant kept from being an orphan. Even looked at objectively, here was something truly to rejoice the heart.

On the fringe of sleep, I mumbled to myself that I must not exaggerate

146

the happiness I felt at the moment. In the nature of things, tomorrow would bring something ugly or hateful, and the inevitable slump into depression would be all the more shattering because of my earlier exultation. All the same, I mused, only this moment mattered, this soaring moment of feeling so good, so wonderfully free and rewarded. I thanked God for answering my plea at the bedside of the sick young woman, and prayed again: *just this one time then, just for one short minute, let me be happy* . . .

The incomparable sense of well-being welled from my heart into my throat and up into my face until I could feel it glowing. *For one little minute, God,* I begged, *let me keep—* Then a soundless laugh began to make my face tremble and, from there, spread to my entire body until my eyes were drenched in tears.

Then I slept.

9

I Am Accepted; Poker Passes the Time; Don Socrates Philosophizes; I Am Asked About Paternity; Daguero Likes Good Meat; The Rain and the Blues

I had saved a mother and, in a way, I had saved myself. I never lacked for patients now. They came confidently and on their own, and my stature in the community improved day by day. Don Socrates was overjoyed by the change. He postponed his trip back to Santa Morena from *mañana* to *mañana,* and he shared my triumph as the great *gringo* doctor who had defied the *curandero* and brought a dying woman back to life. It was all very gratifying, but my healthy skepticism remained; if they loved me now, they could hate me again just as quickly. A mere swing of the pendulum and I would be a pariah again. As simple as that. But it pleased me that Don Socrates was happy, continued to postpone his trip, and kept his sons with him.

Of course, they were having a good time and so were delighted to stay on in Rojas. Don Socrates was proud of his tough, handsome, lusty sons, and he didn't fool me a minute as he railed about their behavior.

"*Ai,* these sons of mine are like devils. Every night they are out till all hours serenading the *muchachas,* and I don't know what else . . . Young people today have no respect for their elders. They refuse to listen, they do what they want, and . . ."

I smiled. I had heard it all before.

Life was no longer so sluggish in Rojas. Things picked up with the arrival of the first of the *estancieros,* just back from driving their cattle to the Brazilian border. They were in an expansive, good-time mood. Their pockets bulged with money, and cash flowed freely in the *pueblo.* The hard work

148

and still harder riding were done for the moment, and this was the time for spending, for fun and games. Diversions were few in places like Rojas. There were women, there was drinking, there was gambling. The gambling house was crowded every night now. I was accepted and trusted after my successful bout with death and Malvenido, and I found myself joining the card games as a respected member of the community and almost, but not quite, "one of the boys." But it was only to kill time that I participated at all, and I was more fascinated watching the gamblers than in my cards, good or bad. At least so I told myself.

Still, playing cards requires attention, caution as well as daring, and I did enter into the spirit of the game more than I acknowledged to myself. And I smarted at the fantastic run of good luck being experienced by Don Arturo, the man with the bridgework and the gap above it. He won the biggest pots night after night, and the story of his luck spread over the province. People came to watch him, shake their heads, and marvel. He was a hero. I went along with the amazement of the others, but I took his incredible luck as a personal insult. It also occurred to me that he might be cheating.

I preferred smaller games without an audience, so I was glad to accept the invitation of the subprefect to play at his house. He said he loved privacy and that crowds made him nervous. His guests for a game of "pokercito," as he called it affectionately, included the village's few prominent citizens, and I suppose it was something of an honor for the *gringo* doctor to attend. They were long sessions. The subprefect's wife prepared the *sala* carefully for her distinguished guests and even kept a *sirvienta* up all night to serve distilled coffee to the gamblers.

"It is pleasant playing at the university," said Don Socrates. The fancy name was his little joke for the subprefect's gambling den. "But, you know," the old man confided to me, "it is not really the crowd that bothers our friend. It is Don Bonaparte. Why?" His eyebrows shot up. "Because in his gambling house, Don Bonaparte takes a tribute from every pot. It is a kind of personal tax, and it adds up. Yes," he mused, "it adds up enough to make one like a private game better."

In any form of competition, particularly where chance plays a great part, it takes a major effort of the will to control the emotions. The true poker-face can do this, but these good men could not. I liked watching them as they played, their gestures and expressions betraying their emotions, tics, and twitchings giving away the fact that they held good hands. Tall, broad-shouldered Don José stroked his beard nervously, as if he were trying to clean a paintbrush that refused to be cleaned. In his attempts to bluff, he was tense and motionless, staring fixedly at the table and refusing to look anyone in the eye. As for Don Alfonso, the *alcalde,* the signs of a winning hand were unmistakable. The mayor was a thin man with a protruding Adam's apple that never failed to bob in a victory dance when he held the cards. The subprefect, on the other hand, always began to tell jokes when he held winners.

Don Socrates was terribly nervous during a game. A streak of luck reddened his cheeks alarmingly, his facial muscles quivered, and his fingers trembled so uncontrollably he seemed barely able to hold his cards. Winning was not important to me. I held my own, however, and I suppose I could have plunged successfully had I wanted to profit from the psychological advantage that I enjoyed. Even when they were not playing, these men discussed poker with the utmost seriousness, much as baseball is picked over in the United States, soccer in England, and politics in France.

"You will never lose much at poker, doctor," said Don Socrates. We were sitting on stools on the little sidewalk outside my house, good friends now, exchanging small talk, gossip, and ideas. "It seems to me that you are able to remain calm because you really care nothing for the game."

"That could be," I admitted. Then, wondering if I could risk some personal criticism, I said, "You take it hard, don't you, Don Socrates? You are a bundle of nerves during a game."

"*Ai, hijo.*" It was as if he had confessed some dreadful sin. He made a face, a grimace that seemed to exaggerate his self-disgust. "It is a vice, and it has me in its grip." He sighed deeply. "But what else is there to do out here?"

He glanced at me, a mocking light in his eyes, and I said nothing. Then Don Arnulfo, who was sitting next to us, his chair rocked back against the wall, began to speak. Because his mouth was paralyzed on one side, he could not talk and smoke at the same time, so he had to remove the *cigarillo* from his lips, then search for words.

"Yes, what else? There is no distraction for us in Rojas." He frowned thoughtfully. "But in the big cities they have books and theaters and concerts." Then he added, "And even electrical treatments to cure a man's disease."

Back to that again! I cursed myself for mentioning such treatments, feeling a stab of guilt at my rashness in suggesting they might help him.

"It is not absolutely necessary, this electricity, Don Arnulfo," I said, wanting to make the man feel better. "Your face is better already. Be-

150

sides, you have something in Rojas that will help you more than all the electrical treatments in the world: peace and quiet, good clean air, and the time to enjoy the good things of life."

Don Socrates inhaled on his *cigarillo,* blew out the smoke, and looked across at me in surprise. I knew what he was thinking and smiled. Meanwhile Don Arnulfo continued to complain over his dull lot.

"Nothing to do. Nothing. All my life I have longed to see the great cities of Brazil and Chile and Peru. All my life I have begrudged those who have enjoyed the advantages of living in those busy, exciting places. If they want light, they have only to turn a switch. If they want to travel, they have railroads and automobiles. Why, they even move their cattle by the railway. They live, really live, while we waste away our years. And now I am crippled and will never visit the big cities. I haven't the hope left—or even the time."

I noticed Don Socrates scowling as Don Arnulfo's complaints died away on the evening air. Some time ago, perhaps in a moment of weakness, he had confided to me that he was almost seventy years old. It had been hard to believe at the time. He was a man of action. He could ride a horse three days on end and arrive at his destination still fresh enough to sit up gambling all night. He was one of the most intelligent men in the province, certainly the most progressive; he owned several thousand head of cattle, at least forty horses, and his home was the pride of the community. He was honored, sought after, and respected. He was an able man and a vigorous one; the fires of youth had not died in him; he had a sharp eye for women and, from what I had heard, still gave his wife cause to be jealous. But now, as Don Arnulfo's whining lament hung in the gathering dusk over Rojas, as it remained suspended in the stagnant vacuum of this backwoods village, I felt that Don Socrates suddenly looked every day of his age.

"*Compadre,*" he said heavily, "I have experienced the things you crave— the cities, the railways, the factories and theaters, all of it." He sighed, his eyes dull as he stared into nothingness. "And I say no. You are not right in envying the people who live there. Everywhere, man is born and man dies. Is that not so? And we call the time in between life, and we wish only to pass it in happiness. That is what the two thousand inhabitants of Santa Morena want, what the three thousand people in Rojas want—and the same with the two hundred thousand citizens of La Paz, and two million in Paris, too."

He held out both hands, palms upward, as if testing for rain.

"We all wish for happiness, we all seek it, but the way to achieve it, the

151

manner in which we traverse those years between birth and death—ah, that is where the problem lies. And the difference, too. The difference between the city people and ourselves. I spent years of my youth in the cities, and I tell you the people there do not understand. No. They forget that there is an end to life's span; they forget that every day away from the beginning carries them closer to the end."

He paused, and there was silence as the *cigarillos* glowed in the dusk. Don Socrates cleared his throat before going on in the same severe, eloquent voice. His shirt was open and loose, his trousers baggy, but they did not detract from his presence. He was an impressive patriarch, and I felt his words carried as much weight for me as for Don Arnulfo.

"As I say, these city people act as if the end would never come for them. So every day they exhaust themselves preparing for a tomorrow—and some day that tomorrow they look forward to so eagerly will not come. Don Arnulfo, you and I, the simple people of Rojas—we do not close our eyes to death. We are there in the room at the instant a newborn baby opens its mouth for its first cry. Similarly, we are present when the hour strikes—*quando llega la hora*—and one of us has to die. Nothing that happens, neither love, nor poker, nor *aguardiente,* can make us entirely forget the end of our time."

As he finished, the *cigarillo* dropped from his hand, flashed momentarily in flight, then seemed, almost symbolically, to extinguish itself in the dust. It had been a long speech for Don Socrates and, I felt, truly meaningful. He had not merely indulged in incipient garrulity, nor had his undoubted eloquence given his words all their weight and color. It was more that he was a man near the end of his time, and he knew it. And he had a clear, strengthening self-knowledge, a lack of illusion about himself and his life. At the same time, reaffirming the bitter, imprisoning truth that man was born to die, his words were also a passionate avowal of the realities, the close-at-home facts of life. He could still laugh at himself though.

"We do not forget the end, doctor," he went on, turning to me, "but we also enjoy the time allotted to us so long as it lasts, yes, right up to the end. Poker and *aguardiente* and love—our people enjoy them without remorse and without worrying about paying for them in the hereafter. So what does it matter if my fingers tremble when I uncover my cards one after another with slow, burning impatience and the gambler's lust? When I rise from the table, I can say *me gusto.* I am content. If I tremble, it is only my nature, and I wish to let my nature live today."

"True," I broke in, "but nature is—"

But Don Socrates had more to say and did not hear my interruption.

"What if our sons give way to their desires and go after women all night? They are men and do as men do. It is their nature, and I will not advise them to hoard their manhood. Why? Because tomorrow the poison of the rattlesnake, the horn of the mad bull in the pampas, or the fever and chills of malaria or some other sickness may make an end of the life of my sons."

Now the old men fell silent, but the velvety night air seemed full of unspoken words. His philosophy both moved and repelled me. I felt bound to ridicule his idea of total acceptance, but I spoke without thinking.

"But what about humanity's progress?" I asked. It was put as a *gringo* might have been expected to put it—high-sounding, pompous, and alien. I regretted the words immediately, but had to go through with my thesis. "Doesn't that count at all?" I added.

Don Socrates did not hurry his reply. Apparently my question did not strike him as out of place, and I felt relieved.

"It seems to me," he said slowly, pondering his words, "that the happiness man has received through progress is hardly worth the happiness he has had to sacrifice to achieve this same progress. It is true that in Rojas we have no electric lights, no automobiles, no railways, no factories. But it is only for one machine that you need another machine. One demands another so that there is no end to it, and man has long lived without any machines. Tell me, doctor: can you deny that there are people in our region who are happy as the happiest in your big cities? Or that there are men and women in the cities who are more unhappy than the unhappiest here?"

I couldn't, I suppose, but the atmosphere had become too serious. Definitions of what constitutes happiness can vary greatly.

"And can you deny, Don Socrates, that sometimes we need machines. Without the airplane I probably wouldn't be here. An airplane is a machine, and a doctor in these regions has become a necessity. You've said so yourself."

"*Ai*, doctor, *picaro*. You are the crafty one." Don Socrates laughed. "But that is different, is it not? You cure our evils of today."

"Granted. But," I persisted, "Doctor Malvenido's followers say they have always managed without a modern doctor and that they can go on living without one. A *curandero* is enough for them. They say that if one has to die, one dies when his hour has come."

Don Socrates responded violently to this thrust. His shadowy figure shot upright and his stool clattered to the ground.

"They're ignorant animals, all of them!"

Consistency can be a vice as well as a virtue, and it amused me that my oracle of the pampas was not too concerned with it. But there had been enough of talk, and the contradictions in Don Socrates' philosophy quickly dissolved in the darkness at the prospect of the poker game due to begin at the "university." We played far into the night, and it was a sleepy, sullen doctor my patients faced the next day. I had had to get up for an early call, and I was amazed to find Don Socrates bursting in on me looking so fresh and wide awake.

"I must go home, doctor," he announced. "My son should arrive today or tomorrow in Santa Morena. He is returning from Brazil with the money for our cattle, and I must be there. Besides, the raintime is approaching, and there is much work to be done around the *estancia* before it sets in."

There were no delays this time. I had barely finished with my next patient before Don Socrates was back with his two other sons, all mounted and ready to go. We went through the usual Godspeeds. With one after the other I shook hands, embraced, and shook hands again. It was no longer a mere formality; I was attached to these people. I handed Don Socrates a bundle wrapped in paper, holding my letters. I had included no message for Carlotta. After all, what could I say? "Having wonderful time, wish you were here." Hardly. "I miss you and love you." My God! She would no doubt expect a letter, but her father would surely open her mail.

"Do me the favor, Don Socrates, and give this to the postmistress in Santa Morena to dispatch to La Paz."

Don Socrates took the bundle and slipped it into his saddlebag. He said nothing and, patriarch that he was, he managed to make his silence eloquent. Waves and smiles, a clattering of hoofs, and they were off. My stare lost itself in the palm trees as the riders disappeared around the corner. How gray and lonely the trees looked, the bent one all crumpled and sick. Their leaves were sun-scorched, drab, and listless. My good friend was gone, and I had an empty feeling in my head and stomach. I was alone and friendless. Not quite though. Daguero stood at my side, his tail and ears drooping. Just like his master.

*   *   *

In a way Daguero was my salvation. We settled into a routine of our own, but I must admit that it was infinitely more satisfying to the dog. The sick and the not-so-sick all day, a little poker at night, small talk of Rojas, and the rest deadly monotony. About the only break came when Rudolfo called to me from the threshold.

"Doctor, Don Salustine has hoisted the red flag over his door!"

I couldn't get excited. "What does that mean? A new revolution in the country?"

"No revolution, doctor." I couldn't see his eyes behind his dark glasses, but he sounded hurt. I didn't care. "It means that the mail carrier has arrived."

Mail? That meant news from civilization, a breath of life come into the doldrums. Without bothering to grab my hat, I dashed into the street and over to the little house flying the red flag. It was an occasion for Rojas. The short, middle-aged postmaster was only able to indulge in his official function half a dozen times in the whole year. He was all bustling self-importance, and gave me a benevolent smile as he gave me my mail.

"Ah, here you are, doctor. There are letters from La Paz, from across the sea, and also newspapers from the representative of the province. You have good reason to be pleased."

Like most small-town postmasters in any part of the world, he seemed to know my mail so well that I was sure he was familiar with the contents. Not that I could blame him. As they say of contract bridge, one peek is worth two finesses.

On my way home, I tore open the oldest postdated letter after arranging the others in careful chronological order. I told Rudolfo to hold off my patients and to take care of as many as he could himself. I was taking time out for my mail and would respond only to an acute emergency. In my *sala* I leaned back in my hammock, deliberately prolonging the precious moment before I plunged into the familiar world I had left behind—the only real world. The first letter was from my friend Herbert. It was flat and predictable with I-did-this and I-did-that, all cut and dried. He spoke of Karl, who was still working as an accountant, and Karl's wife, Maria. I knew his own wife had joined him by now, but he said nothing of her. His letter closed with the briefest—and most infuriating—of postcripts: "Are you happy, Martin?"

Don Socrates would be amused. Here was a chance to compare big city and village happiness. Are you happy, Martin? Really now! I had strayed, left the mainstream in La Paz, and deliberately gone off to lose myself in the wilderness. Oh, yes, I had turned my back on my friends, left them flat, gone off to seek my fortunes. And now—was I happy? Damn Herbert!

It reminded me of the time the circus had come to town when I was a boy. The colorful advertisements in the newspapers, the garish posters on the wall had fascinated me. The acrobats, the tumblers, the ropewalkers, the animals, the big tent, the exotic displays. For weeks I dreamed of nothing else. I knew every detail of the show. I worked up an intensely personal relationship between myself and all the animals and performers, until I was convinced that they must know me as intimately as I knew them.

I was sleepless the night before I went to the gala opening with a relative.

155

But there was a big crowd at the gate, we got separated somehow, and I was left standing outside the fence. Why, it was just as if I had been refused at Paradise. No escort, no ticket. Then I heard the blare of the band as the show got under way, cheers, bursts of laughter, and applause. My astonished hurt went too deep for tears. How could it be that *my* circus had started without *me*. That the animals, the clowns, the performers that I knew so well—and had known so long—did not care whether I was watching them or not. It was like cold-blooded murder.

And now, all these sad and bitter years later, it was an older, but no wiser, Martin who had slammed the door behind himself and run away from the main tent. But this time nobody came to the main office to report a lost child; nobody came after me, nobody missed me. I was not a participant, not even a spectator. I was left outside in the jungle while the performance went on in La Paz. My friends did not write of their common problems, just a few casual remarks about the weather, they were well, getting used to the altitude, and a mocking question: "Are you happy, Martin?" Happy! How dare Herbert use that word when it had as little meaning for himself as it had for me and all the other refugees? But one thing was clear: Herbert no longer thought of me as one of them. I had dived into oblivion.

I found I had missed one letter, the most painful of the lot. It was from my Lisa in Paris, and had followed a circuitous route to Rojas. At first I was grateful that she had remembered—how I had pounced on the envelope when I recognized her handwriting!—then I wished she had not. She wrote only of her office and her activities there. No personal matters any more. I had cut myself off, and this was a follow-up courtesy. She would have followed me, if she had loved me. But she hadn't, she wouldn't, and—well, to admit the truth, I had never really loved her, and I had never told her that I did. I was a fool, and she was a woman, an intelligent woman. So what right did I have to feel sorry for myself? Why did I behave as if my heart were broken and I had lost a great love? Carlotta would marry me like that. Not so Lisa and, curiously enough, I must have known it all along because I had never asked her. Or would she? Or had I? Odd how blurred and blunted my memories had become in these past months. But I had to be honest with myself: the truth was that I was simply envious. All these people had somebody to whom they belonged. They were loved and cherished and cared for.

I turned in the hammock, and letters and envelopes and papers fluttered to the floor like old snow from niches on a canyon wall. I could hear

156

Rudolfo's voice in the *officina* painfully improvising some far fetched medical explanation. Time I got back to work and forgot myself and my stupid troubles. Love and loneliness and that rot. But it hurt and I hurt. My hand dangled over the side of the hammock, and I started as a large tongue, like wet pink flannel, licked across the back of my wrist. I looked down at Daguero and scratched his ears.

"Are you happy, Daguero?" I asked. "Are you? Tell me, boy!"

The dog barked and wagged his tail frantically.

There was an answer for you! I'd a lot sooner have Daguero with me in Rojas than Herbert.

* * *

Although September and October were months belonging to the dry season, they had known rain. But then this infrequent rain had fallen like tears of joy, impatiently yearned for by a thirsty soil and so quickly absorbed that I could almost detect sucking sounds. The water disappeared as quickly as drops flicked on a hot stove, wet spots drying instantly in the burning sun that followed the showers, and soon the ground was as dry, baking, and dusty as it had been before.

It was far different in November when rain came as if tilted from a huge bucket, cascading down from the sky in great waterfalls. Its unending steadiness was both doleful and depressing. The reservoir was inexhaustible and the tap never stopped. On and on and on until the streets were gluey, muddy grooves between the drenched houses, and walking was a tortuous progress around puddles, over puddles, across puddles, and, finally, in desperation, through puddles which seemed bottomless. Then the rain would let up, the puddles would melt away, then just as suddenly be replenished by new downpours. But these rains were feeble forerunners of the torrential storms that were unleashed on the earth in the beginning of December.

They thundered from an inexorably gray sky for days and nights, filling the atmosphere with walls of water that splashed, splattered, inundated, and washed away Rojas. Or so it seemed to me. For days and nights the hard strings of rain descended on the *pueblo,* pattering down on the streets, houses, and huts in an awesome curtain. From the eaves of the slanting roofs, thick ropes of water swirled incessantly, while great hoses foamed from the corners of the houses that had gutters. I had to work by lantern light at all times, and I felt I was going blind. Gray were the mornings, gray were the noons, and gray were the long hours before the still longer evenings. People huddled in their houses before the rain like troops under an artillery barrage. There were leaks everywhere in the thatched roofs of the village. The interiors were dank, and everything smelled of mold, rot, and wetness.

Roaming cattle and horses streamed into Rojas in search of protection from the enemy elements. Ordinarily they never tired of the pampas, its cold and wind, heat and storms, but the unceasing deluge had defeated them. They were sodden, congealed, forlorn, and bedraggled. They limped and stumbled into the village like dazed survivors of a shipwreck looking for some security, some shelter to ward off the pelting rain buffeting them. But there was no shelter, no overhang, and the beasts clustered under the sparse tree crowns, standing there like pitiful statues, whipped and beaten, resignedly letting the water have its way down their damp, shrinking hides.

Situations and circumstances change, bad as well as good, and it is a mercy, or none of us would ever survive or find the strength to go on to greater joys, triumphs, sorrows, or disasters. Sometimes then, and always miraculously it seemed, the torrent would subside for one, or perhaps two days. The sun shone on the drenched, eroded soil bright and warm, as if to remind the remorseless rain gods that it would reign supreme once again with all its old strength, when the downpours had finally dissipated and dried away to nothingness. Like so many weary, unbelieving Noahs emerging from the Ark to marvel at the warmth and blue sky, the people of Rojas crept out of their leaking, battered houses to blink in the sunlight. It was only a respite, much like the tranquil eye of the hurricane, but this was the way it would be soon, and this certainly made up for all the torments of the flood.

As red-hot wires steam when dipped in cold water, so the land steamed now in the burning rays of the sun, smoky vapor drifting and eddying up as far as the eye could see. Like thousands of separate campfires, the mist rose, swaying in a ghostly dance across the fields before it climbed into the cooler upper air, where it immediately huddled in thick rain clouds ready to fall back to earth again, as soon as the sun retreated.

My spirits had risen with the sun. I stood in the open door of my house, breathing the good clean air and rejoicing in the dazzling play of sunbeams over the soaking fields. I watched the mist rising and rolling across the grass almost like the surf, it seemed, and just then I spotted Daguero returning at a jog from his morning excursion to the *pueblo*. He looked pleased with himself, head and tail high, until his attention was caught by the thick plumes of fog swirling around him. He eyed them with openmouthed puppy astonishment, then set off in pursuit of one of these elusive, unsubstantial ghosts. He lunged, he darted, he snapped, he twisted, but not even his most spectacular leaps availed him. Unable to get his teeth into the mist, either through speed or a direct approach, he tried guile. With infinite care he stalked his chosen ghost, crept along on his belly, poised himself, then jumped, his mouth wide, and caught nothing. His reaction to failure amounted to a canine double-take. He had missed completely, but there was his adversary dancing all around him.

It was a remarkable performance, and Daguero was not the kind to give up easily. His antics captivated me. Soon I was laughing helplessly, more refreshed in spirit than I had been in weeks. I admired him for chasing will-o'-the-wisps and trying to attack them. We were a lot alike, dog and master, but Daguero was the more tenacious. Although he came when I called him indoors, he was clearly dissatisfied. The ghosts still floated un-challenged outside, and his chest contracted as he looked up at me, the whining, imploring notes of his canine pleading coming through his teeth. I stretched out on the hammock. He plodded over, put his muzzle on my chest, and eyed me beseechingly. I had to speak to my faithful friend.

"Qué tal, hombre?" I said in the gentle tone I used when we were alone. "What's the matter, old boy? Are you hungry? *Quieres carne?* Shall we go buy some meat, eh?"

I was sure Daguero understood every word. He gave a long, high growl of agreement and thumped his tail on the floor for emphasis. But I was lazy, failed to follow the suggestion immediately, and the tail-thumping slowed to a measured, speculative tempo, and he gave a few affectionate barks un-derlining impatient reproach.

"All right, all right."

I got up and yawned. Daguero's tail accelerated cautiously, I moved away from the hammock, and he began to jump back and forth between me and the door, his tail swishing like a metronome gone crazy.

"You've made the rounds of Rojas, eh? You've already found out who slaughtered a cow today, is that it?" I asked.

Daguero gave a few ear-shattering barks, rose on his hind legs, and hopped about wildly just as if he were spring-mounted. I pretended to return to the hammock, and now he lunged at me, swiping with his front paws and giving staccato barks. I gave in with a laugh, patted his silky head, and went to the door. Once on our way, Daguero saw no further use in per-suasive tricks. He walked close to me with a befitting dignity, only now and then giving an impatient little growl or scrambling ahead a few paces. He stopped suddenly and, looking up at a house two blocks away, I saw a big, bloody side of meat hanging from a beam by the front door.

"Well, well!" I said. "It beats me how you dogs always know who is butcher for the day. This time it appears it is the *alcalde* who is selling meat. I hope the meat is fat, Daguero. The mayor is an old skinflint, and I'm afraid his animal would have to be half dead before he could make up his mind to butcher her. Look at that bloody mess! We ought to have a professional butcher in the *pueblo,* old boy. Then you'd have fresh meat every day—and the people of Rojas would enjoy good meat under sanitary conditions." Daguero pressed against my leg to hurry me on. "But you don't starve, do you? That dried meat isn't so bad when it's cooked soft for you. Besides, with those dragon's teeth of yours . . ."

Daguero and I were close to the *alcalde's* house now, and I stopped my one-sided conversation so as not to be labeled *loco.* A man didn't walk the streets talking to his dog, no sir. So I put on my friendly *gringo* doctor's smile and joined the crowd of Indio women in the patio. They were waiting patiently for the attention of the stout official, who was bent over the carcass of the cow satisfying the demands of two white women. They were pointing at the sections of meat they wished, and Don Alfonso was trying to give them just the cuts they designated.

The mayor's two sons were helping their father and, like him, they were wielding machetes and laying about clumsily with bloodstained hands. I had the impression that they were hacking to death some great beast which still writhed beneath them. A number of dogs, snarling and snapping a short distance away, now retreated as one of the butchers heaved a rock in their midst. The blood and smell of raw meat were driving them wild, but they kept abreast on an invisible line, a wolf pack held in restraint by threatening gestures and flying stones. As a newcomer, Daguero felt entitled to sniff the carcass under my protection. He did so, and the wolf pack snarled and growled as one.

"*Buenos días,* doctor," said the *alcalde,* looking up. "How have you arisen?"

We were both respectful and polite in exchanging the usual morning amenities and then, the conventions observed, I was free to place my order. I pointed to a shoulder.

"That's almost too good a piece for a dog," said one of the boys.

I smiled, looked around at the women, but no one responded. It was clear that no one present approved of giving a lowly dog a good cut of meat. Well, I must be consistent, I thought ironically. If a *gringo* doctor was different from these people, then his dog must accordingly be different. Like father, like son. I pointed again at the shoulder, Don Alfonso promptly applied his machete, and broke out laughing.

160

"I just remembered, doctor, that you still owe me money from the last time I killed a cow. You were busy then, but not your dog. He came by himself and I sold him two pounds of meat." He pointed with his bloody machete. "He ate it up right here."

I grinned. "I honor all of my dog's debts. Was it good meat?"

"Like this." Don Alfonso held up the shoulder I had just bought. A hole had been bored through the meat and a piece of rope looped through it for easy carrying. "The best. Your dog has expensive tastes."

"Don't we all sometimes?"

I paid for the shoulder, plus Daguero's earlier "purchase," then started back for the house with the bloody meat dangling from my hand like a scalp. I could feel eyes on my back, but I ignored them. The sun was pleasant, the sky bluer than I remembered, and Daguero was prancing happily around me.

"The people here think I am too good to you, old boy," I told him. "They don't know that you're all I have, the only living thing that belongs to me. Nothing is too good for one's best friend, eh, Daguero?"

He barked loudly, then bounded ahead to the patio of my house, where a sleek black dog was waiting for us. Rudolfo's Hordimales was Daguero's pal, and Daguero always went half mad with joy at the sight of the older dog. They jumped on each other excitedly, then hurried back together to greet me, Hordimales evidently expecting a handout. His disdain, his customary superior calm were abandoned in his eagerness. He danced around as frantically as Daguero, just as much a puppy at the prospect of food.

"Ah, your friend Hordimales is a smart one, Daguero," I said. "Because the rain has stopped today, he knew we would bring meat back to the house and so he comes begging. But Rudolfo's mother does not like us to feed her son's dog. Did you know that, Daguero? She says we spoil him, that a dog should have to fight for his food. But she's an ignorant woman. It won't hurt Hordimales to take food from us—not if she doesn't find out about it. And she's wrong, too. Dogs shouldn't have to fight for their food any more than men . . ."

As I reached my patio, I took out the knife I usually carried with me and began to cut off chunks from the shoulder of meat. I tossed them to the two dogs, who jumped high for their treat, catching the pieces on the fly in their open mouths. Barely had their legs touched the ground before their throats worked convulsively, they had swallowed the meat whole, and they were ready for more. I kept on feeding them for a while, then threw some pieces as far out as I could to show Daguero and Hordimales that the

161

game was over. I cleaned my knife, folded the blade, picked up the now jagged and depleted shoulder, and started for the house. I was just passing close to my own half-opened shutter as I heard Don Arnulfo's scratchy voice and, guessing that he could only be talking about me, I stopped to listen.

"I have not heard of a woman or a *muchacha* to whom he has gone in the night. But, I will say, there is gossip about the time when he was in Santa Morena. In any case, it is true he works in Rojas, but during his leisure hours he seems nervous, restless—like a man who has not had a woman for a long time."

"But he has many women at night," Rudolfo insisted indignantly. He spoke strongly in refuting this slander on his chief, his matter-of-fact calmness put aside in my defense. "He has *bastante* of them, and it is not his custom to talk about such things. You must see that, as doctor here, he has to use the greatest discretion. *Sí, sí, bastante* of women," he repeated, as if to stress his point. "This nervousness, this tenseness you speak of in him, it has other causes."

I smiled at my assistant's commendable exaggerations, then strained to hear what Don Arnulfo would say next.

"Could it be then that he worries about the *curandero* still having more patients than he has?"

It was a typically dirty insinuation, and it made me bristle until I heard Rudolfo's strong rebuttal.

"No, señor, of course not! That quack is not so quick with his talk as he used to be. That I can tell you for sure. Malvenido has respect for the doctor now. Why, we passed him on the plaza just the other day, and the old man did not even dare to look up. Think of that now!"

There was a pause as Don Arnulfo gave it some thought, and I smiled reminiscently at the scene Rudolfo had remembered. In spite of the assurance of the woman in the coffeehouse, that night we had returned from our bout with death *and* Malvenido, the official introduction he had sought had not yet been arranged. But, subtly, ever since that life-and-death struggle over the daughter of Señor Nunez, there had been a difference in our relationship. Then, as Rudolfo had just said, we had indeed come face to face on the public square. The old *curandero's* eyes still burned with the same fanatical fire, but it seemed an inner blaze now, not so personal, and no longer directed at me. He had even worked himself up to sketch a faint ghost of a salute with his cane. And I had replied with a vague gesture, which could be taken in any spirit the *curandero* chose, and we had passed on quickly, leaving me—for some reason I couldn't explain—elated out of all proportion to the significance of the episode.

Don Arnulfo was muttering something unintelligible now, but I had heard enough. I withdrew, chopped up the remainder of the shoulder of meat for the dogs, then went inside, all innocence. Don Arnulfo broke into a coughing spell at my sudden appearance, his features assuming an alarming redness, while Rudulfo smiled and smiled at some joke only he seemed to understand. I behaved as if nothing was out of the ordinary, we exchanged civil banalities for the moment, as Don Arnulfo's color became more normal, and presently he was setting forth the problem that was troubling him. I had suspected that there was something. People did not pay casual calls in Rojas, any more than in other places, but his roundabout approach tickled me.

"Doctor, I have come to see you on a matter *un poco delicado . . .*"

I waited for more, but he hesitated and I found myself saying, more sarcastically than I had intended, "And you wish perhaps that I should ask Rudolfo to leave?"

Don Arnulfo shook his head. "I have talked to him about it already."

"Have you now?" Again, fortunately, my uncalled-for sarcasm did not register.

"Yes, doctor." He licked his lips. "Do you remember Don Ernesto?"

"Don Ernesto?" I repeated. Was I an idiot? "Certainly I remember him!"

"Then you must recall that you treated the widow Señora Domena when she gave birth to her last child not long ago."

"*Como no,*" I said. "Yes, of course." But I had to make a slight correction. "But it was the matron who delivered her. They only called me in when the bleeding would not stop afterward."

"That is so." Don Arnulfo was working up to the crux of his problem. "I have come to see you, doctor, *pues*—because Doña Domena has declared that Don Ernesto is the father of this last child."

"Ah!" I smiled understandingly. "And now there is family row in Don Ernesto's house. His wife doesn't like this business."

Don Arnulfo eyed me blankly. "The wife of Don Ernesto has nothing to do with it, doctor. It is none of her concern. The thing is that he is willing to recognize the child as his and let it bear his name, but only if you will confirm the fact that the infant is indeed his."

"I see," I said, although I did not quite see. "But do you mean to say that Don Ernesto's wife really knows nothing about it?"

Don Arnulfo stared at me unbelievingly for a few seconds, like a man called on to explain something that had already been made abundantly clear.

"Don Ernesto's wife certainly knows," he said politely, if a little impatiently. "But this is of no importance. If a husband is of a mind to tell his wife about his affairs, he does so. It is up to him alone. But, in this case, Don Ernesto holds that Domena had been living all this time with another man, Carlos, who happened to be staying in the *pueblo* for several weeks. The problem is one of paternity, you see."

I swallowed hard. I could see where matters were heading, and they seemed clearly above and beyond my line of medical duty.

"Well, there are medical procedures which, in many cases, can determine the father of a child. But these call for laboratory tests and, as I have no such facilities, I could hardly perform them here."

"*Vea Usted.*" Don Arnulfo looked disappointed. "It is not a matter of such extraordinary importance as to require laboratory tests. After all, Don Ernesto has previously recognized several children as his own just on the word of their mothers. But he is obstinate this time because he didn't want this Carlos sneaking under Domena's *mosquitero*. I have come to you purely for the child's sake. Don Ernesto is an honest man. Although not one of the richest men of the community, once he recognizes a child as his, he always helps the mother bring it up and gives it his name. Although the mothers of his other children are all strong and able to work, he still supports them. But, as you know, doctor, Domena is weak yet, very weak."

I still had much to learn about Bolivian morality and sexual customs, but there were surprising points to Don Arnulfo's story that appealed to my sense of humor. At the same time I was not tempted to laugh.

"Do I understand that Don Ernesto is an honest man because he supports his children?"

Don Arnulfo shrugged. "I do not argue that, doctor. But we have many wealthier men in Rojas, and they leave the burden entirely on the women by whom they have children. Don Ernesto, on the other hand, is one of the few who feels an obligation. Therefore, it would be pitiful if he could not be convinced that the little baby girl is his."

I pondered this a few seconds. "And you tell me he has several other children and not from his wife?"

"*Como no.*" Don Arnulfo nodded enthusiastically. "The man is *muy hombre*. He is only a few years younger than I am, but, not so long ago, he fought the tiger with just a knife in his fist and his dogs to help him."

I smiled. "I guess him to be about fifty years old. For his age, he is skilled with women."

164

"Ah, doctor," Don Arnulfo repeated admiringly, *"es muy hombre.* You should have known his father. He was at least eighty when he died three summers ago, and this old man left a little *muchacho* who is now five years old. He is not from the same mother as Don Ernesto and, if you look at the *niño,* you cannot deny the likeness."

"Did this old man have many children then?"

"Oiga." Don Arnulfo blew out his cheeks. "In Rojas alone, not counting the other *pueblos,* there are besides Don Ernesto and the little one at least a dozen others. *Qué hombre!"*

He clicked his tongue sadly, looking off into the distance. Don Arnulfo's facial paralysis had afflicted him after emerging from under the *mosquitero* of a bosomy Indio woman, and ever since he had been afraid of the chase and avoided it with reluctance. "I am afraid if I do not stop," he had confided to me, "that it will extend to my arms and legs."

But now he continued his effort to convince me. "You must know that Doña Domena is not well. Her oldest child will live with her mother-in-law, and the other with the people of its father, Don Manuelo. *Pobre muchacho.* Don Manuelo's wife is a wicked woman, and she probably will not give the child enough to eat."

"If so many of the children born here did not die, your population would multiply rapidly." I was thinking aloud as I spoke.

"Ai, doctor," said Don Arnulfo. "If all the children born here were to live, we would be very fortunate and have enough people."

"True, but would the children be happy?"

"Porqué no?"

"Pues, it seems easy for the people here to make children, but I think it an even greater responsibility to bring them up."

"In a large house, doctor, feeding another stomach is no problem. If it is a little boy, when he grows up to manhood, he will help on the pampas with the cattle. If it is a girl, there is always enough housework to be done."

Don Arnulfo had all the answers, but I wasn't satisfied. "Forgive me, señor, but what about children such as the one you have come to speak to me about?"

"Ah, this little one is an exception because her mother is weak and cannot work. That is why I have hoped you will speak a favorable word."

I shook my head. With some proof to go by, I would not hesitate, but not this way, just on my off-the-cuff say-so. "For the sake of the baby, it might not harm anyone to tell Don Ernesto that he is her father. I saw this man Carlos and, for the girl's sake, I hope she does not grow up to look like him, but I must confess that I do not go along with the careless way men

165

live here—planting their children whenever and wherever they have the opportunity. It is too irresponsible, not wrong, but irresponsible, that's all."

"*Sí*, doctor." Don Arnulfo scratched his head. "Some of us do live like animals. But, as you know, there is not much else for us to do here."

I had heard this plaint before and had to laugh. "So you make children, eh? And the more children a man has, the more you say he is *muy hombre*."

"A man needs a señora for his house—and to represent him, doctor. Sometimes he also needs another woman—to keep his mind clear. Then, if children result . . ." He pursed his lips and shrugged.

"At least nobody is surprised. But I wonder whether a señora could do both, represent her husband and keep his mind clear, as well as being the mother of *all* his children." It was evident that none of this sat well with Don Arnulfo. He had tried and failed, he was anxious to go, and I tried a final joke. "This has been most interesting. When I see your *compadre* Don Socrates again, I will not tell him your opinions. Somehow I feel sure he would not approve."

At that, Don Arnulfo broke into another coughing spell, reddened, and took an abrupt departure after a single, curt *"Gracias."*

I was puzzled and a little vexed. It had been silly of him to expect me to declare on paternity as freely as a water diviner or, more close to home, a *curandero,* and yet I suppose it would have made friends for me without injuring anyone involved. Yet, if I stood on and for nothing else, I had to rely on my medical principles and accepted medical practices. I wasn't God. All the same, I feared I'd been sanctimonious in my sexual arguments. But why should he go like a man just stung by a bee?

I turned to Rudolfo, my loyal assistant, who had been sitting quietly in the corner during my long, rambling conversation with Don Arnulfo.

"Did I say something wrong?" I asked. "He seemed to act so queerly when I mentioned Don Socrates."

"It was nothing," said Rudolfo evasively. "Don Arnulfo is like that sometimes."

"There was something, Rudolfo. Tell me what it was."

"No sé," he said and flushed.

"You're giving yourself away, my friend. You might as well tell me before I hear it elsewhere."

He denied it again, but I was firm in my insistence and finally he told me the story about Don Socrates. It seemed, he said halfheartedly, that not too long ago Don Socrates had been smitten by a pretty sixteen-year-old *muchacha,* whose mother had been Indio and whose father was unknown.

The old man had been so taken with the girl that he had brought her into his house. He had lived with her there openly under the eyes of his family, giving no consideration to their feelings. His wife had become so disgusted that she had moved out to the *estancia* with her daughter.

"Then, when you arrived in Santa Morena, doctor," Rudolfo went on, "Don Socrates wanted you not to know about the girl. He sent her away, this *muchacha,* and ordered his señora and his daughter to return to his house."

My reaction to the story was mixed, but I roared with laughter as Rudolfo finished, and my hilarity sounded unnatural even to myself. Still the idea of the old patriarch making love to a sixteen-year-old schoolgirl in the presence of his ever dignified and highly annoyed señora was as grotesque as it was absurd. What was even more absurd was the reformation induced by my arrival. Why, Pierre had stopped drinking in my honor, I thought with savage irony, and Don Socrates had topped this by foregoing his affair with a young girl. And then I had turned around and made love to the willing Carlotta, crept under her *mosquitero* pantingly as soon as her father was away. So who was absurd and grotesque now, eh? Ah, the *gringo* and his tiresome sexual platitudes. What must Don Arnulfo think of me—and all the others?

"How many children have you fathered, Rudolfo?"

The young man was taken aback at my serious tone, but he showed no resentment at the personal question. "I have one *hijo,*" he said seriously.

"You are not married, of course?"

Rudolfo's shrug—as with all these people—was more eloquent than a Parisian's. "One cannot marry every woman with whom one has a child."

In vain, this time, did I look for any telltale crimson to flood my assistant's fair cheeks or mark his sensitive features. Rudolfo was entirely unconscious of any reason for embarrassment. In fact, I admired him as an honest man— a man far more honest with others and himself than I was or ever could be. These people would not understand the European meaning of sophistication, but I was the naive one, not they. Their life was their life; mine was—well, no life.

If I could have willed it just then, I would have blushed for myself. I ministered to these people, cared for them, doctored them, lived in and among them, but my dog Daguero understood them, was of them, and belonged far more than his proud, ignorant, bigoted master.

All right, then, where did I belong?

10

Thoughts on My Bolivian Prison; The Shocking Death of Doña Eulateria Roca; The Near Fatal Illness of the False Priest; Malvenido Helps Me Perform an Emergency Operation

The torrents of rain that continued to thunder down during January and February filled the ravines, until they became lakes, and made mad, surging rivers of what had been insignificant creeks. They kept on and on, and there was nothing else to do but to accept the situation in the same spirit as the inhabitants. I was still a doctor, my professional duties came first, and I traveled as much as I was able, to take care of the sick. I did things that normally I would never have dreamed of doing, never thinking of myself as a glamorous or heroic figure. Nor was I really.

Although I defied the elements, soaked myself to the skin day after day, stumbled through swamps infested with poisonous snakes, swam beside my horse through rivers filled with treacherous alligators to reach patients in the outlying *campo,* my excursions, dangerous as they were, had little to do with bravery or triumph over fear. It was true that I was no physical coward, in spite of my fear of snakes, alligators, and other jungle terrors, but the opportunity to be active, helpful, and productive, while willingly riding myself into exhaustion, was important to me. That way I had no time to worry about myself, the nagging restlessness of my brain was appeased, I fell asleep as soon as I tumbled into my hammock, and my hours of rest were good and easing—an unconsciousness of body, mind, heart, and soul.

But as the weeks crawled by with infuriating sluggishness and my tours of duty were less demanding, for one reason or another, the boredom that came over me was an active worm in my brain. March was a miserable, unending month of drizzle and gray clouds, a permanent curtain set to hang, low and oppressive, apparently for the duration of time. Grim, inexhaustible, inexorable, asphyxiating . . . Day after day I stood staring through the bamboo bars that cut my window quadrangles into vertical strips. To the north and west I could see the iron curtains of the rains, shutting off the free air above the mountain peaks and preventing the *avion* from ever reaching the province. Through the bars to the south and east were only swollen rivers and flooded fields. Then it struck me. My God! It was just like being a prisoner again.

Still, I thought defiantly, being a prisoner of the elements was a different thing. One could fight the elements; they harassed and attacked a man's body; they did not try to break what made him a man, the power of his will and the strength of his soul. I could ride out the torrent, let the wind and rain whip at me. I could defy them, struggle joyfully against vicious nature, all the time sucking the free, fresh air into the deepest alveole of my lungs. The choice was always mine. But in prisons made by men, in the concentration camps, monsters broke the wills and souls of other men, even if their bodies survived.

In literature, during times of stress or emotion, it is amazing how often men and women call to mind passages of great poetry which seem to express, with a passion of which they are apparently incapable, exactly what they feel. I have always had little faith in such writing or in such characters and yet now, as I clung impotently to the bamboo window bars and asked myself for the hundredth time what I was doing in Bolivia, I could hear my darling, troubled Lisa quoting her favorite lines from A. E. Housman:

> "And how am I to face the odds
> Of man's bedevilment and God's?
> I, a stranger and afraid
> In a world I never made."

I turned away from the window and pressed my arms to my trembling body. Lisa! Lisa! I began to doubt my own reasoning; man or the elements, where was the difference and what did it matter? A jail was a jail; a jailer, a jailer. I looked at the bamboo bars on the windows around me. This *was* a prison, and I *was* inside it.

*   *   *

The day had been long, overcast, and, of course, rainy. The time had passed with grinding slowness, and it was late afternoon when I heard the noise outside. Any distraction was a relief, and I rushed to the window. Two teams of strong oxen were pulling a rough *carreton* past my house toward the center of the *pueblo*. The usual stiff cowhides roofed over the wagon and, along with a piece of sackcloth, also curtained it off in back. I knew that it carried a passenger, and then my attention was drawn to the man on horseback following the *carreton*. Whether it was the dripping rain or the dim light, I couldn't tell, but this silhouette assumed fantastic proportions outlined against the gray sky. No horse, no man could be that big! The great animal had a wooden pace, its hulking rider sat stiffly in the saddle, and both moved like figures in a poorly animated movie cartoon. The man wore a wide sombrero, much like my own. I couldn't see his face because of the shadows cast by his hat brim, and a heavy rubber *poncho* encased his big body to well below the thighs, leaving exposed to the rain only the coarse shoes in the stirrups.

In contrast, a stooped Indio rode on a small mule a few lengths behind the giant rider and massive horse. The Indio's black felt hat hung over his face, as if the drenching rain had collapsed it like a moldy melon. His *poncho* was thin and worn, and his bare feet jutted out in broken, wooden stirrups. What a pair, I thought, and how much like Don Quixote and Sancho Panza. I looked after them, finding pleasure in the queer procession and making it last until they were out of sight, like a gourmet savoring some exotic delicacy.

I was still standing there as I noticed Rudolfo walking toward the house. Only a few minutes had elapsed since the arrival of the *carreton* and its dissimilar outriders, and now everyone in Rojas must know about it. Rudolfo's prompt appearance, from just that direction in which the covered wagon had gone, made me certain that a medical call had been sent out, but he certainly did not walk like a man with a mission. He dawdled along, his hands buried in the large pockets of the gray coat he had salvaged from his year of military service, circling puddles as if they were lakes, drawing away from ruts as if they were canyons, and cringing from the rain as if he were under a deluge. I went toward the door, and Rudolfo spoke as soon as he came in.

"Señor Simon Bolivar Roca has brought his wife, Doña Eulateria, from his *estancia* in the *campo* to you here in the *pueblo* to consult you about her health. Uh, he sends his greetings and, uh, expresses his desire of your visiting his humble house whenever convenient."

Rudolfo spoke without enthusiasm and, from his stilted delivery, I had no doubt but that he delivered the message exactly as the tall man on the great horse had given it to him. When he had finished, my assistant pulled up his shoulders, then let them sag in a helpless gesture without taking his hands from his pockets. I couldn't fathom his attitude, but I gathered that "whenever convenient" meant right away. After all, the man had come all the way from his cattle ranch in the deep country, a long trip which meant some kind of emergency. So I started out, Rudolfo behind me carrying my bag. A successful city doctor wouldn't be so eager, I reflected, but I was curious about this man and then, bitterly, I had nothing better to do than come at once.

We stopped at a house I had passed many times before. I had never seen a living soul in the place, and it looked just the same, desolate and empty. It was very much like the houses around it, except that a halfhearted attempt had been made to replace the timbers, which formed the usual sidewalk for most homes in Rojas, with a more solid wall of masonry. But the project had apparently been abandoned, and the little that had been done was falling to pieces. In one corner of the patio, I noticed the big horse that had carried my Don Quixote and the little mule of my Sancho Panza. They were standing drowsily under a tree, and the teams of oxen, still paired two and two, were bunched at the rear of their wagon, blinking resignedly into the rain.

Daguero, who had come with us, went over to sniff at the animals, then rushed to my side. The little Indio was waiting for us at the entrance to the *sala*. He was holding an unlighted kerosene lantern, and I wondered why. Daguero sniffed him, then backed off uneasily. He always went ahead of me at a bound, but now he hesitated and stayed outside, as I scraped the mud off my boots and crossed the threshold. Odd, I thought.

"*Entra,* doctor," a deep basso profundo voice called out.

It was just the tone I expected, a big man had to have such a deep voice, and I smiled. He got off a stool, came over to me, and shook hands. Out of custom, I automatically lifted and curved my arms for the embrace that always followed, plus the second—and final—handshake, but my host made no corresponding moves, and I was left flat-footed, my arms still outstretched, like a lying fisherman.

"Sit down, doctor," he said in his booming voice.

I lowered my arms and sat on a stool covered with a cowhide so worn that it was rubbed smooth in places, and I could feel the legs sticking into my buttocks. We made conversation, and I was taken aback as he apologized for his "humble home." I felt I was supposed to contradict him out of pure courtesy, but I didn't because it would have been ridiculous. The *sala* was bare to the bone. There were our stools, the saddle gear heaped in a corner, and nothing else.

I wondered that he should beg compliments, but the man himself was noteworthy. At first I was disappointed that he had no beard, as I had imagined he must have, and then I decided he did not need one. It was sufficient that he had short, curly black hair bristling on his elliptic head, fiery black eyes, and a big mustache. His patrician air was emphasized by his long protuberant nose and thin lower lip. He looked so much like a Spanish aristocrat that I tried to picture him in the elegant breeches and velvet jacket they usually wore. He had the poise and bearing, everything but the correct clothes. His trousers were bleached and old and, now with his leggings removed, were bunched and baggy around the ankles. Over his shoulders he wore a ragged scarf and his shirt was open at the neck. The skin here, as well as his long, lean, wrinkled hands, gave away his age for all his black hair. I guessed that he must be close to seventy.

The dimness of the room flattered him. The only light came from a rancid-smelling candle that had been set on a piece of wood. It was on the floor, close to the man, and his huge, wavering shadow was thrown against the wall behind him and high up into the rafters holding up the thatched roof. As we chatted desultorily, the stooped Indio shuffled into the *sala* carrying a battered tray with two cups, one of tin and one of pottery. The strong aroma of coffee seemed to make the room a little less gloomy. The tray also held an old tin can with a protruding wooden spoon—the sugar bowl.

"*Sírvase,* doctor."

It was given like a royal invitation. I took the tin cup from the proffered tray, expecting that the earthenware one would be offered to Rudolfo, who still stood at the door of the *sala* like a beggar, not even having been asked to sit down. To force my host's hand, I looked around now at my assistant, but Don Simon haughtily ignored the gesture and, ever the lord of the manor, took the cup himself.

"How do you like our sorry country?" he asked between noisy sips, his little finger stiffly away from his cup in what was meant to be dainty, high-society style. Then, before I could reply, the basso voice went on in what was bitter lament. "*Ai,* there is no more discipline in this world. The young no longer have any respect for their elders . . ."

He pointedly refrained from looking to the door, where Rudolfo was standing on one foot, then the other, and I felt uneasy. What did Don Simon expect him to do—grovel? Kiss his hand?

172

"Believe me," he continued in his deep, lordly voice, "forty years ago, even twenty years ago, things were different. Then those of us who knew the Castilian language were at least masters of our own houses. But when these—these Turkish peddlers began to invade our country one by one, with their suitcases on their backs and nothing else, urging us to buy their worthless merchandise . . ."

Contempt was on his face, bile on his lips. He put down his cup with shaky fingers and rolled a *cigarillo* with neat, precise motions.

"Today they own nearly all the land and cattle here. Every store belongs to one of them. Why, some of our sons and daughters have even lowered themselves to marry these Turks." His thin lips curled as if he were going to spit. "And now we, the conquerors, have to do business, have to deal with the Indios from whom we wrested the land."

I had to repress the urge to mad laughter. Here was the superiority of the high class, the first families, the aristocrats, the super-race of warriors, the landed gentry agog at the infiltration of the inferior, the commercial travelers. Why, he talked like the Nazis at home, or what had once been my home. The same propaganda, the same snobbism, the same supernationalist hatred of all newcomers, especially when they turned out to be successful in business or industry. It was pathetic, sickening—and disillusioning. What kind of New World was this? Why, it's the same all over, I sighed, and now I understood Rudolfo's lack of enthusiasm for Don Simon and his problems, whatever they might be.

My host paused now, and I looked up to meet a probing glance from under a nest of bushy eyebrows. He was sizing me up, trying to determine which side I was on. I pressed my lips together and struggled to show nothing. Don Simon could not tell which side I favored. My friendship with Don Socrates was well-known, however, and he was from Turkey or Syria, as Pierre had once told me. But damned if I'd give this King of the Pampas any satisfaction. I didn't want to take sides. I had never wanted to. It was all so tiresome, so childish, just like this little set speech of Don Simon's which, I supposed, he had given over and over to any ready ear.

Now his hard look softened, and his features took on a melancholy cast. "We have been very stupid," he acknowledged. "Very stupid," he repeated sadly, then his eyes lighted up. "But not all of us, doctor, no. Let me tell you. Let me prove it to you! Some thirty years ago, as short a time as that—doctor, I swear to you that there wasn't a pauper around who didn't have a cup of gold sterlings, yes, a whole cup full of English pound sterlings. You know, they had to pay us in pure gold for the precious rubber that our trees yielded. *Sí*, señor, we swam in gold." The gloating sheen was brilliant in his eyes for a few seconds, then they became veiled. He looked around mysteriously, beckoned me close, and put his lips to my ear. "I could tell you a few places where lots of the coins are buried. *Sí*, señor, and they know it, the Turks. That is why they hate me so."

Suddenly, I was achingly, terribly bored. He was dotty, senile. I'd come to this haunted house to see a patient, not to listen to fairy tales about the good old days. I wanted to get up, turn him off, and get down to business.

But Don Simon hadn't finished, his broken record had to play through to the cracked end.

"They came to me one day," he went on loudly. "They came and paid a great deal of money to buy seeds from all of us. They wanted to plant rubber trees in the Malay, you see, and all our foolish people sold them gladly for such high prices. Everyone sold them seeds, everyone except one man. So they came to me and, *sí*, señor, I gladly sold them seeds, too. But, but—" he broke out into cackling, triumphant laughter—"I boiled them first."

The recollection gave him such a kick that he bounced to his feet like a young man. Oh, how he'd outsmarted them! Taken their money, their gold pieces, and twisted their tails as they, of course, deserved. He was a man among men.

"Yes, boiled them," he repeated happily. "And now let us go and see your patient."

He marched to the door of the adjoining room, and pointed to a wooden bed. On it lay a woman of about fifty, her head propped up uncomfortably against some bulky pillows. Her yellowish face had a hollow look, her legs and arms were thin, and her abdomen hugely swollen in something like the last stages of a grotesque pregnancy. Her breath, I immediately noticed, came fast and shallow.

"Permit me to introduce," said Don Simon in his basso profundo. "*Querida,* this is our new doctor, a professional, not a faker like the Indio quack they have here."

The sick woman gave me a brief, formal smile. I made a little bow, chatted for a minute about nothing, then felt her pulse. It was fast, but strong. As far as I could tell in such a superficial examination, the lungs were certainly congested. There was fluid in the basal parts, and it was remarkable that her legs were free of edema. Don Simon no doubt expected me to come out immediately with what was ailing her, but a snap diagnosis was impossible. He was the type of man who demanded a quick cure, which was

174

also impossible, but I could at least make the poor woman more comfortable. Don Simon's eyes were piercing me, and his wife looked up at me with pathetic eagerness. I was no faker; I was a professional, not a magician. I wished I could like Don Simon, I thought, but this woman . . .

"I think we can relieve you of some of the fluid in your abdomen," I said to her gently. She eyed me questioningly, not understanding, and I turned to Don Simon. "The señora would then be better able to breathe," I explained.

"Doctor, she is in your hands."

He said it without hesitating, and I couldn't help wincing. It was a standard sickroom reply here, but to be given such unquestioning confidence was always troubling. But what was there to worry about so long as I was extra careful not to hit a loop of the bowel in inserting the trocar? Theoretically, shock was always possible—and dangerous, sometimes fatal. But I had often done abdominal parcenteses on patients who had looked far more ill than this woman, and nothing happened. Of course, there was always a first time. Even if I waited and examined her thoroughly in my *officina,* but that meant carrying her through the streets in the rain and mud, and . . . I bit my lips. The woman looked at me trustingly, Don Simon smiled with a serene confidence that I could not share.

"Rudolfo!"

My assistant darted inside at my call, and I instructed him to fetch the trocar, an instrument which was nothing more than a giant needle, from my office. He went off promptly. I gave further instructions, and Don Simon gave orders to the Indio, who soon heaped twigs on a dry space under the thatched roof. He started a fire, set a pot over it, and presently there were sounds of water boiling.

"That's fine," I told Señor Roca. "Now we need something like a pail to catch the fluid."

But the pot for the water had exhausted the resources of this impoverished aristocrat's house. There was nothing like a pail and, instead, the Indio produced a dozen shallow receptacles, which were the halves of shells from some coconut-like fruit. Then, feeling like a householder putting out pans under a leaky roof, I arranged them on the floor by the bedside so that they would catch the ascitic fluid as it ran out. The barren room, the crude preparations, the primitive shell containers, all put me in mind of Malvenido. I felt just like a *curandero* myself. I ought now to mumble some charms, murmur incantations, and start doing a medicine man's dance around the bed of the stricken woman.

I hadn't paid much attention to where the Indio had started his fire. I knew it was under what passed for a chimney, but the rain, beating down so steadily, was making for a bad draft. It was seeping into the patient's room now, curling low and thick, rasping the throat and stinging the eyes. I could hardly work, choked and blinded in this fashion, so, as soon as Rudolfo came back, I asked him to put out the fire. I put the instrument in to boil for a short while, then waited for the smoke to clear from the room.

When everything was ready, I asked that the candles be brought close, and Rudolfo helped me set the patient up as straight as she could manage. I raised her skirt decorously, with Don Simon watching, lowered her undergarments to expose the belly, and painted the lower left quadrant with iodine. Smiling assurance and telling the señora to relax, I injected novocain so the insertion of the trocar would not hurt her. I took up the trocar, holding it low so as not to frighten the woman, then slipped it quickly, firmly, and smoothly into the swollen abdomen. The first hit was lucky: a stream of thin amber fluid spurted out and squirted to the floor. Quickly I placed one of the shells on the spot, and the liquid bubbled into it.

My audience had increased. Besides Don Simon, Rudolfo, the Indio I thought of as Sancho Panza, there was also an Indio woman who had come out of somewhere and was watching now, sucking one of her fingers. Things were going well, the fluid was jetting out, and I was relieved. The magic was working.

"So simple." I smiled at my audience.

More than half the shells were overflowing with fluid now, it was still squirting out strongly, and I suggested to the Indio that he get some extra ones. He shuffled off, and I followed his exit dreamily. The room was so dim, my audience so quiet, and the only sound the dripping of the fluid into the shells. No alarming sound or movement alerted me, but it was just as if an icy fist suddenly gripped my heart. I jerked my head toward my patient just as she simply and silently keeled over. Her eyeballs rolled upward so that only the whites were visible, she gave one sharp gasp, and her face all at once seemed to double in size. Then she turned blue, and her jaw sagged.

"*Por Dios!*" I snapped.

I reached back for my kit. Rudolfo thrust it at me, and I wrenched it open, and with trembling fingers broke the neck off an ampule. Hurriedly I aspirated the liquid into the syringe and jabbed the needle under the señora's skin. Another quick injection, then again caffeine and coramine. My heart beat wildly, my eyes burned, and I hoped, hoped, hoped, although deep down I knew that it was too late. Back of me, except perhaps for Rudolfo, everyone was ridiculously calm. There had been no crisis, no moment of life or death, and everything had seemed so simple. My God! Hadn't I even said it myself, so sure, so smug. Damn! These people either did not realize, or were afraid to realize what had happened. It was up to the magician—that criminal!—to tell them that he wasn't going to pull the white rabbit out of the hat, that there had never been a white rabbit there. Death was that swift.

"*Está mala!*" I cried out. "She's in a bad way."

A stunned paralysis came over them as I continued to fuss over the woman. Don Simon edged closer, stared at his wife unbelievingly, then stepped back again to stand rigidly, like a man turned to stone at some awful sight. Rudolfo, hat in hand, dark glasses off, grimaced, his eyes white in despair. The Indio stood with trembling lips, and the Indio woman, close like all her kind to death as to life, let out a shrill scream that was more babylike than adult. And that was all there was. No one was prepared for any great emotional display, and the atmosphere was one of unfinished business. A question had been put, answered suddenly and forever, but no one had as yet heard it good and loud.

"Señor," I said hoarsely, turning to Don Simon, "Señor . . ."

But the old aristocrat did not seem to hear. He stared at the bed and past it. His wife lay there, crumpled and broken as if she had fallen from the heights, and the fluid was still running out of the trocar. *Drip, drip, drip.* I removed the instrument, got up, and my knees felt so weak I almost collapsed. The Indio man and woman straightened out the body. With Rudolfo following with my bag, I staggered back to the *sala* where the tray, the tin and earthenware cups still stood, accusingly now, on one of the stools. I sat or, rather, fell on a stool. My head in my hands, utter bleakness consuming me, I sat for what seemed a long while. How had it happened? How *could* it happen?

I looked up as Señor Roca came toward me like a sleepwalker. He said nothing, saw nothing. I should have warned him, I reprimanded myself. Sometimes, too often at that, the magician's tricks don't work or he can't work them. And it's dangerous down here for a doctor to be too sure. You must always explain. If you tell them before and something happens, then it's usually not so bad. But all this line of reasoning made me feel more miserable; I was thinking of myself, not the patient, not of Don Simon, whom I had so obviously failed.

I hardly recall leaving his house. Certainly we did not say good-by. I was just walking back to my own house, this time with Rudolfo in the lead. I felt even worse the next afternoon as the funeral services took place. The procession, such as it was, passed our house on the way to the graveyard. Only Don Simon, big and implacable, the stooped Indio, and the lowly Indio woman followed the hurriedly made casket.

I came away from the window and paced my consultation room. I had thought of going and tried to induce Rudolfo to come. He had surprised me by refusing—it was one of the rare instances in which he disobeyed me—and there was some logic in his argument.

"You must not waste pity on the man, doctor," he said. "Look at the way he treated his wife. You know, he has two women living with him on his *estancia*. You heard him talk, too. You know how he treated others."

I knew all that, and it didn't help. A doctor was supposed to save lives; he was not required to be friendly with his patients, like, or admire them. And in all Rojas I was the only one who was upset at the señora's death. Nobody made a bad remark, no one criticized me, and it was not a question of anyone hiding his opinion. They seemed not to care for or about Señor Roca.

"It's just that you can't always save people," Rudolfo summed it up.

Just like other men, a doctor must balance his luck, the good against the bad, the flukes against the bad breaks, and all the rest. I had defied Malvenido and saved the woman who couldn't expel the afterbirth, just when it seemed that she hadn't a chance and couldn't possibly survive. I wouldn't have taken odds on her coming through, from her looks and the advanced stages of her illness, and it was a minor miracle that she had. And now this Señora Roca, who hadn't looked like a dying woman, had succumbed just at the instant she was being relieved. It was incredible in a way, as I compared the two cases, and no simple explanation would suffice. I knew there were doctors, the tough, older, experienced ones, who wouldn't give the señora's death more than a passing thought, who would shrug and say it was only in the nature of things—you lost a patient, saved another, and that was life, wasn't it? But I wasn't made that way.

If the young woman had died under my hands, after the *curandero* had put his curse on both of us, as it was, I would have lost both face and position in Rojas and all the province. And here Señora Roca had died, almost at my touch, and no one thought ill of me, no one thought anything except that perhaps that it was a fate that the proud, aristocratic Don Simon well deserved. All because he no longer belonged and was one of the few survivors of an unmourned and dying breed. Values were just as confusing here as elsewhere, and it did no good to remind myself that where doctors were concerned they never changed.

The weather continued as miserable, it even worsened at times, and my spirits sank with it. I was busy enough, but never so busy that I hadn't time enough to brood. It was no surprise then that the good news meant nothing to me. It was three weeks before Easter, and the incredible report spread through the village like a bolt of lightning exploding and shattering impenetrable gray clouds. The priest had arrived!

I heard it from a beaming young woman as she rocked her baby in her arms. The infant had some kind of digestive upset, and I had just examined the baby boy, and prescribed some medicine. My diagnosis was uncertain, but it seemed to me just the kind of intestinal infection which had taken the lives of so many little children in the province. It was either that, or something much milder. Only time would tell, but it hardly mattered to the young mother that her baby might be seriously ill. The priest was in Rojas!

"At last," she said, smiling contentedly. "At last, this son of mine is going to be baptized in church, and he is ten months old already."

Just after she left, completely unworried, the village's notary public dropped by for his ten-day supply of digitalis. He was the *alcalde's* father-in-law, a frail, tottering man with a stuttering heart. His lips were blue, his breath short, and he seemed ready to collapse at any moment, but today the radiance transforming his face put all his symptoms in shadow. The priest was in Rojas! I gave him his digitalis, and he sighed happily. If his hour should strike now, he explained, the man of God would be near.

Everyone in Rojas reacted the same way. Men and women were pleased, delighted he had come. You would have thought Santa Claus was making an appearance in the toy center of the local department store or, looking at their smiling faces, that this cursed rainy season had come to an end. I didn't think I was being cynical, but the arrival of the false priest left me cold. He was a good man and all that; I respected him, but he was no more a priest than Malvenido was a doctor. And, perhaps, for all I knew, he could do as much good—or harm, depending on how you looked at it.

Still, it's always good to have something to look forward to, and I was envious of all this burgeoning happiness around me. I'd like to jump for joy myself, but there was nothing in Rojas, in all the province, to work such a change in me. Looking out the window, I saw only the same muddy, rain-drenched streets, poverty, desolation, decay, nothingness. Rojas might be a village on the moon for all it meant to me. Then my attention was drawn to the subprefect. He had just come out of the church and was hurrying, sloshing along, head down and preoccupied, toward my house. Trouble, I thought. Some woman in difficult labor, a baby dying, an old heart failing. The false priest needed the doctor. All right, the false doctor then.

I waited at the door for the subprefect. He looked unhappy. He was panting so that he couldn't find words to express himself.

"*El Cura,* doctor—you must come immediately—he is very ill—please come—"

"*El Cura* is ill?" I said, astonished.

I couldn't believe it. How could that good, strong man with the metallic voice ever succumb to insignificant germs? But the subprefect was all worked up, I grabbed my emergency kit, and began walking quickly down the street with the official stumbling along at my side.

The subprefect tried to speak, took a breath, expelled it, then inhaled again. "I do not know, but he must be suffering from the same disease my *mozo* had two months ago when you operated."

"Pray heaven not!" I said fervently, remembering his servant's all but ruptured appendix and the difficult operation. "Some fever perhaps."

"Well, it is a miracle they made it at all in *El Cura*'s condition, what with the rains, the rivers so high, the flooded areas. No wonder the oxen are half dead."

The priest's official residence in Rojas was a small building close to the church and so low it was dwarfed by it. The place had looked empty and forbidding since I had come to the village, something like a monument to or a statue of a national hero, awaiting only the anniversary day to achieve honors and significance. Rudolfo had explained that the priest was expected a day or two before Easter, and then his house would become the center of activities for the village. I saw now, as we approached, that the boarding over the windows had been removed and the little house looked alive for a change. The subprefect paused now, gasping and clutching his side, and I guessed he had a stitch from his hurried trip to my house and back. I stopped, waiting for him to catch his breath. Looking inside the house, I made out the priest's blond, bearded manservant—he was a deaf mute, as I remembered—stooped over a small table.

The sound of running footsteps made me turn around. Rudolfo. He probably had heard of the priest's illness and gone to fetch me. He ran awkwardly, swinging his arms wildly to gain speed, but he only seemed to stay in place, kicking up mud. The subprefect had recovered now and took my arm, but I wanted to wait for my assistant. Rudolfo and I conferred briefly, it was as I thought, and we went inside together behind the subprefect.

180

The house had been shut so long that the stale air was still heavy with mildew. The large room was almost as empty of furnishings as that in Don Simon's house. A wooden bed stood in a corner, its *mosquitero* stiff and grayish from disuse, tucked back over its own top. On a lumpy red pillow, minus a pillowcase, rested the striking, white-haired head, now so changed I could hardly recognize the man I'd met and been so impressed by at *El Cementerio*. The nose protruded from the haggard face like a long, dull knife blade; the eyes, blind and blazing in delirium, were so deeply embedded that the cheekbones were as prominent as the breasts of plucked chickens; the skin of the priest's neck hung down in limp, dry folds.

What could have happened to this strong, confident man? He seemed close to death, and I thought this is too much, much too much, I can't do it, I can't do anything for him, and why should they expect me to? The manservant saw me, began to make grunting sounds, grimaces of pains, and at the same time rubbed his own belly. It was about as explicit as a deaf mute could make it, but he repeated the performance to make sure it got across. I nodded in understanding, then he pointed to the bed as if he had done his part and was referring the whole matter to his patron.

The man was an apostle in the province, a saint. How did you go about examining a man among men? I frowned, gathering myself together. Sentimentality was out of place, dangerous. Whoever he was, a sick man was a sick man. I went to him on the bed, pushed back and lifted his soiled black robe and the shirt underneath. The lower abdomen, as I expected, was stiff as a board; only above the navel was the flesh soft and yielding to my carefully palpating fingers. The priest surely had peritonitis. No doubt about it. But I could not assume, as blithely as the subprefect, that it was caused by a diseased or ruptured appendix. It could be any number of things—and it could be just that.

Understanding came momentarily into the glazed eyes of the priest as I bent over him. *"Agua,"* the parched lips murmured beseechingly. *"Agua."* Then delirium took over again, the cracked lips quivered with irrational babbling, and I choked at the lump that came into my throat. But I had no time for sad thoughts. The subprefect was at my side and on me, eager, confused, and excited.

"The same thing, no?" he said brightly. "Exactly the same thing as my *mozo,* as I told you. When are you going to operate, doctor?"

Oh, shut your stupid face, you blunderer! I said to myself. What do you know about it?

"But he must be operated, no?" the man persisted.

I said nothing. His question implied, demanded a positive answer, and I was so exasperated I wanted to throw him out of the room. Sure, operate. Why not? Silently but furiously I argued with him. What have you got to lose, *caballero*? What's it to you? It's not *your* responsibility. Talk is cheap and you own the store. Suppose I open him up, find a malignancy, sew the priest up, and then he dies? Whose fault will it be? Who will be blamed, damned for killing a saint? Only the *gringo* doctor, that criminal. And this is not Señor Simon Bolivar Roca's wife; this is the great man of the province. There must be no mistake. And perhaps an operation would be just that, while letting him be, letting nature—and God—take over would be much safer for all concerned.

I glared at the subprefect and calmed down. I was a doctor. There was no hospital, no time for hospital procedures, and it was my duty to do what I could with what I had. It could very well be an abscess from a ruptured appendix. If it was that and I could clear the abscess, I would be doing something, and there might be a chance. The priest was entitled to my best, just like any patient. I'd do a laparotomy, if he could stand it in his weakened condition. There was nothing to lose because he would die anyway. If he should die after I operated, then everyone in Rojas, the whole community, the entire province, would scream for my head. But that didn't matter, my feelings couldn't matter at all . . . I'd have to take my chances just as the priest would his.

I examined his heart. Hmm. Now the pulse. Dangerously sluggish for a man burning with fever. But the lungs were clear. I drummed my fingers on the wooden bed and thought hard. I made my decision and looked up, right into the popping eyes of the idiotic subprefect.

"All right, we'll operate," I said in a strong voice. "But where?" I looked around the room. "Maybe we could do it right here. That table will do and then we wouldn't have to carry him to my house, although after his difficult trip here, it wouldn't matter much. But then again," I continued, thinking aloud, "we'd have to carry my office equipment over here. A big job, but not impossible. And the light by that window is good. Yes." I raised my voice. "We're going to operate right here."

The subprefect's eyes popped some more. I turned to the mute servant.

"Listen to me well. I want you to get water and soap and wash *El Cura*. Wash his entire abdomen. Scrub it well!" I put my hand on it. "And do it as carefully and delicately as you would his face. Then get his razor—" With his beard he couldn't have one of his own, but the priest must have one, I reasoned. "Get his razor," I repeated, "and shave him there so no hair remains. None at all."

182

The deaf mute nodded his shaggy, blond head. I trusted the man; for his master he would break his back.

"We'll need a couple of big pots for water, too," I went on. Immediately the subprefect went to the window, snapped out an order, and a *sirvienta* scurried off to obey. "And we're going to need help to carry our medical equipment over here."

"Don't give it a thought," said the subprefect importantly. All of a sudden he had become a leader of men. "My *mozo* will report to your house instantly."

It seemed to me the advance preparations were fairly well organized. The priest's house quivered with activity, all to one great purpose, and now it was time to get back to my own house and begin selecting all the things I would need. I started off deep in thought, then almost tripped in astonishment over the threshold when I saw the crowd gathered outside, as if in a line at a ticket window. Groups of men had appeared from nowhere, it seemed; they stood around now debating in low voices, and more people were running up from all directions.

"I'll be damned!" I said. "That's all I need—a big audience."

Rudolfo, walking at my side, didn't seem in the least surprised.

"Everybody loves this *cura*. Everybody."

"I know, I know." My tone was impatient. "I met him at *El Cementerio*. Let's hope that's not a bad omen."

"Everybody loves this *cura*," Rudolfo said again, as if to impress on me the supreme importance of our exalted patient.

But it only made me more cynical. "It must be so, but nobody was excited when we took out the appendix of the subprefect's *mozo* in a similarly risky operation. In fact, his patron wasn't disturbed enough to interrupt his poker game. After all," I said sarcastically, "they were also raffling off a mule at the time."

"But you cannot compare the *cura* with a *mozo*, doctor."

If Rudolfo had spoken insolently, rather than so matter-of-factly, perhaps I wouldn't have been so angry. As it was, my blood boiled. A servant here was less than dung, his life didn't matter at all—no more than that of Jew in Nazi Germany. My superman assistant, I thought, and glared at Rudolfo. But his face was all innocence; he had no idea of how offensive his words were to me. What's the use? I told myself. False philosophy and a false priest . . .

We gathered all our equipment on a table in the *officina*, the hemostatic forceps, the scalpels, scissors, sutures, and the drugs we would need. A young Indio came to the door, scratching his head and muttering that he

183

had been dispatched by his patron, the subprefect, to carry "the doctor knew what." He was the man I had operated on two months before, and he was nervous, his eyes darting about the office suspiciously as if he were in danger of having his appendix forcibly removed a second time. We gave him the metal instruments, I slapped him on the shoulder, and he hurried off.

"Where's the novocain, Rudolfo? Ah!" The flask was half full, but it was all yellow. Useless! "Throw it away and boil some water, quick!"

I filled my bag as Rudolfo set to work. He was quick. I took our supply of the drug, weighed out a gram on the scale, and I told Rudolfo to pour a hundred cubic centimeters of boiling water into a flask. To this I added the novocain powder and shook the flask.

"I like a one per cent solution best." I was talking to myself in a low, confidential voice like a man in desperate need of a friend. "We ought to prepare another hundred cubic centimeters just to be on the safe side. You know, until we get to the peritoneum, we're going to operate with local anesthesia."

Rudolfo grunted what I took for assent, prepared the extra solution, and I packed several glass syringes in some towels. Then I looked around my depleted office and concentrated for a few seconds.

"I think we've got everything," I announced.

Rudolfo nodded, and we left. Shuffling noises made me turn before we had gone very far, and I saw Daguero, tail and ears up, eyes alert, trotting along with the casual air of one who belonged to the privileged medical unit.

"*Váyase, hombre!*" said Rudolfo.

Daguero hesitated, sizing up my feelings and no doubt expecting an outburst from his master. Faithful, loyal as he was, he seemed the only one on my side. I looked at him, smiled, and went on. Daguero jogged along behind, and Rudolfo said nothing further.

The crowd had doubled in front of the priest's door. By now the whole village had gathered there, every man, woman, and child in Rojas, and their silence, as we approached, was somehow ominous. Some women were sobbing openly, black shawls over their heads, *ponchos* on the muddy ground for them to kneel on as they prayed and fingered their rosaries. They made way for Rudolfo and myself, glaring at Daguero. I told myself that it was only because I hated the thought of making a noisy fuss that I did not send him away. Close at my heels, he followed me inside, chose a place close to the door without blocking it, and flopped down to judge, observe, and give me friendly support.

184

Water was already boiling in the large pots brought by the *sirvienta*. I threw in the metal instruments, watched them tremble in the bubbling froth, and began rolling up my shirt sleeves. The subprefect, still front and center like a master of ceremonies, was looking at me for a signal. Fussing with my cuffs, I jerked my chin toward the bed.

"We need some strong men to lift *El Cura* on the table."

The official huffed a few words toward the window. Instantly the door crashed open and a good two dozen husky volunteers trooped into the room. Far too many but, bursting with zeal and good will as they were, there was surely no sense in trying to restrain this thundering horde. Somehow they lifted the priest's limp body from the bed with the greatest care and set it down gently on the table, all without pushing or falling over each other.

"Now the table," I said. "It's dark there. Let's carry the table to the window—no, this way—so the light will fall where we need it. That's it! *Gracias.*"

Their work done, they beamed at my approval, and I waited for them to leave. Then, given no further orders, the whole crowd marched to the wall. The men took off their hats, scratched themselves, and stood like rocks. Operating room kibitzers in front-row seats. Well, really! I thought then, helplessly, what the hell? It was all right with me.

"Rudolfo," I said, "I think you better take soap and water and wash *El Cura* again." The deaf mute was nodding and pointing. I examined the priest's bared abdomen, then tried a joke. "The shaving job seems to be a good one, especially for a man who never shaves."

I smiled as I said this, but it didn't go over. I had missed both lines and cue. Everyone was deadly serious. It was life or death in this packed room, and a joke was an obscenity. I turned my back on the spectators and went to the stool on which Rudolfo had put a basin of hot water. I grabbed the small scrubbing brush, the cake of soap, dunked both, and began to wash my hands methodically. In the operating rooms of most of the hospitals I had worked in, a ten-minute hourglass stood on a certain shelf at eye level. Now, as I scrubbed in this Bolivian hovel, I found my glance going automatically to that corner of the room, where my eyes were accustomed to find the hourglass with its sand, running smoothly from the top to the lower bulb, marking the all-important ten minutes decreed by the textbooks and the laws of sterility. The vital ten minutes of soap and hot water that transformed a man and gave him the right to plunge his hands, now purified, into his fellow man's insides.

Where was my mask? Where was the nurse to help me with my rubber gloves? Where were my skilled assistants of the operating theater? Not here, neither was the hourglass. I would have to forego exact timing and guess, but what did it matter to a renowned *gringo* doctor-magician about to perform a glamorous appendectomy with the entire population of a provincial capital looking on and holding its collective breath. I almost giggled. And who was this *gringo* doctor, this medical superman? Would it ever occur to any of these good people that only a relatively few years ago I wore short pants and stood trembling before my geography teacher because I did not know the name of some obscure whistlestop in the Alps?

All eyes were on me, shifting like those of spectators at a tennis match, as I drove soapy foam up and down my arms. An appendectomy, a simple appendectomy. How many times it had been performed before! Under water in submarines, on board ship, on railway trains, and, for all I knew, probably in airplanes, too. And hadn't some wilfully eccentric doctors done it on themselves? And hadn't writers also usurped the operation for their fictional marshmallows? What would their doctor heroes do without an appendectomy performed with only a broken razor blade, paper clip, toothpick, or hairpin? Where would these medicos find refuge from their own mental anguish, sanctuary from their shaky nerves, if not in the depths of the peritoneum, where their hands knew exactly what to do, where there was no alternative—only one way to proceed—and therefore peace of mind? There was only one thing to do: go ahead.

A sigh caught in my throat as I scrubbed the fingers of my left hand, one after the other, for the third time. Yes, there were no alternatives, but fear rode heavily on my back now since that tragic business with Señora Roca, an unexplainable fear of unpredictable, unforeseeable disaster. It might strike at any time, from any place, and certainly *now* from this diseased peritoneum awaiting the bite of my scalpel. Like specters on a dark night, all the possible and the worst consequences of the operation rose to haunt my imagination: the agony and death of the priest, the scorn of those who called themselves my friends, the anger of the people turning to mob fury. All my enemies would have a field day. And Malvenido . . . To him, especially, my failure would be sweet revenge for the defeat he had suffered when the woman with the retained placenta had defied him by living.

Malvenido. In my place, would he be thinking of his fears, wrestling with alternatives, worrying about consequences? Were *curanderos* bothered by ethics and the like? Did I really know so much more about the human body than this medical faker? Did a true priest know any more about the human soul than this miserable "false" priest on the table? The crowd outside, al-

186

ready silent, seemed to become more silent. My hands still in the hot water, I glanced out the window. The people were giving way, a little alley had formed in their midst, and down it came the *curandero* probing the dust with his metal-tipped cane. Now he was at the door, through it and inside, and past the crouching Daguero, whose hair was rising along the backbone from tail to neck.

Damn the man to hell! I don't want him here, I raged to myself. The nerve of the fraud! I'm going to throw him out. After the way he behaved at Señor Nunez' *estancia,* putting the death curse on my patient before I even . . . My sight blurred, veins throbbed in my forehead, but not a word came from my constricted lips. My hands were trembling, but they were plunged in soapy water, and no one could notice how they betrayed my feelings. Now Rudolfo joined me and began to scrub. How calm he looked.

"Everything under control?" I said.

My effort at nonchalance was spoiled by my hoarse, tense voice. Besides, it was a foolish question. After all, what was Rudolfo expected to say in reply? We had no operating room procedure. It was all nerves. *My nerves.* I dipped my hands in soapy water again, squeezing one with the other as if I were holding someone under, squeezing hard until he choked and drowned. Malvenido, of course, but, no, he had taken up a commanding position at the foot of the table, his gnarled hands resting on the knob of his cane. Then it occurred to me that, apart from looking for revenge or sitting in judgment, it might well have meant considerable personal sacrifice for the old *curandero* to come and watch the *gringo* doctor operate on the province's most illustrious personality. Life and death were no longer in his hands. New times, new ways, new medicines.

I jerked up my head and stared at the wiry figure. No longer did I feel hatred, gone was that malevolence he seemed to emanate. Now I seemed to feel something close to understanding, an *esprit de corps.* Strange, I thought—and ridiculous. Then I turned my attention to the fingers of my right hand. But I felt much better for some reason, my fear set aside. I noticed through the window that, for a day of the rainy season, the weather was beautiful. The sun was shining brilliantly, but the humidity was low. Ideal for the patient who, dehydrated as he was, would not lose too much fluid, and also good for the doctor and his assistant, able to work without the sweat running into their eyes.

"Now, Rudolfo!" All eyes were on me as I clasped and folded my hands before my chest, air-drying them. "Paint him, please."

He took the forceps that held the sponges, soaked them in the diluted solution of tincture of iodine, then neatly smeared the lower abdomen, as I had taught him, first the right side, then the left, and, finally, the leftover spots.

"The navel, too," I reminded him.

Rudolfo grimaced as he dug the sponge into the umbilicus. He could never understand. It was such a sensitive place, so far from the appendix, and the iodine burned so. He looked at me, I nodded, then he bathed the abdomen with iodine a second time. All the while *El Cura* never moved; his breathing was half snoring, half moaning, painful to listen to, and he burned with fever. He was a sick man, far sicker, I felt, than most of these people realized.

I took my freshly laundered towels and draped them on a stool as if they had just come out of an operating room autoclave. I motioned, and the priest's deaf-mute servant brought forward the pots containing the instruments. Rudolfo had washed out my instrument trays with alcohol and put them on a small table. Now the subprefect moved the table close, Rudolfo put the instruments on the trays, and adjusted them within easy reach. Turning for the syringe, I deliberately avoided looking at Malvenido. I did see the strangely greedy countenance of the subprefect, the intent faces of the row of husky men against the wall, and the open mouths of those outside the house. Only in the eyes of the mute servant did I read sorrow and anxiety. He knew.

I felt surer and calmer now, and I made my motions deliberate and exact. I jabbed the twenty cubic centimeter syringe into the novocain flask, withdrew the plunger, and watched the solution stream inside. Holding the syringe in my right hand, I turned it upside down, expelled the air and, after I had palpated McBurney's point with my left hand, I squeezed up a furrow of skin and inserted the needle. The priest did not move. I studied his face, then began to do a careful, block anesthesia, pushing the plunger with easy firmness, withdrawing from time to time to make sure the needle was not in a vein.

As I went through these preparations, almost automatically, I concentrated on the details of the operation according to the accepted techniques which I had studied. Take the scalpel with sure, unswerving fingers, guide the sharp edge so it will make a fine incision. The blood will seep slowly, a deep red line on the white neck of a swan, or on equally white snow. I recalled everything that I would see and touch, once beneath the skin, the muscles, tendons, blood vessels, organs in the abdomen . . . I tried to

188

fasten my mind on these things to the exclusion of everything else. The people watching, the venomous *curandero,* and I were mere trivialities like time, yesterday, today, and tomorrow. We did not matter, we did not count, we would be wiped off and away just as, in a few moments, the sponge would clear the bloody line of incision.

Ah, but this was reality and quite different. I shook my head and loosened the syringe from the needle that remained in the tissue. I refilled the syringe, again thrust it upside down and expelled the air, and then connected it to the needle. I thrust it farther down into the subcutaneous tissue and made sure the novocain was spread deep in a circular area.

Practice was so different from theory and literature. This skin was brown from iodine and hardened from a rough, exhausting, demanding life. This man had given everything of himself unremittingly, and now his life hung in the balance. The risk was great and, dear God, I simply had to pull him through. I suppose, though, that the scalpel blade will not be sharp, as had happened with the Indio only two months earlier, that I would have to press and force. ". . . Experience, my dear Watson." And it did not seem the least bit odd that I should be thinking *à la* Sherlock Holmes. I had the proper explanation on the tip of my tongue. "Elementary, my dear Watson. You see, this moist jungle climate will blunt any edge in time. And, to make it worse, I have observed that the tissues, now infiltrated with novocain, appear buckled and not at all as smooth as the neck of a swan. Look for yourself."

I paused, Sherlock Holmes and his doctor friend retreated to the depths from which they had come unbidden, and I studied my patient's face intently.

"Better check his pulse, Rudolfo." How far away my voice sounded! "He might have a novocain reaction. Count the beats, then scrub again."

I couldn't help thinking that I was talking to hear myself talk, seeking reassurance and a sort of rapport with my fascinated audience. Rudolfo responded to my bidding with his usual alacrity. I studied my patient, and now the dry skin around the priest's neck gave me warning. He was dried out. It would be necessary to inject a saline solution into a vein before . . . I cleared my throat nervously.

"The patient is quite dehydrated." I addressed my public like an operating room lecturer. "Let us therefore improvise an infusion." I turned to the subprefect. "Will you kindly have somebody boil some more water? And have someone else buy a few ounces of good salt and bring it here as quickly as he can. Thanks very much."

189

The subprefect gave me his best official nod, moved aside, and again snapped out orders. Two persons hustled out of the room, and I could not help smiling to myself. This was efficiency Rojas style! Rudolfo said nothing and, judging from his expression, the priest's pulse was apparently no weaker. I filled the syringe for the third time and infiltrated the remainder of the affected area. Tricky stuff, novocain. My thoughts began to stray again, and I was the inexperienced doctor just out of medical school involved with a charming young woman of good family. Against the advice of her parents, she had entrusted me with the removal of a small sebaceous cyst from her pretty neck. I had been flattered and proud—my personal interest so much greater than my professional one. I had casually injected the novocain, then, all of a sudden, the small cyst had buried itself in the infiltrated tissue. I had lost the damn thing! I remembered my wildly beating heart, the horror of the situation, the struggle to remain calm, think professionally, and do—what I was supposed to do. Now I smiled to myself and touched the priest's bared and painted abdomen. From fingertip to abdominal muscle I seemed to communicate with him and the message was: Dear priest, do not worry. Have no fear. I have improved since those days. I know what to do and how to do it.

I pulled out the needle and swabbed the blood-tinged liquid oozing from the puncture. Well, that was about it and what was I waiting for? I looked up and met Malvenido's glance sheepishly. The *curandero's* eyes were impersonal and, over a ways and back in command, the subprefect's features had lost their look of habitual greed and were now merely tense. What would these two think if they knew what was passing through my mind? Rudolfo's dark glasses and set face made me feel good. Here was somebody truly loyal to me. At least I hope so, I added cautiously and somberly, remembering his devotion to the priest. Ah, well, here goes . . .

I put my thumb on the edge of the scalpel blade. Not too bad. After a few tries the skin was cut; a few more tries and the incision had deepened to the fascia. And now the skin had a shiny marble-like appearance where the severed blood vessels had begun to bleed through the infiltrated tissue.

"Hemostat," I mumbled, grabbing the instrument before Rudolfo could give it to me. I dug the spread tips into the tissue, pressing them together as they caught the bleeder. "Another!" This time Rudolfo had it ready. I applied it quickly. "More." For an old man who was not too fat, the priest's incision was bleeding a good deal. Almost all the hemostats were clamped down now, and a final sponging assured me that all the bleeders had been attended to. "Now let's do some tying."

190

Rudolfo snapped the vials containing the catgut, and the smell of the phenol preservative seemed to fill the closely packed room. I looked up at a scratching sound on the ground near the door. Daguero had raised his head and was sniffing the pungent air. Now he made a complete circle, lowered his head, and settled it between his paws. I took a deep breath, untangled the thread, and nodded at Rudolfo. He held up the hemostats. I slipped the catgut around the tips, crossed the ends and pulled, and then once more.

"Cut," I said, and Rudolfo snipped efficiently.

Again I pulled, my movements hard and firm, to make the knot that choked off the life-giving blood vessels. How necessary and yet, in a way, how cruel this tying off of the blood lines. My mind slanted off again, and I remembered the gentle Rabbi Deutsch, who had suffered such pains in the concentration camp. His trouble had been correctly diagnosed as appendicitis, and he had been promptly operated on with Teutonic thoroughness. Oh, how kind they were to him! Why, during his convalescence they even gave the good rabbi matzos to eat because it was the Passover, the Jewish Easter. Three weeks afterward he had made an excellent recoverey—so excellent that he was pressed into file with other potential victims, the official Nazi thumb jerked to the right, and he was chosen for death.

I was breathing heavily. With the last of the bleeders tended to, I dug my fingers into the incision, pulled the muscles apart, took up the forceps, and worked with the blunt end to separate them more. It was almost as if I had rough hands in the guts of the rabbi's executioner.

"You so-called priest from Barcelona," said a vicious part of my brain, addressing the patient before me. "You false priest, whose fascia of the musculus obliquus externus I am now splitting, can you tell me why those depraved bastards had to cure him before they killed him? Exterminated him like a louse! Were they perhaps afraid that his God might cheat them, take him away before he could be satisfactorily tortured?"

El Cura groaned, and instantly my fingers relaxed. I had reached the peritoneum. My breathing had calmed, my brain cleared, and I was aware of sweat dripping down my forehead and into my eyes, stinging and blinding. I blinked them in surprise. It couldn't be from the heat, I thought grimly. I better watch myself. These people will begin to think I am nervous and unsure.

"All right, Rudolfo, let's have the small retractors. Then get the ether."

I inserted one of the blades on my own side, hesitated, and looked around for help. Damn! I hadn't thought—I'd have to have volunteers quick! Then

Malvenido, the *curandero,* was suddenly close to me. Lifting his arm carefully, so that his shirt sleeve would not touch anything, he took hold of the other end of the instrument. For an old man, I admitted grudgingly to myself, he certainly has a steady hand. But more help was imperative.

"Now you!" I said to the priest's deaf-mute servant, as I inserted the other retractor on the opposite side. "Come on!"

A look of horror came over the blond-bearded man, and he froze in place. The subprefect moved in, snatched at the retractor with eager, trembling hands, but, in his haste, lost his grip on it. The instrument fell to the dirt floor with a muted, clunking sound. A fleeting movement swept over those filed along the wall, as if all wanted to jump at the same time, but not a man stepped forward. Rudolfo bent down and retrieved the retractor.

"Boil it!" I said.

The subprefect, pale and excited, took it from Rudolfo and hurried to the patio, where the fire still burned.

"Go ahead anyway," I ordered Rudolfo. "We can't waste time now."

He put a towel around the mask we had put together from old wire and gauze, moistened the mask with several drops of ether, and carefully set it down over the priest's face. Again a movement at the door distracted me. From the corner of my eyes I saw Daguero lift his head. His nostrils quivered, he stared gloomily, and jumped to his feet. His cut ears erect, he retreated to the far end of the room.

"I wouldn't use a towel," I said quietly to my assistant. "We want the patient to have as much air as possible."

Rudolfo removed the towel from the masked face. The subprefect, a bulky, panting man, stumbled in with a pot in which water was boiling madly. Using the large forceps, I extracted the retractor from the steaming, bubbling water.

"Good," I said. "Now please pour some alcohol over the instrument."

Grunting, the subprefect put down the pot and did as I had told him. I waved the retractor in the air to cool it off, then inserted it in its proper place in the incision. As the subprefect grabbed the end that I indicated, his teeth clamped his lips into bloodless lines. His hand was unsteady, and I could feel the tension in his arm. On the other side no such effort was evident in Malvenido. He was cool, his hands steady.

"All right," I said. "Now let's all pull a little—easy—just like that. Fine!"

The priest no longer moaned. His breath was a regular snoring, and he was limp. As I went on, I could feel Malvenido's eyes staring at the operating field just as intently as my own. There it was, the peritoneum, the most sensitive protector of the abdominal organs. With a mouth-tooth forceps I tried to lift it up in one place, but it was impossible.

"It has thickened and there are things adhering to it," I said, but I was really speaking only to Malvenido. "We shall have to make a small incision without lifting."

I took the scalpel, barely nicked the serous membrane, and then greenish pus pushed out thickly with considerable force. At once the heady ether fumes were overcome by a vile, foul smell that turned the stomach. The subprefect gagged and turned green. Rudolfo swallowed hard. Only Malvenido stood unmoved. A howl of misery made me start. I saw the men who lined the wall glaring at poor Daguero. His eyes were sad, his head down, his ears drooping. Tail between his legs, he went out the door.

The pus kept on streaming, green and nauseating. I cleaned and wiped and cleaned again, then carefully enlarged the incision I had made in the peritoneum. A suction machine would have made the job much easier, but I had no such operating room luxuries. I reached for my largest syringe, dipped into the abscess, and aspirated the pus. The syringe filled quickly, I wondered where I could empty it and, after a moment's hesitation, squirted it out on the floor where I stood. (*El Cura's* servant could cover the place with dirt later.) Then, using the syringe, I sucked up the pus again and again, drawing out less each time, until the cavity was decently clean. Then—

"Will you look at this appendix!" I exclaimed. "My God, I never—"

Medically, it was fascinating. There in the depths, something like a snake sleeping off a heavy meal and swollen to the size of an adult's index finger, as against its normal pencil thickness, rested the villain. Greenish yellow and stiff—helpless now.

From his stand at the patient's head, Rudolfo bent over to get a good look. The subprefect, now a pale yellow, took a quick, flinching peek. And Malvenido, his arm poker stiff, studied the useless and diseased vermiform appendix with calm, almost professional interest. Enough of the classroom though! If the priest were to move suddenly, if the intestines should suddenly move, God alone knew what might happen.

"Let's take it out quickly," I said.

I took the forceps and put its jaws around the appendix ever so delicately. It was friable, ready to crumble, and slipped from my grasp. It took me three attempts to get a good hold at the base.

"Doctor Malvenido," I said, preparing for my next move, "will you please hold up the forceps?"

With his free hand the *curandero* had continued to cling to his cane. Now it thwacked on the dirt floor, he switched hands neatly, and held up the forceps as I had asked. I wound the catgut twice around the base of the appendix, secured it, then cut firmly. Malvenido, like a priest with the Host, held up the sausage-like organ in triumph for all the congregation to see.

"Quick, now!"

I wiped, cleaned, threaded a needle with a length of catgut, and took hold of the peritoneum again. The patient stirred under my hands.

"Shall I give him more ether?" asked the observant Rudolfo.

Stitching away as fast as I could, in and out, in and out, I didn't answer my assistant; in fact, I hardly heard him. "Get me the jar with the rubber pieces. Hurry!" I had the drain in before I had done with the last stitch. "Now for the muscle and the fascia." For an active man like the priest it was important, if he should survive, that there be no danger of incisional hernia. Enough things go wrong as it was. Now to stitch the outer skin. My fingers flew. "All right, Rudolfo, off with the mask."

I stepped back and stood motionless, momentarily drained of all thought, emotion, or feeling. For all these tense, concentrated minutes, in spite of the twists of my mind, I had really forgotten the priest, the *curandero,* the spectators, Rojas, everything. Nothing had mattered except muscles, pus, and guts. Experience and training had taken over. So perhaps the fiction writers were right, after all. I shook my head wonderingly as I watched Rudolfo bandaging the wound. Very good. He had put on gauze and fastened it loosely so that the pus could ooze from the drain. I swung around to the men, still ranged motionless along the wall.

"Now we'll carry the table close to the bed."

They eased it over gently, moving with precision and co-ordination, then lifted the priest with loving care and set him gently on his worn mattress. Outside the windows, where all of Rojas seemed to have gathered, a wave of hushed sounds—"Thank Gods" and sighs of relief—came to my ears, then subsided like distant surf. But there was still more to be done. The operation was over, but its success still hung in the balance.

"The salt," I reminded the subprefect. "Did you get the salt?"

Hands moved up and down across the room, then the subprefect was handing me the package. Rudolfo had a container ready. It held about two quarts of water, and I threw in what seemed enough salt to make a satisfactory infusion.

"That ought to make a fair saline solution," I said to Rudolfo. "Now, let's get the other fifty cubic centimeter syringe and inject the fluid inside the skin. You know what I mean. It's just as we do it with babies."

He looked at me like a man stunned. "Do you think he will live, doctor?"

"*El Cura?*" The others were listening now. How easy to say yes. I sighed. "Rudolfo, his life is in God's hands now."

My assistant's eyes brightened. He looked joyful and certain.

"Then he will live. He will live!"

I wish I could have been half so sure.

11

The Priest Recovers; Know Thyself?; I March in the Easter Procession; News from Santa Morena; A Visit from Pierre; I Protest a Public Whipping; I Come Down with Malaria

A truce of sorts had been achieved, but our war had not yet been won. All that long afternoon, the still longer night, and the next day and night, Rudolfo and I battled for the priest's life, barely stopping to eat or grab a moment's rest. The men of Rojas, all of them optimists at heart, it seemed, no longer gathered in knots before the house; they took it as a foregone conclusion that their beloved *cura* was out of danger. Most of the women, however, were realists who trusted their instincts. They continued their vigil day and night, kneeling in the street along the wall of the church in spite of rain, storm, and cold, praying ceaselessly for the priest's life. It was just as well.

The old man did well, much better than I had expected, and continued to improve. But on the third day after the operation he suffered a sudden attack of chills and fever, and I was worried. Malvenido, who had remained in the fight with us, knew what it was immediately. "Malaria," he said, as I relieved him of his watch early on the fourth day. We still weren't friends—we probably never could or would be—but he had been helpful, he was courageous, and, if I weren't careful, I'd be admiring him. This time the *curandero* was quite right.

Weak and sick as he was, the priest could not keep the atabrine down. He'd swallow it, then vomit right away. There was nothing to do but give him intramuscular injections of quinine and plasmochin. These were painful. He cried out pathetically each time the needle penetrated the tissue, but he grew used to them. I was sure that these injections, plus the subcutaneous saline infusions, were responsible for saving his life. Another week passed before the priest, haggard and emaciated, was able to talk.

"Good morning, my son."

His voice was heartbreakingly weak, but his eyes were wide open and clear—a good sign—for the first time.

"How are you feeling, padre?" I asked.

"About as well as can be expected for a man who has come back from the dead." He looked into my eyes. "You did well."

"I did only what I was supposed to do," I told him.

"Only what you were supposed to do, eh?" His eyes wavered and his voice fell to a faint whisper. "I would like to thank you anyway, my son." A ghost of a smile flitted over his lips. "Especially after the way I insulted you at *El Cementerio*."

He grew stronger with every passing day, his eyes gaining luster, his body flesh, his muscles tone. Invariably, his eyes sought mine, and he looked at me curiously. It made me a little uneasy. There was a lot on his mind that he wanted to discuss with me. I could guess what it was, and I didn't want to talk about it.

"You know what pleases me most, son?" he remarked one morning. "The way you and Malvenido co-operate. It is heartwarming, an inspiration."

"What?" I exclaimed, startled. "Malvenido and I? Why, we don't even talk to each other except in emergencies."

It must have been my resentment of the quack, still seething below the surface, which led me to make so ridiculous a statement. A shadow passed over *El Cura's* striking, pain-haunted face.

"*Hijo,* who are your friends here?"

So now comes the cross-examination, eh? I'll keep my own counsel, I thought, steeling myself—and my own secrets.

"Oh, I have lots of friends," I said brashly. "Everybody's my friend. Don't you hear them call me *querido hermano, amigo?* Ah, yes," I went on, far more sarcastically than I had intended. "I'm everybody's dear brother in Rojas, but when I want a real confidant, I talk to my dog."

The priest nodded vaguely, as if it were something foolish that I was entitled to say and that he was forced to listen to, then went on unerringly.

"To be a doctor, to have had your training, to be able to save lives, as you have mine, is a good and noble thing. Tell me, doctor, have you ever thought of all you could do to help the people here? I mean the improvements you could introduce. Perhaps even a small hospital."

I think I blushed. In any case, I had no flippant reply ready.

"Well," I muttered, after a time, "When I first came here, I thought—I hoped—you see—" I threw up my hands. "Padre, there are so many things to do down here, so many things to think about . . ."

"Such as? Tell me, son."

He waited patiently for my answer, but what could I say? What could I tell him except that I was lonely, frustrated, tormented, and, more often than not, so bored that I cared little for anything. So I simply smiled mysteriously and shrugged. I doubted whether the priest was deceived. I knew it for sure two days later. My patient was strong enough to sit up in a chair, but he seemed terribly troubled.

"What it is now, padre?" I asked, concerned. "Don't you know that good spirits are essential for recovery. You must cheer up. Now what is it that's bothering you?"

"You. I am worrying about you."

Because I knew the answer in advance, I was annoyed. "Worried about *me, padre?"* I gave a false little laugh. "Then you are in good humor after all."

But the priest would have none of joking and lightheartedness. He waved an impatient hand that was still much too thin.

"Son, I have been watching you. You live from day to day. I see it, I feel it. You take things as they come without thinking; you live more by instinct than by reason." He shook his head. "And that is not good for a man like you."

"It isn't, eh?" I said bitterly. "Then you no longer believe that I am one of those who wants to get rich quickly."

A look, part anger, part sorrow, crossed the priest's expressive face. He stretched out an emaciated arm in appeal.

"*Hijo,* in that trunk there is a little book. Fetch it for me, the one in the leather binding. That's it. Now hand it to me." I did so, he weighed it in his palm, then held it out to me. "I wish to give it to you. Don't make a face. I am giving it to you, not because it is Plato, in the original, but because the leather cover will preserve it in this tropical climate. You see, I want you always to keep in mind what is written there on the first page."

It would be best to humor the old man, I thought. I sighed, flipped the book open to the first page, read as directed, then jumped as if a rattler had bitten me.

"Padre, padre." I gasped out the words because what I had read had hit me like a punch in the stomach. "How did you—how could you—this one phrase." I swallowed. "Did you want to hurt me so much?"

198

I saw fire burning in his eyes, but he feigned innocence.

"What is it, son?" he said easily. "Can a simple phrase, a couple of words, upset you that much?"

"It is not a simple phrase, nor a couple of words. It is—"

"—a philosophy of life. *Of your life.*" The fiery look in his old, knowing eyes had turned to one of cold steel. "*Por favor,* read it to me."

Reluctantly, almost gagging, I read: " 'Know thyself.' "

The priest inclined his head and started to speak, but I wouldn't listen. I couldn't bear it. I was pacing the room now, close to tears for a reason I could never explain, and the words fell from my mouth like spittle.

"Listen to me, padre. Listen well. For eight years I went to a Latin school to get a humanistic education, as they called it. The school had a large auditorium, and the students gathered there several times a year. And— I'll never forget it—one entire wall of that great room was taken up by that inscription in Greek: Know Thyself.

"I didn't know what it meant until the older students told me. Then, after Greek was added to my curriculum—oh, padre, you don't know how proud, how overwhelmed I was when I could read that inscription myself! How I loved that school, all the philosophizing, the analyzing of men, things, motives, the digging into the meanings of words . . ."

I kicked viciously at the floor. "Yes, padre, I admit that I loved my school and what I learned there, fool that I was. It was the only world in which I was at home until—until the time came when to know oneself was only to add contempt to misery.

"Do you know what is going on in Europe, in Austria, in Germany? Not only the rape of a land and people, but of the mind and all reason. A whole race is being systematically exterminated by madmen and brutes!" My voice had risen to a shout, and I paused to control myself. I wanted to hurt this pious old sage, ram his philosophical clichés down his throat, and I went on slowly and savagely. "No, padre, we have spent too much time studying—that's the trouble with people like me. And we have studied the wrong things. In the end we finished by not knowing ourselves. Worse, we did not know our neighbors, what they thought, nor the ultimate horrors they were capable of. We, the theoreticians of life, debated in the darkness, finally came out blinking into the cruel light of day, and our fellow country-men then turned around and practiced *their* theories on us."

My bitterness had marred my speech. I was spewing out Spanish with a marked guttural accent that grated in my own ears, and I didn't care.

"Say 'Live by instinct,' padre, and you've said it right. That's the great truth I've learned recently. Another one is that it would be easier if I knew *less* about myself. It would be easier, too, if our parents or our schools had taught us how to defend ourselves in time; if, instead of giving us fancy and meaningless philosophies like 'know thyself,' they had taught us how to break jail or to kill before we were killed." Saliva dripped down my chin, but I did not wipe it away. "Ask Pierre in Santa Morena! His reasons may be a little different, but he'll say the same thing. The objective thinking we absorbed makes it hard, no, impossible, to accept the world and life as it is today. 'Know thyself,'" I sneered. "Bah! What rot. Where does it get you? To know oneself is to know futility, failure, defeat. To acknowledge a complete lack of faith, hope, and charity!"

Although I had said a lot, there was still much more to say. But I stopped, swallowed, and cursed the tears of anger and sorrow prickling my eyes. What a sniveling fool the priest must think me in spite of the immortal truths I had uttered. I choked back the vituperation rising in my throat, wishing that I could, but still unable to hate this emaciated old man with the wide, clear eyes and snow-white hair.

"Son, son." He pointed at the leather-bound book. "Whether you like it or not, this world will always be your home. Here, or in the city, it does not matter which, but nothing can alter that. Your kind cannot escape. You are a man of intelligence, a man of reason. If you ever stop knowing yourself, you will become a wild beast, kill others, and in the end perish yourself. That is what has happened to those who have taken over your country and persecuted you. They may be victorious, they may subject the whole continent to trials and torture, but—and I say it with all the power of my faith in God—they, too, will perish in the end. If one lives as a beast, one dies as one." Now his voice softened in pity and weakness. "Peter is a case in point."

I looked at him in astonishment.

"I do not judge, nor call him a beast. He is what he is, Peter, the poor man they call Pierre. He is going to perish, and liquor will do it. We have tried terribly hard, but he has finally succumbed. He has given up and lost with God's mercy on him. The poor child no longer has the strength to resist."

It was strange to hear him speak of Pierre as a child, yet it was fitting, quite fitting. He was a child, yes, a baby, and it broke my heart to think of him. I wondered if the priest knew about his wife. But then did Pierre really have one? He had told me so many stories about himself. What was the truth, I wondered, and, most puzzling, did even Pierre know now?

The priest and I continued to look at each other like debaters who had furiously launched their best arguments and failed to impress each other. A pause, the tension left the old man's face, and he smiled.

"Now that there is hope that I shall be strong enough to officiate at the ceremonies, doctor, I wish to invite you to be a standard-bearer at our Easter procession."

How neatly he had changed the subject! Here I was still in an uproar after my outburst and the feelings that had boiled up in me—and he thought he had solved everything with his damned "know thyself." It was really foolish to get excited about an ignorant fanatic who was not even a real priest.

"You forget I am not a Catholic," I said sharply. And was he?

He did not even look up at me. He stared at his hands, meditating with himself. "I could not have forgotten, son, because I did not even think of it. Let me see . . . I help my brethren to live, you restore their lives." Now he did look up at me, and it hurt to see his honest eyes. "If there is any difference, why, it's all in your favor."

*　　*　　*

The Easter procession was the climax of the *fiesta*. It was held after dark, and this somehow made it much more colorful and exciting. The marchers trooped around the plaza three times in a long, snaky file with gaps that opened and closed accordion style. Torches had been stuck all around the plaza, filling the air with smoke and flashing light which brilliantly il-luminated the gaudy figures and statues being laboriously held aloft by hard-breathing men, whose weatherbeaten faces glowed with an unearthly exaltation. Behind the largest of the statues, the most imposing standard was carried, with the subprefect holding the pole, the *alcalde* on one side, and me on the other, spreading the silken purple.

I hadn't really wanted to take part in the procession, but I felt I owed it to *El Cura* and, again thinking of my precious self-esteem, I knew it would be taken in bad part if it were learned that I had refused to be a standard-bearer along with the dignitaries of Rojas. The subprefect on one side of me, the mayor on the other—I was in select company, honored, respected, looked up to as the man who saved the priest. All the same, I felt out of place and ill at ease. I didn't belong. I was Judas.

Around the plaza we went, once, twice, and again. The torches smoked and spat fire, colors seemed to whirl about me, and I was dizzy. The streets of Rojas were a boggy mire still, but the sticky mud meant nothing to those who marched in reverence and devotion. I felt they would have walked through fire with as little concern. And even those too sick, old, or infirm to walk in the procession threw themselves in the mud, prostrated themselves in front of their houses as the figures were carried past, sobbing and praying and calling out to God to have mercy on them.

After the procession had circled the plaza for the third time, it headed for the church. It was the first time I had been inside it, and I watched my neighbors curiously. The occasion was doubly great for them; they were celebrating Easter and the return to life of their beloved *cura,* a miracle faintly paralleling the Resurrection. Men, women, and children kneeled on the hard adobe floor, hands clasped fervently together, faces lifted to Heaven, eyes half closed in adoring ecstasy, lips moving with the chanting of the priest, whose voice rose above the whole congregation.

I was not of their faith, nor really of any faith, and it pleased me to think that the spectacle, the Mass, and the religious intensity of these people did not move me. After all, what else did they have to cling to, these wretchedly poor, ignorant, naive, goodhearted people? All right, all right, but if I was not moved, neither was I completely unmoved. If a man has nothing and doesn't mind such a state, well, what of it? But that was just my status and I had found I did mind; I minded terribly. And these people, lacking in material possessions and in intellect, had something. They knelt, adored worshiped, and, most importantly, believed.

Now *El Cura* turned away from the primitive altar to address his people. I tried to listen, but I was too distracted, nor did I particularly want to listen to this man. He had nothing to say to me except "know thyself." But his voice was strong and clear. I had to listen.

"A fifty-mile trip in our province is not a mere hour's ride, a brief whirl over manmade asphalt highways. No, it is a day or two on almost impassable roads, hard work all the way, but when we have reached our destination, we have achieved something. Our labors have been rewarded. We have overcome woods, jungles, mountains, and rivers; we have won over the terrain— we have triumphed over ourselves.

"Similarly, disease is not just a dry compilation of laboratory findings, X rays, and textbooks. It is a flesh and blood enemy, one we must fight tooth and nail, while all the time that merciless umpire, Death, the Man with the Scythe, stands by waiting, waiting . . ."

I looked up. *El Cura* was speaking directly to me. *To me.* I must listen very carefully. Now he raised his arms, as if in benediction, and his sepulchral voice seemed to descend from far above.

"This is still new land, virgin land. This is a land in which to begin, to fulfill and find fulfillment, a land to pioneer. It is always so. First there is nothing, then we humans create and, in so doing, we come closest to our most intimate self. For is not creating the noblest form of enterprise and therefore closest to Heaven? And what better place for creation than here, where the sun accompanies the days, where the stars and the moon kindle the nights, where human values, both good and bad, lie exposed on the surface for all to see? What better place, I ask you, than here, where a man, the good and the bad, can find himself easily among his fellow men; right here, where he can lie down to rest after a hard day's work, feel the throb of the earth under his tired body, forget his neighbor's shortcomings, as well as his own, and learn to be thankful—oh, how thankful!—for the gift of life."

I was moved, and admitted it. Never had I heard a priest speak of God before without making him prosaic, and I marveled. He has touched me. *El Cura* has touched me! I must go and apologize to him for my rudeness, I said to myself. I must talk to him, *must* talk to him.

I lay awake thinking a long time that night and slept badly. Early in the morning I rushed to the priest's house. I noticed that the *carreton* was no longer in the patio, and the boards had been nailed back across the windows. The priest was gone, so was his deaf-mute servant. I walked back slowly to my own house, head down, hands in pockets, and oblivious of Daguero trotting happily at my heels.

I felt dejected and abandoned. For a moment, almost for a moment, I had seen the light—just a glint in the darkness, faint, but unmistakable— then it had been snatched away. I was alone again, back alone with myself, and I didn't like it.

*　　*　　*

Things that seem never to end, never to have any prospect of giving way do, of course, alter, change as they must, and revert to what they were. But the process has been so tedious, so protracted, so grinding an ordeal that the change, once so intensely longed for, can hardly be appreciated. The rainy season was over at last. The water had subsided, but the memories of raintime lingered on. Soupy mud, gaping, brackish puddles everywhere, and small swamps between the houses that, as the sun shone brightly and the days grew hot, hatched and harbored myriads of deadly mosquitoes.

The tiny bloodletters and disease carriers took possession of Rojas like conquerors, making me look back to the floods of rain almost with longing. They made the days a burden and, with their maddening whine, the nights hideous. There were no screens in the windows, no insect repellents, no sprays with which to kill them either on the wing or in their breeding places. To the people, the invasion was simply another phase. They accepted mosquitoes as just another of God's inexplicable curses all of the years of their lives. They were harassed, yes, swore, complained, swatted, and scratched, but they endured the plague as they had always endured it. I found it intolerable and thought I would go mad having to submit to being punctured, bitten from head to toe, and drilled repeatedly by the killer swarms.

But they, too, like the days of rain, passed and were forgotten until next time. Rojas' period of grand isolation was over. Travelers from all around began to arrive more frequently into the little provincial capital. The going was better, according to their reports, and the Rio Yucoma was shrinking back to its own bed after inundating miles of lowland on either side of its banks. Even the big cities were sending out feelers. A man I talked to, whose *estancia* was located midway between Santa Morena and Rojas, swore that he had heard the rumble of airplane motors above the clouds only a few days earlier. I doubted it, but then perhaps it was a thing they did each year: sent out a search plane to see whether the rains had washed the hinterland villages away.

As life picked up with good weather, the episode with the false priest quickly submerged itself into the sea of happenings. It was way, way back and, only at rare intervals, did I ask myself: did it really happen? Was there an operation? Did he survive so miraculously? And did he really lecture me and strip off the skin of my self-esteem. For all the reality of the episode, I might just as well have dreamed or imagined the whole thing. So much that went on in Rojas came to seem like a product of my fantasy; I had the feeling I was treading in quicksand rather than on firm ground.

Yet, all the same, the priest had undeniably left me with a real, tangible fear nestled deep within me. Over and over, during the day, I found myself staring intently at Don Salustino's house, but no red flag was hoisted above the postmaster's door, there was no mail call, no excited clamor by the post office. If the mail had arrived, it would be made known, but time and again I strolled by the house, glancing casually inside and feeling ashamed— ashamed to betray my frustration to people who would not understand it. And how could they when Rojas was all that mattered, when their lives and all their human relationships were centered here? What could mail mean to them? They didn't need any reassurance that they were alive, remembered, and cared for.

How my heart leaped as Rudolfo walked into my house briskly one bright May day. He looked so jaunty, so bursting with news.

"*El correo?*" I said eagerly. "The mail. It's here?"

"No, doctor," he said apologetically, "but the first traveler has come in from Santa Morena. It is Don Fausto, and he stays at my mother's house. He says that the plane has landed there twice already since the end of the rains."

The fact that it was this new arrival, rather than the mail, that had so set up Rudolfo enraged me. They were all gossips hanging over their backyard fences for the latest word from civilization. Still, when Rudolfo suggested I go home with him, I went along. Don Fausto had attracted a crowd. The modest *sala* of the house was full of people perched on stools set in a half-circle around a hammock in which Don Fausto was sitting. It was a decorous, dignified occasion. I felt I was intruding, but, as soon as he saw me, Don Fausto broke off his dissertation, got up, and greeted me with elaborate respect.

"Ah, *querido* doctor! How are you? How have you fared since you left us? Ah, we have missed you in Santa Morena!"

I did not remember the man at all, but, like old friends, we embraced and shook hands again. Rudolfo brought a stool for me, and I was seated in a favored position close to the hammock. The audience hushed. Don Fausto shut his eyes as if to ask himself, "Now where was I?" then cleared his throat importantly.

"Doctor, the news I bring will probably not appear so extraordinary to you as it does to us."

"*Pero,* Don Fausto!"

It might or it might not, but I was still the *gringo* doctor under observation, and it behooved me to act the part. So I refused to believe what he had said and managed to put on a courteous smile to indicate my intense interest in his words.

"Doctor, they have brought shiny steel equipment to Santa Morena—many mysterious machines, a generator, a motor, and gasoline for it. They have also brought a young man. He is from La Paz and is a radio operator employed by the airline. Following the instructions he carried, they put up a little house at the end of the airfield." Don Fausto's eyes rolled eloquently. "I tell you, so quick were they, so efficient, that it was finished before anybody saw it being built. Up in a flash!"

He paused for all of this to sink in.

"How excited we all were in Santa Morena. We all put on our best clothes and hurried to the airport to see it. Ah, it was like a *fiesta* in that little house! The operator only touched a switch and a glass bulb spread electric light like that." He spread his arms. "It was just as the citizens who have been to La Paz had told us, and as we ourselves had seen in the pictures in magazines. Then—listen to this!—the young operator manipulated his machine and a voice came out clear between the humming and the whistling noises. It spoke to us and said, 'This is Radio Buenos Aires.' *Les juro,* it was exactly as if the man were speaking in our midst. It was a miracle! Then, after the announcement, the most beautiful music you ever heard came out of a loud-speaker, as the man called it."

The room buzzed with the excitement of the assembled citizens. Incredible! Amazing! Some of the men rolled their eyes and slapped their thighs. How lucky they were in Santa Morena! How fortunate! Too bad that Rojas . . .

Rudolfo's mother spoke now, her shrill voice cutting through the babel. "Doctor, you have not yet heard *all* the news."

I had been nudged. Now I was happy to carry through. *"Por favor,* Don Fausto. Please oblige by telling us everything."

"Como no!" He licked his lips and sat up straighter in the hammock to get the maximum effect from his next blockbuster. "On his last trip to Brazil, Don Fulgencio bought a kerosene refrigerator. What a thing, I tell you! Four little cubes of ice fit into one glass, and the people pay as much as three *bolivianos* for them."

"Qué barbaridad!" exclaimed the *alcalde,* who was also among the front-row listeners. Greed at the thought of so much money for so little ice reddened the mayor's round face. "For that amount I could sell them six pounds of the most excellent cow meat."

I got up from my stool with an odd sense of personal gain against a dark background of uneasiness. I had known these things well and these people knew it, but it was so long ago and they were so far away as to be miraculous novelties. I was as awe-inspired by Don Fausto's recital as if I had never drunk an ice-cooled bottle of beer, or as if I had never before listened to a radio. For having known and lost these things, for now living in a land where they were unknown novelties—and for failing to belong to that land, much less accustoming myself to it, I was somehow a double stranger. As I thanked him and took my leave, Don Fausto handed me a letter. I saw it was from Don Socrates and waited until I got home to read it.

"With tears in my eyes," he wrote, "have I watched my people make the acquaintance of the technical progress achieved by a world of which they are almost ignorant. Ignorant not by their own fault, but by a fate which led them to live in a region badly isolated from the greater part of their own country, as well as other lands. And now the young people of my *pueblo* are torn between two sensations. They do not know which is more captivating—to crowd the fence around the radio station or to try to catch a glimpse of the white box that produces ice in Don Fulgencio's house. As for me, doctor, I am content to saddle my horse from

206

time to time, and to ride to the airport where the operator lets me hear the news from the capital of Argentina. But what changes for Santa Morena!

"Pierre has been seriously ill all these months. I have asked him to write to you about it. *Pobre diablo,* with nobody to look after him but that black woman.

"I earnestly hope that it will be possible for you to free yourself from your duties for a few days so you can celebrate with us the *fiesta* of the foundation of Santa Morena in the latter part of June. My house and its humble owner will consider it a great honor to receive you as an illustrious guest with whom talking about world problems will be the greatest pleasure for your obedient servant . . ."

I was amused at Don Socrates' changed philosophy regarding machines, progress, and isolation. But the news of Pierre's long illness worried me. I supposed that the priest was right, and he was drinking himself to death, but surely something could be done for him. Why hadn't Pierre written? I hadn't even had a single letter from him in all the time since I had left. For that matter, since the plane had come, there should be letters for me from Herbert, my other friends in La Paz, and from abroad—perhaps another from Lisa. Damn it all! What was going on? I rushed to Don Salustino's house and asked him about the mail.

The little postmaster shrugged his shoulders. "*Sí,* doctor, I have heard about the arrival of the *avion.* I have also received notice that the *mozo* with his bags left Santa Morena ten days ago." His eyes grew wide and popped at me. "I really do not know what to say. There has been no accident for a long time now, but the Rio Yucoma is still dangerous. There is still much water around to slow the courier. And," he added soothingly, "it may be that there was no mail from overseas this time."

Overseas or not did not matter so much as getting no mail at all. The letter from Don Socrates didn't count, since that had been delivered personally, and I couldn't understand why I should be so forgotten and neglected. It couldn't be deliberate. Life could be cruel, but not that cruel. Back home and away from curious eyes, I let myself go, storming, kicking about, and cursing in my office. This wretched career in this miserable out-of-the-way place. They may have thought so and I may have, too, at one time, but these people didn't really need me any more than I needed them. Daguero licked my hand and pressed against me, but I pushed him away. I wanted something I could hold on to; something that would mean promise for the future, a break in the monotony of the maddening present.

*   *   *

Perhaps it is bad to wish for things too violently. When they do come, it's often more than was hoped for, much stronger than expected. My break came early the next morning as I opened the shutters. I saw a big, muscular *carretero* hitching his oxen to the fence. His broad face was furrowed with worry and indecision, and I noticed that his right arm shook in spasms. Then he saw me watching him and seemed to breathe more easily. I felt I had seen him before somewhere.

"*Ai,* doctor, I have a sick man here—a very sick man who wanted to be taken to you."

"Say!" Now I placed him. "Aren't you the man with the malaria who was at *El Cementerio—El Trimotor?*"

"*Sí,* doctor." He nodded and jerked a thumb toward his cart. "Do me the favor and take him into your *casa.* He said he is your *amigo* and cursed when I said I wouldn't bring him to you from Santa Morena. He was too sick to ride a saddle ox. Then he said he would tell you if I didn't take him, so I . . ."

"Countryman!" The voice wavered between a whisper and a low-pitched scream, making my spine prickle. "Friend."

I ran to the back of the *carreton.* "Pierre, *hombre, amigo.* Why—?"

His eyes were enormous now. His face was gray and haggard, the skin of his neck hanging in folds like a shirt grown much too big for him. Pierre's body was still bulky, but it no longer had substance. He was a hulk. *El Trimotor* and I managed to carry him inside the house and put him down on my bed.

"Martin, *mein Junge,*" he gasped, "to see you again, you can't—you don't know what it means."

"It's all right, Pierre. You're here now and I'm glad."

"Are you, countryman?" He struggled to breathe. "You know they even have a radio now in Santa Morena."

He spoke of the phenomenon in the same snide way that he used to refer to sexual matters, but it was of no moment. He was here. He made a terrible journey under conditions of great physical suffering. He was a sick man, but in no immediate danger. Doctoring could wait, I thought, and the best stimulant would be a glass of whisky, the old friend-maker. It was assuredly most welcome. Drinking it revived him, he asked for more, and I poured out another half glass as he grimaced.

"Why didn't you write?" I asked, later on in the evening.

"Why don't people do what they're supposed to do?" A little boy's smile was lost in the shriveled skin around his loose mouth. "Ah, Martin, you ask that. When I face paper and ink, I have to be true, look at things honestly." He sighed. "I can't hide myself."

"We are alike, Pierre. We must face ourselves all the time. You should have written. I was worried about you."

208

"Were you?" he said thoughtfully. "I cause myself pain; I cause others pain. I thought I would get used to being alone some day, but I never have, never did, never will. And a man is always alone, Martin. Did you know that? Did you?"

It pained me to hear him go on like this. He was ill, exhausted; he should rest.

"You've talked enough, Pierre," I said gently. "You must rest, get well."

"Let me talk," he pleaded. "You don't know what it means to have somebody to talk to. You haven't learned yet, but you will know if you stay out here long enough."

He was wrong there. "I do know already." I looked at him. "I give you my word, Pierre. *I know.*"

I was so intense it should have registered, but his eyes had glazed over, turned in on himself and the past.

"Countryman, countryman," he mumbled. "Did I ever tell you that I had a daughter, a little girl with blonde curls? She died of the flu—you remember the epidemic after the World War. Oh, she was my joy and my pride, next to my wife. I was thin, then, and a man." He tried to sit up straighter, but hadn't the strength. "Yes, a man. But then the flu got me, too, and afterward I got the mumps with complications." He gave a bitter, grunting laugh. "I don't have to tell you what kind of complications. When the fever went I was left the way I am now, fat, monstrous, and no longer a man. Not even a filthy eunuch!"

I wanted to sympathize and reassure him, and I had to bite my lips to keep back pity. How Pierre had degenerated since I had seen him. How much older he had become, and not only old, but repetitive and drenched in self-pity. What hurt most was the certainty that I, that no one, could do anything for him. He was midway down the slide to death and oblivion—both of which he may well have longed for many times over. No drugs or medication would help, his best and possibly his only comfort was liquor, the friend-maker. And what did it matter if it only hastened his end? There was nothing to lose because he wouldn't live long anyway. He was weak, his resistance low, and his heart could not stand the strain of pumping blood to that huge, blubbery body.

Pierre gulped his drink greedily, held out his glass again, and I poured generously. He swallowed it straight down, coughed, then looked me over with a knowing leer that I found repulsive.

"Have you got yourself a girl in Rojas, eh, fellow countryman? There must be plenty of them hot and panting to know what it is like with a handsome *gringo* doctor."

It was a good try, but it lacked the salacious sting of the old Peter. He coughed again and his eyes seemed to clear.

"Why I came and sought you out—I'll tell you. I heard about you and the priest. The miracle operation you performed, and saved his life. They are talking about it all over. All over, and you are famous now, Martin. But, tell me, did he try to give you the leather-bound book? Did he force on you that great Greek cure-all, 'know thyself'?" he asked sarcastically, before breaking into hoarse laughter. "These damned *curas* . . . What do they know of life? Of anything?" His voice sank to a whisper. "I threw it right back in his sanctimonious face. Yes, I did! Why, he isn't even a priest." A peculiar expression, part fear, part anxiety, crossed his slack, ravaged face. "You didn't fall for his cheap game, did you, countryman?"

I said something brusque and noncommittal and, because he was tired and had talked himself out, it seemed to satisfy him. I gave him a strong sedative, and spent a restless night in the hammock, staring into the darkness, while Pierre snored and gurgled on my bed. He baffled me. He had come all this long, painful way, not for treatment apparently but to talk and, mostly, just to discover whether I had fallen for the false priest's philosophy. What a peculiar mission and yet how typical of Pierre.

I still had many office calls and operated a catch-all clinic. As I awoke toward morning, after a few hours of fitful sleep, it struck me that fitting Pierre into my daily medical routine would present a problem. He was still snoring as I got up, stretched, went to the window and, out of habit, opened the blinds. I looked out, saw three familiar figures standing silent and stolid in front of my house, and knew my problem was solved. Pierre's Indio woman and her two boys were back on the job. I mentioned their presence to Pierre after he had awakened. All he did was nod at an accepted fact.

"Always she follows me, countryman." His voice had a note of pride as he said it, a pride that was almost manly in its deep resignation. "I have to go back with her."

"Why?" I said.

"Because I have to. Because if I have any home, it is with her and her sons in Santa Morena."

There are times when it does no good to argue even if better judgment is on your side. This was one of them. Pierre had come for his own reasons; now he was going back for them. He was sick, ailing, still in no condition to travel, but two days was as long as I could persuade him to stay on.

"Shakespeare said it best, countryman: 'This above all: to thine own self be true.' That is not 'know thyself,' and you and I are alike. We carry the seeds of our salvation inside ourselves, the seeds of salvation as well as the seeds of our doom. And, you know, Martin, I have learned they are the same, exactly the same."

"Pierre," I began.

"It follows that false priests carry false philosophies with them."

"Pierre, for God's sake, *hombre,* take care of yourself," I begged him, gripping his hand. "We shall talk again when I come to Santa Morena."

Then they started out, Pierre lying in the *carreton,* the Indio woman riding beside him, silent and impassive, the two boys sharing a saddle ox. (Where *El Trimotor* had gone off to all this time, I had no idea.) I stood watching them until they disappeared. Significantly, Pierre did not once look back.

* * *

In the days following his departure, Rojas was dull and hot, and the thought of Pierre haunted me. I felt moved to take some kind of drastic action, but I knew not what. Of course, Pierre had urged me to get out of this country before it was too late, but I wasn't an alcoholic, saw no likelihood of my becoming one and, after all, what else could happen to me that hadn't happened already? True, I had plumbed the depths of depression and despair more often than those of happiness and fulfillment. All the same I had kept busy and done my job.

I have achieved what I wanted, I told myself. I am a member of the community, a man who fills an important place and has his pressing duties. Good, but perhaps not good enough, since I was somehow unable to convince myself either of being really needed, really belonging to the community. Then there was the loneliness that so often swept over me like the tide. At times the whole countryside seemed so remote, so alien, so apart from me. Then there was also a feeling of impalpable danger at every turn, a fear of disaster, some slip that would plunge me into hell. The absence of mail hurt, too. One stale letter from Herbert, then silence, not a line. Perhaps it would be a good idea to move to Santa Morena. Just watching the *avion* land and take off would pick me up. (Couldn't I leave, go back to La Paz whenever I felt like it?) And the *fiesta,* Don Socrates' warm invitation—and what about my recent promise to Pierre? All I needed was the opportunity, and I had it. So that very day I decided to discuss a leave of absence with the subprefect.

211

Approaching the official's house at a leisurely walk, I was suddenly struck by terrible screams coming from the patio. They could only come from a man in extreme pain or mortal agony, and I began to run in their direction. I cleared the back of the house, jumped over the beams of the corral, then rounded a clump of trees and shrubs from back of which came the screams, louder and more excruciating than ever now. A few more bounding steps and what I saw stopped me dead in tracks, shot through with horror.

An Indio, stripped to the waist and all but naked, was tied to a tree. He had been forced to hug the trunk, a rope wound tight around his wrists where his hands met. The two village policemen, whom I knew on sight but had never talked to, were swinging whips, striking rhythmically and alternately with all their strength, the leather cutting into the raw bleeding flesh each time, and the Indio groaning and screaming at every lash. The subprefect stood nearby counting the strokes unconcernedly. The policemen might have been swatting flies for all he cared. A flicker of a grin crossed his face as he saw me. He gave a casual greeting, but when I did not return it (I was incapable of anything), his smile froze, and he looked embarrassed.

The policemen went on whipping, the man groaning and yelling with pain, and the subprefect counting like a remorseless boxing referee. Paralyzed, I could only stand and stare. Then, as feeling returned, I covered my eyes with my hands (although I could never block out that dreadful scene), I rushed away to my own house. I locked myself in and for hours saw nothing, said nothing, did nothing. Rudolfo banged on the door, the sick came and went, and all the time the doctor remained stunned, sick at heart, dazed, and *hors de combat*. This brutality was something I never would have believed possible here. Were they Nazis, too, bullyboys and sadists?

I had recovered a little by the time Don Arnulfo called on me that evening. I knew what this miserable intermediary was about, and I glared at him bitterly. He was a little shy. It was clear that he did not know how to come to grips with his subject. But I certainly did and, after enjoying his discomfiture to a point and pulling myself together so I could speak calmly, I put the matter frankly.

"Don Arnulfo, I witnessed a terrible thing today. I cannot describe to you my emotions when I saw this grown man being whipped by other men. Nothing I have seen in Bolivia thus far has so upset me. I don't care *what* the man did, whether or not he was an Indio. He's a human being and should be treated like one!"

My caller nodded and scratched his chin. "You must be careful how you express your opinions, doctor. We have our own customs here, and most of us like them. Don Arturo says that you *gringos*—well, it appears that in Europe your kind commits unheard-of brutalities and atrocities. You say nothing, you permit them, but when you come to one of the Americas, you suddenly grow tenderhearted."

What a mess of lies and shameful half-truths! Who else would mouth them so glibly except this Don Arturo with his beautiful voice and the gap between gums and teeth that would let a fly crawl in and out?

"Do me the favor, Don Arnulfo," I said stiffly. "Go back and tell Don Arturo that a *gringo,* who does not like brutalities here, did not like them in Europe either. If the *gringo* is tenderhearted here, he has been just as tenderhearted in Europe. Things that are morally wrong in one place remain so in another. And perhaps that is the very reason why he came to this country."

Don Arnulfo twitched uncomfortably. He blinked, wet his lips, and put up a reassuring hand. "I know that, doctor. So do most of us. But, you see, there are always a few who only look for an opportunity to say that the *gringo* wants to interfere, to change our way of life."

My stony expression showed that I was not convinced, that his explanation hadn't made a dent in my thoughts. Now he looked for a scapegoat and, finding an easy one, lost any shred of sympathy or understanding he might conceivably have gained.

"But these Indios, doctor. One has to show them who is master. I inquired about the one you saw being punished—I inquired personally. He left his master's house for many hours while he was supposed to be working. Some of them are like animals. They live and think like animals, and they must be so treated. It is the only way to make them understand."

"Nonsense!" I said as I paced the room. "If they are animals, which I deny, then treat them as such. If your horse jumps the fence during the night and runs off into the pampas, do you whip him? You do not! You go after him intelligently with corn in your hands, trying to lure him back. And if you catch him, you don't whip him because he is an animal, unless you are stupid or a brute. If the Indio is an animal, as you say, then for God's sake don't whip him. If he is not an animal, but a human being as I insist he is, then other human beings should not shame themselves in the eyes of God by whipping him!"

Don Arnulfo scratched the back of his head and stared, saying nothing. It hadn't sunk in. He couldn't, wouldn't, or didn't want to understand.

"Don't you know inhumanity to man when you see it? Living in a community where men are whipped reminds me too much of the concentration camps from which I was lucky enough to escape. When I was in one of them, I often wondered how and what the people felt who lived just outside the fence. Now I think I have a slight inkling. If they thought they were guiltless because they shut their eyes to what was happening, I cannot agree. In fact, I can't stand such reasoning.

"For me, America—North or South America equally—has always meant human freedom shining like a beacon for all the world to see. When I stepped ashore in Chile, when I crossed the great, barren mountains from the Pacific Coast to the valley of La Paz, the air was thin, breathing painful, and our faces blue as the train climbed to the thirteen-thousand-foot level, but it didn't matter. I tell you, Don Arnulfo, we were all refugees from the Nazi hell, and our eyes shone because we saw freedom. Not only saw it, but breathed it and smelled it. Our ears rang with it. Our hearts pumped it into parched veins!" My voice dropped. "But after what I have seen today . . ." I had to stop because of the lump rising in my throat.

"No one is without fault, doctor." Don Arnulfo's face twitched spasmodically. "No one. We all have to learn, you know."

My God! Those tired, shopworn, meaningless platitudes.

"Yes, yes. But some—far too many—never learn. And I don't believe they even want to!"

We talked more, desultorily, but although we both spoke in Spanish, for all the contact we made, we might as well have been speaking different languages. We were on different levels in different worlds. I saw him out of my house still a baffled man, a man for whom, by the grace of distance and geography, the great war of 1914–1918 and the years after it had been no more and no less than a matter of business and life as usual. He did not understand a man like myself, a man who had been through the mill of tyranny and dictatorship which ground so exceedingly fine. And why should he? I asked myself. Perhaps the worst thing was that he did not really understand anything, had no moral concepts, and gloried in his safe, secure ignorance that made him feel superior to the humble Indio.

The Indios! The salt of this earth, tillers of the soil, the laborers and workers, the true natives who had lost their land and everything. I might know it, believe it with all my heart, insist on it, defend them, but how much better were they than animals? Why, during my first week in Rojas, I recalled, I had been hurriedly summoned to treat an Indio who had been carved up in a drunken brawl. Fired up on *aguardiente* or something just as potent, he had argued with a fellow Indio, and taken a razor-sharp, curved-

214

tip machete through the chest. The vicious weapon had come in through the man's back and penetrated clear through the breastbone as if the bone were paper. There was nothing I could do. Crumpled, bloody, and practically dismembered, the Indio was very dead when I reached him. And his assailant, rambling drunk and disarmed, was being beaten over the head by the same two village policemen I had seen in action today.

It was a brutal beating, but, drunk or not, he was a murderer, justice was being done, and I remembered thinking that the whole situation was well in hand. Only later did it strike me that no one in Rojas was the least stirred up, excited, or disturbed by the tragedy. An Indio had killed another Indio— and so what? Who cared about another dead Indio? Who gave a damn about the live ones so long as they kept their place, did as they were told, and did it fast and well? I heard the murderer was to be taken away for trial, but no move was made, and he stayed on in Rojas working by day and in jail at night. Then suddenly he was removed by the policemen, the news came that he had been convicted and sentenced, and then a few months later he turned up in Rojas working as before.

No one thought anything of it. I was told it was a long way to the penitentiary, wherever it was, and it was not at all unusual for convicted Indios to "escape" en route. It was too much bother anyway to escort them hundreds of miles over the mountains into captivity. Besides, they were needed in the fields. And this fellow here—well, what had he done except to kill another Indio, another animal? Oh, they were always killing one another. As for an Indio killing a non-Indio, ah, that was quite a different bottle of *aguardiente*.

I thought of this now as I continued to pace my *sala* in the darkness, setting one foot mechanically before the other, just as I used to during the endless days in my Austrian prison. The wall stopped me, I made a right turn, went on to the next corner, then another right turn. The wall closed in on me, *all* the walls closed in on me, and I wanted to turn. I wanted to bolt, to escape from what, until I had seen that wretched Indio being whipped today, had been a new, free life in the jungle—a life which now seemed to lie in ruins and from which came only groans, screams of agony, and the laying on of whips. Desperately I yearned for another chance to start anew somewhere else. One more chance . . .

I laughed suddenly, loudly and bitterly. By now I ought to know that life's ruins could never be left behind. They remained with you, and they accumulated. You were forced to face them, paw and scrabble through them looking for survivors, returning again and again in memory and in

215

fact like a criminal to the scene of his crime. I shook myself in anger. I rushed to the window and grabbed the bars. A prison in Austria, another in Bolivia. The comparison was no accident. From whips cutting the flesh of the Indio animals to Nazi thumbs pointing the way to death for the inferior Jews was only a step.

But then if this is so overwhelming, so vital to you, why didn't you try to cut that Indio loose, to stop those brutes from beating him? my conscience demanded of me. *You just ran away as you always do. You bleed at injustice, you sob and beat your breast over it, but you never fight it. You simply run, don't you?* True! True! I ran. Oh, but I was correct, perfectly so. I was against it, I argued, I objected, but I never dared to interfere with the authorities, assuming that, whatever they did, was really none of my business. *How brave of you, doctor!* my conscience sneered. *Sticks and stones will break your bones, but names will never hurt you. Nor words either.*

I should have stayed with my refugee friends in La Paz. They were accustomed to my running away. I could still hear Herbert's accusing words the day I had taken the plane in La Paz: "I still can't believe you're going. Why, you belong to us and you mustn't be alone. Isn't Bolivia far enough from Europe? Isn't La Paz small enough a town for you? *Must* you bury yourself in the jungle?" How unjust Herbert's charge of desertion had seemed when he made it. How wrong until now. I felt dizzy and nauseated all at once and shut my eyes. Was I in South America? Or was I still in Europe pacing my prison cell, languishing behind the barbed wire? Panic came over me, the same cold, unaccountable panic that came over me in Paris that day when I sat through that old, American film over and over again. Tom Sawyer was lost in the caves, trapped and wandering in the blackness, screaming, shrieking, calling for help . . .

I opened my eyes, blinked back the dizziness, and went to my office. That bottle I had opened for Pierre the other day. It was still a quarter full, and there was another one. I pulled out the cork and drank the liquor straight. More and more and more until it drooled down my chin and oblivion beckoned.

* * *

The spirit of *fiesta* was abroad in the province that summer, and everyone was leaving for the big celebration in Santa Morena. By the middle of June *carretons* filled with men, women, and children, and piled high with supplies, were leaving daily. And one morning thirty men on horseback had gathered in front of the subprefect's house before starting out. I was sup-

216

posed to be among them and they were waiting for me, but I still lay in my hammock.

I had gotten up early for the trip, but no sooner had I awakened and hauled myself out of bed I knew I wouldn't make it. I had a blinding headache, the room revolved around me, and my legs were so weak I could barely stand. Rudolfo had been planning to accompany me, and I hated to tell him how ill I felt. He had been looking forward eagerly to the trip. He was bubbling with good spirits like a city boy leaving for the country, and I could hardly recognize my serious and subdued medical assistant of old. He only nodded when I told him, but even with his ever-present dark glasses hiding his expressive eyes, he could not conceal his disappointment. But he was a good boy and a loyal assistant, and he quickly forgot his frustration—we could go another time, couldn't we?—in his ready sympathy for his chief.

He saw me back to bed, hurried to the subprefect's house to account for our absence, then came back to look after me. Rudolfo remarked on my pallor. That was nothing in itself, but I felt listless and infinitely weary. My body ached with an uncalled-for fatigue. Rudolfo thought I should eat something, but the thought of food made me vomit.

"If I were a *boracho,*" I said to Rudolfo, "it could be that I was suffering nothing more than a hang-over."

He insisted that I would feel better with something in my stomach, and at noon brought some chicken and fried bananas from his mother's house. The aroma pleased me now, I thought that perhaps it was just a matter of weakness, and began to eat greedily. But two bites were enough. I felt filled to bursting and as uncomfortable as I'd ever been in my life. The room was hot and sticky, Rudolfo took away my plate, and I closed the shutters and fell weakly into my hammock. I fell asleep quickly, but I did not sleep soundly. It was a sickly doze, a series of connected nightmares. I would awake with a start, go off again, and then jerk back to semiconsciousness. This kept on until Rudolfo shook me awake.

"Doctor! Doctor!" Then he mumbled something I couldn't catch.

"Yes, what is it?" I sat up painfully, as if my body had broken in two, drunk from heat and sleep, my heart beating a wild tattoo. "Oh, it's you," I said, blinking owlishly at Rudolfo. "What the devil is it? What do you want?"

Again he spoke, but I couldn't make any sense of his words. I held my head in my hands. I was soaked in sweat like a ball of cotton pulled out of the water, but I felt like a dried-out husk inside. I could feel my brains—

217

what brains, doctor?—rattling inside. The fresh khaki shirt and trousers I had put on for the trip were a sodden, wrinkled, and clinging mass of cloth, and my stomach felt like a rock underneath my heart.

"What was it you said, Rudolfo?" Speaking was an effort, and my words came out slurred. "Do me the favor and repeat. I did not understand."

"Don Antonio has asked," he began, speaking as he would to a deaf person, extra loudly and distinctly, "Don Antonio has asked if you would come over and see the *joven* Roberto. He cannot catch his breath."

"*Joven* Roberto—cannot catch his breath. Hmm." I had to concentrate hard to give each word its proper meaning. "That must be the skinny little boy who suffers from—let me see—yes, asthma. No wonder they get it, Rudolfo. No wonder. I feel as if somebody were squeezing my own wind-pipe. And this awful heat! I think we're going to get a change in the weather."

Rudolfo looked at me oddly, then out the open door. He took a deep breath of air, as if he were sampling it. "The heat is not so great really and, if there is a change, it will be cold. It might be a *surazzo*. Something must be in the air to make people's breath whistle."

I groaned. A *surazzo?* What was that? "Did you say the *joven* Roberto?" Asthma, that's what he had. And what did we do for that? "You will have to go and give him the needle yourself, Robert. Mind you give him only half an ampule. Don't forget to take cotton and alcohol."

Rudolfo quickly prepared what he needed. I had managed to sit up, but after he left, the rock under my heart became so unbearably heavy I toppled backward into the hammock. It seemed that I had just shut my eyes when Rudolfo was standing over me. He reported that the *joven* was much better. Then he held up the glass ampule to show it was half full and to prove to the great *gringo* doctor that he had done as told. I watched him put cotton and a piece of adhesive over the neck of the ampule where the tip had been broken off. Very good. At least I could trust Rudolfo to carry out professional instructions.

I shut my eyes and tried to convince myself that I was better too. A scratching sound reached me distantly and, slowly and carefully, I turned my head, and blinked my eyes open to see Daguero lying against the wall with his nose resting on one of my sandals.

"Daguero," I mumbled. "Daguero, you lazy *hombre,* you."

He opened his mouth wide and gave an ecstatic, neck-straining yawn. Then he loped over to the hammock and plastered my limp hand with wet kisses. Through the half-open door the sunlight shone in blurred, dusty beams. How thick the outside air seemed. Everything was hazy. Daguero whimpered, waited impatiently for his master to play the familiar game, gave up at last, and rolled over on his back for me to scratch his stomach, all four legs stretched skyward stiff as sticks.

The heat bore down on me, squeezing sweat out of all my pores. My nausea was as bad as when I had been seasick crossing the ocean. The *sala* was larger compared to that cabin on the steamer. It had been no more than a hole for four, foul-smelling, seasick men, a dark hole without windows, portholes, or air shafts deep below deck. Just thinking about it made me more ill. I tried to force my mind toward more pleasant thoughts, but it only spun dizzily like pictures fastened to a moving wheel. When it slowed down momentarily, I could recall individual scenes, but they all seemed grotesque—my whole life in the New World had been grotesque.

That *baile* given in my honor that night in Santa Morena. That incredible ball. Grotesque was the only appropriate word for the elegant dancing slippers, so prized and so important, in which the *muchachas* skipped gracefully over a floor that was nothing but dirt stamped hard by heavy boots. But then, in retrospect, those pretty shoes, brought to Bolivia from Argentina, were no more fantastic than the daubs of thick make-up on the eyelids, cheeks, and lips of the girls dancing under the unflattering light of the single gasoline lamp illuminating the squalid room. Hardly a room at that, more an oversized stable with the horses removed for the night. And I remembered so vividly Carlotta's shoes, absurdly high-heeled and tiny and snub-toed, tied in frivolous bows around her slender ankles. Nice ankles.

Carlotta! Whatever had become of her? Was she pining for her *gringo* "mosquiteer" or was there no lack of successors? It was really a shame to forget her so completely. But I hadn't thought much of women lately, or much of anything, I suppose. My thoughts lurched to Lisa in Paris. How loyal she had been to a man without a country, a doctor without a practice. Thinking of her fresh good looks and cool beauty, her warmth and passion, her allegiance to me now seemed so improbable that it was hard to believe that this exciting and desirable young woman had ever been in love with me. Or had she at that? Or had I really been in love with her or—what? *What,* for God's sake! Hot blood boiled inside my head, and my thirst was suddenly overwhelming.

"Rudolfo," I shouted hoarsely. "Oh, Rudolfo!"

His head popped into the doorway almost immediately, but it seemed like hours to me.

"Do me the favor and prepare me a glass of water with fruit salt."

"*Ya está,* doctor. Coming right up."

He poured the fruit salt into a glass containing yellow, brackish water from the *currichi*. My craving for filtered water had passed. It took a whole hour to get one glass of purified water using the filter. Who cared about worms and sanitation? I was doing as the Romans did now. Standing over me, Rudolfo stared with wide-eyed concern. The mixture in the glass he was holding foamed and frothed. The drink tickled my parched mouth and was sour, but in a few minutes the rock in my stomach seemed to move of its own accord and crumble piece by piece. Why, I ought to write a testimonial, I thought wryly. "For rocks in the stomach, nausea, weakness, and hot sweats, Dr. Martin Fischer says there is nothing like Rojas Fruit Salts, the medical cure-all . . ."

More noise, the scratching of canine claws on the floor. I tried to focus my eyes on the dogs. Hordimales came out of the consultation room stretching his body fore and aft. Daguero made his usual puppylike overtures to coax the older dog into a game, but Hordimales was cool and superior. He sniffed Daguero with great care, also fore and aft, as if to assure himself of his identity, then ignored him to stalk past haughtily. Daguero had no pride. He ran after his snobbish playmate eager to make amends for any slight, and I thought he looked silly lowering himself so, because he was already much bigger than the insufferable Hordimales.

"Rudolfo." His name came out a croak from my cracked lips. "What time is it now?"

He took my arm, turned over my wrist gently, and I realized I could have looked at my own watch. "Close to five o'clock," he said. I thanked him, smiling painfully to cover my lapse. Where had the day gone? Where had all my days gone? My face burned with its own inner fires and my thoughts bounded along with my racing pulse, always trying to get just one step ahead. Rudolfo was a good nurse, but I needed a woman in a situation like this. Even Pierre had a woman, such as she was, with him constantly. In spite of his impotency, his spiritual suicide, he had a faithful woman on whom he could rely. And on whom could I rely? On nobody and nothing. Love was old-fashioned and the stuff of novels, just an empty word for sex, passion, and fornication (check one, please!) in a charming setting.

"Doctor!" Rudolfo was shouting, and it came to me that I had no idea how many times he had repeated the word before finally capturing my attention. "Doctor!" he bellowed again. "Since we are not going to Santa Morena today, my mother wishes me to ride with her to my uncle's *estancia* a few kilometers away." He scowled. "But I feel I cannot leave you."

"You must go. You must accompany her." I nodded so violently that

220

I was afraid the effort would cost me my head, which fluttered like a heavy flower on a weak stalk. "You must, Rudolfo. I insist. I am perfectly all right, but be back in the morning so we can make an early start for Santa Morena."

"Start for Santa Morena in the morning?" he said incredulously.

"Of course. I'm all right, I tell you! Now go."

Reluctance and indecision played over his boyish face; he started to protest, then thought better of it. He put a glass of water next to me, asked whether I wanted anything else, shrugged, and went out. Daguero ran playfully after Hordimales, but stopped abruptly at the door and looked back at his master in the hammock. I didn't make a move—I couldn't, really—and Daguero studied me seriously, then, a dog with a purpose, came back to sit near the hammock where he could watch my face. I wanted to thank him, pat his dear head, but couldn't find the strength. I was glad to be alone, glad to see Rudolfo leave, but I was fearful too. The instant he shut the door the room seemed to darken with terrifying shadows, and nightmarish images rose like mist all around me.

Shuddering, I slipped into a restless, troubled sleep all through which I seemed to feel the pulsing of my blood all over my body. It was so strong that I could swear the hammock was rocking. I moaned and sang in my delirium. I argued with someone—either a priest or a concentration camp commandant—yelled as loud as I could to make myself heard over the pulsing cataract in my own ears.

"I don't care whether or not he is going to condemn me to death, do you hear? I don't care any more! Better to die quickly than to live in constant fear. And don't say 'know thyself' like that! What garbage! I wouldn't want to know myself if I could. I don't want any part of that miserable, cowardly, self-pitying fraud, Doctor Martin Fischer!"

Like a receding wave, the blood left my head and I was high and dry on the rolling beach of misery. All that remained in my mind was a deep and grievous resignation. How cold I was! I shivered and tried to cover myself, but there was no blanket in the hammock. I stretched an open hand, and my palm felt something cold and moist—Daguero's nose? A chill shook me again. Odd. The cold was over everything. The *surazzo* must have come, and yet it was not raining. I shivered and my teeth began a fine, castanet-like rattle. My body quaked with a chill—chills and fever like *El Trimotor* at *El Cementerio,* the Indio who had come back from Brazil with malaria.

I lay back sick, exhausted—stunned with my stupidity. Know thyself, eh?

Know thy symptoms was more like it. A fine doctor I was! *Malaria*. Out of the cloud in my mind the word danced and grinned, standing out in fiery letters against the background of fog. I wanted to shout, but only a wheeze came from between my chattering teeth. *Malaria*. I wanted to sigh my relief, but only the same wheeze escaped my twitching lips. "It's only malaria, Pierre—only malaria, Don Socrates—only malaria, Rudolfo—only malaria, Carlotta . . ."

The shaking of my body coming in uncontrolled spasms buried me deeper into the depths of the hammock, until the folds and fringe closed over my head, and I had to fight to keep from being asphyxiated. "Rudolfo!" I yelled. "Bring the atabrine. It's only malaria, you hear." No answer. I called out again. Nothing. Where was the clown? Just when I needed him—but he'd gone out, hadn't he? I must find it myself. Physician, heal thyself. I struggled to get out of the hammock, but only set it to swinging nauseatingly. Another frantic struggle. I fell out with a thumping crash and, with a terrific effort, dragged myself along the floor to the consultation room. The dirt was easy, but the wooden floor of the room was full of jagged splinters that jabbed into my hands and knees. The medicine was out of reach, the battle to get it was so painful, but I had to get to Santa Morena, had to, had to, had to . . . Finally I had the little flask in my trembling hands, shook out the yellow tablets, stared at them dully in my sweaty palm, now black with dirt, and forced them between my teeth. Four of them I gulped down. Then I fell back on the floor, staring at the pinpoint of light coming through the closed shutters.

Night came early, a wider slit revealed a strong full moon starting its bright path up the black sky, then it was quickly overtaken by a mass of dark, dark clouds. It was so quiet, the air hushed. The long leaves of the palm trees by the house were unnaturally still and, overhead, the thatched roof seemed to cower in place as if before a menace. As the blackness of night came on, the wind rode in. It rushed through the trees and fanned the palm fronds. The thatched roof rustled in alarm, dryly and insidiously as a rattlesnake. The moon emerged again to shed its silver light, but the wind grew stronger, herded the clouds like cows, and pushed them into a huddled mass that obliterated the moon and spread a deep pall of blackness over all of Rojas. The wind, cold and icy, entered the house through the gap between the bottom of the door and the threshold and attacked me mercilessly where I lay helpless. When at last I opened my eyes again, I could see nothing, but I could hear the voice of the storm, hoarsely vibrant and triumphant.

Numbly I wondered what had become of me. I was not in my bed. There

222

was no *mosquitero* over me, my back was frigid, but there was a surprising warmth on my chest—a living, breathing warmth. One hand was imprisoned under a buttock, my other hand was on the prickly boards, palm down. Straining, I drew the arm toward myself, then I felt the warm presence of a solid, furry body and the sudden, tender licking of a hot tongue.

"Daguero!" I exclaimed, almost tearfully, and recognizing my dog seemed about the most important thing that had ever happened to me. "Good boy, Daguero! You kept me warm. And how big you are. Why, you reach from my knee to my chin. And you're warm, too, so warm!"

I hugged Daguero in exultant gratitude, smiling as his tail banged the floor in affectionate response. I remembered something and began talking to Daguero just as I always did when we were alone.

"That was an attack of malaria, boy, and I should have known it right away. 'Others he has saved, himself he cannot save,' " I said shakily, misquoting some half-remembered Biblical phrase. "It's a good thing it's nighttime and no one can see me. If the people were to find their precious *gringo* doctor lying on the floor of his consultation room, they would say he was a fine medical practitioner who can neither diagnose nor keep disease away from himself. They might have called in Doctor Malvenido as consultant, and we would have a fine exchange of medical courtesies. You call it malaria, my good *curandero?* Extraordinary! Absolutely extraordinary."

I began to laugh, and Daguero licked my face lovingly as his tail beat hard against the boards.

"Daguero, old boy, I'm glad you're the only one here. You understand and you know me and you're my best and only friend. But we have to go to Santa Morena somehow, you and me. Oh, I just want to be there when the *avion* arrives," I explained, caressing his soft head. "I'm not taking it though; that would be quitting. I just want to be there when the plane arrives, just to watch . . . with my back to the wall, remember, Daguero . . . ?"

I hunched up, pulling hard at Daguero, and fumbled for the atabrine flask. I took two tablets, got them down dry as painfully as lumps of coal, and settled back. The bed, I ought to try—I stretched out again and clutched the thick fur on Daguero's neck with both hands.

"Don't you ever leave me," I pleaded. "Never, never, never."

Daguero whimpered, put his head down on my chest, and spread his loving warmth through me. A dog, a brute, an animal. What greater gift than to give of oneself? Pure instinct, someone would be bound to say of Daguero's gesture. Surely—and here an unbelieving sneer, a contemptuous look—you don't think a beast can express love? Who can? I thought, shutting my eyes, and if it's only instinct and nothing more, how many men have such noble instincts? How many men know and can express love, present company included?

Oh, Daguero! I stroked the fur. You are good and dear and loyal. And I am sick, forever sick, and atabrine alone will never cure what ails me.

12

Santa Morena in Fiesta; *I Hear Berlin Direct; Carlotta in Wrath; The* Avion *Beckons Briefly; I Make Up with Carlotta and Turn "Mosquiteer" Again*

It was a stirring, cleansing storm that swept over Rojas for two days and nights before blowing itself out. Somehow it coincided with my mood and I lay peacefully in bed recuperating from my bout with malaria, as the rain exploded in cloudbursts and the wind whipped back and forth, shaking the house, tearing at the thatched roof as if it were made of nothing but paper streamers, and seeming ready to make off with it any minute.

On the third morning the skies were blue and clear again. My malaria had subsided, apparently checked by repeated doses of atabrine, and, even though I was shaky and far from sound, I decided to set out for Santa Morena without delay. I had to leave all the details of packing and preparation to Rudolfo, and I must say he was more than equal to the job there and on the trail. I was so weak that I could do little more than hold myself on the horse. It was Rudolfo who led the way, cooked, made and broke camp, and generally supervised the whole trip, which took longer than usual this time.

In the early afternoon of our fourth day out of Rojas, Rudolfo gave the signal and we dismounted to rest beside La Laguna, the lake that was only about two hours' ride from the *pueblo* of Santa Morena. I was saddle-sore and weary, my muscles protesting and my bones creaking as I stumbled away from my horse. Daguero and Hordimales were drinking greedily of the lake water, and I wandered down next to them, shading my eyes from the glaring sun. It was swampy along the edge of the lake and, bending over the stagnant, green water, I was horrified at my reflection. My face had a drowned, distorted look, and my beard gave me the appearance of a down-and-out bum. It occurred to me that I hadn't shaved in over a week. This was hardly the way to arrive in Santa Morena for the *fiesta*.

"With this scraggly beard on top of my yellowish skin, I must look pretty horrible," I said, feeling my cheeks. "How about it, Rudolfo?"

The only possible answer, I knew, was a resounding "Yes!" but Rudolfo, who would make a good doctor because of it, was always tactful. He avoided a reply that could not be truthful as well as polite.

He stared at me thoughtfully and said only, "Many men wash themselves here before they enter Santa Morena."

It was so well put, so charmingly inoffensive while making a point that I had to smile. I said I'd better shave and wash up then, and Rudolfo got my travel kit from my saddlebag and brought me a tin can filled with lake water. Seated on a thick, fire-blackened section of a dead tree, which had obviously been struck by lightning long ago, I set to work shaving. Rudolfo held a little mirror in front of me so it would catch the light without reflecting the sun in my eyes, the dogs watched the ritual with absorbed attention, and I proceeded to scratch off the stubble of beard with many a nick and a rasp from cold water and a dull, rusty blade. According to the mirror it wasn't much of an improvement—I looked thin, sallow, and sickly—but at least I was recognizably human again.

We went slowly in the heat of the afternoon, and in the coolness of early evening we were close to Santa Morena with our horses splashing heavily through the village *currichi*. Rudolfo pricked up his ears at a fizzing, soaring explosive noise in the distance.

"The drum *bomba*. Did you hear it, doctor?" he said excitedly. "Rolling drums, skyrockets, and firecrackers. Ah, what a gay time it is!"

My efficient, sober-faced medical assistant had been replaced by a little boy worked up and overjoyed at the thought of the festivities awaiting ahead. His enthusiasm gave me pleasure, except that I suddenly felt old and used and tired. What did I care for the *fiesta*? My eyes burned and stung, then I looked up, and something new on the horizon, something I'd never seen— or expected to see—in Santa Morena stirred me more than any *fiesta* possibly could have. Was I dreaming? No, Don Socrates had written about it, Pierre had spoken of it, Don Fausto had described it as a miracle—and there it was! My heart quickened at the sight of the two slender radio towers reaching toward the sky in the far distance. Now both Rudolfo and I seemed to urge our horses on simultaneously, but for different reasons. A fast walk, a trot, and finally a gallop with Hordimales and Daguero flanking their masters on each side, a frantic, happy, barking escort.

226

All of Santa Morena was infected with the carnival spirit. The whole *pueblo* seemed to breathe a different, festive air. Banners and decorations hung from the houses, every door was open, and from each one spilled joyful music, the tunes of a guitar, a flute, a trumpet, a mandolin. The whole village had come alive and breathed conviviality. People shouted and waved at Rudolfo and me, and squads of dogs rushed forward to welcome Hordimales and Daguero and give them the bones, rather than the keys, of the city. The rustic streets, part dirt, part grass, were full of people in a hilarious mood. They waved and called to us, and a burst of music from anywhere was enough to set flushed-face men to swinging laughing women around in simple, rhythmic dance steps like trained bears in a carnival. The population seemed to have doubled or trebled, and behind each house I noticed a number of empty *carretons,* certainly from out of town, the front poles tipped to the ground, the high backs rising far above the axles. They looked exactly like enormous ducks bending over to drink.

Our progress was slow, and we had plenty of time to look around. The fence around the plaza had been reinforced with wooden corral beams, and the benches and chairs around it were filled with villagers and strangers all in their *fiesta* best. They were striking enough, but colorless compared to two frolicking groups of Indios, dressed in bright gaudy clothes embellished with multihued feathers in the style of North American Indians. These two eye-catching groups of Indios were each led by another Indio blowing thin, shrill tunes on his flute as they hopped and danced in short, high steps behind him. From time to time one of the high-stepping dancers would stagger, knocking the others off balance, then fall flat on his face, a bottle of *aguardiente* rolling away in the dirt as he fell. There were shouts of laughter then, the fallen one pushed away, and a scramble followed for his bottle, accompanied by cries of despair because it was always empty.

We rode on, holding our horses in check, and passed a corner of the fenced-in plaza, where some men were arguing over a big tethered bull whose eyes were bound with a black cloth bandage. A little farther, in front of Don Socrates' house, we came on the patriarch himself holding forth to a small crowd of men. It did me good just to see my old friend. He didn't see us until some other high-spirited citizens shouted greetings to the horsemen, then Don Socrates turned, shaded his eyes, and a joyful smile lighted up his brown, weathered features. Even his mustache seemed to bristle with joy, and I was deeply touched as he dropped everything and hurried to meet me. I slipped from the saddle into the arms of the old philosopher, and we embraced wordlessly.

"*Ai, hijo,* doctor." His voice shook with the easy, on-the-surface emotion

227

of age. "We have been expecting you, and I have been worried. All the people said they had left you ready to travel and nobody was reported to be ill." He peered closely into my face, then seemed to change his mind about what he had planned to say. "Well, in any case, you came in time for the bullfight. But, first, come and rest in the hammock and take a glass of *chicha*. It is a long, tiring ride from Rojas."

Don Socrates explained that because the *sala* had been in constant use for dancing, the hammock had been hung across the veranda on the patio side. He led me there now as I wondered what had happened to both Rudolfo and Daguero. I thought of going back to look for them, but the old man had already thrust me into the folds of the hammock, pulled up a stool, and was sitting next to me. He began to roll a cigarette with elaborate care; I immediately understood he had something on his mind, and his concentration amused me. Whatever it was, Don Socrates must think it important, otherwise no citizen of his standing would dream of discussing anything or murmuring anything but the customary polite phrases so soon after the arrival of a visitor. I waited patiently, watching him blink at the *cigarillo*, still unlighted in his fingers. The gaiety of the *fiesta* still reached our ears, but it was subdued now. We were both subdued.

"Doctor, as you must know, I'm not the only one who has been waiting for your arrival here."

"Oh," I said absently, "you mean Pierre. I'm going to see him."

"Yes, of course, Pierre, *pobre diablo,* has been waiting for you to arrive— at least when he was sober enough to remember you were coming." He coughed. "But it was not Pierre I had in mind."

"No?" I was tired, still felt the effects of my attack of malaria, and I hardly bothered to show surprise. I had no time for games or riddles, not in my condition, and, outside of Pierre, I couldn't imagine who should be awaiting me. "I don't know who it could be then, except a patient."

Don Socrates shook his head in fatherly reproof. "*Hijo,* you don't need to hide anything from me. I am your *amigo,* and you are as dear to me as my *hermano, sí,* my own brother. I speak of the *muchacha* Carlotta."

He paused, looking for me to make some dramatic response, and I was nonplused. My reaction should be one of elation or surprise, in order to please Don Socrates, but I felt neither, nor was I up to pretending. I held my tongue and he had to go on, fiddling with his *cigarillo*.

"Don Armando, her father, is a dear friend and my *compadre* and, as you know, I am the godfather of the *niña*. I can say that your choice is a good one. You need a señora for your house. You need a *mujer*, a wife to

228

handle the servants and to care for you when you are sick." He looked at my thin, yellow face. "The *muchacha* is a very good choice and I, who have known her since she lay in the cradle, am in a position to tell you so."

I was acutely uncomfortable. It would have been bad enough had I been well, but now I felt as if all the wind had been knocked out of me. But then it must go all the way to Don Socrates' early matchmaking gambit after my arrival in Santa Morena, and now he simply wanted to make it official, publish the banns. So *I* had made a good choice, eh? What choice? My God, what a mess! I swallowed twice before I could speak, then my voice wavered.

"Don Socrates, I—I don't know how to say what I wish to say. But I have never thought of marrying. Not that it isn't true what you've just said about Señorita Carlotta and her father, but—well, it is that I cannot marry."

His face wrinkled with anxiety, his eyes were troubled. "Is it that you are already married?"

"No," I said truthfully.

"Ah!" The wrinkled face smoothed out a little in relief. "Then what is it that makes you live all by yourself without a señora?" I took a deep breath and remained silent. "You like the *niña* Carlotta?"

"Of course. She is a *muchacha encantada,* a charming, young woman, but . . ."

"They say you visited her often when you were here last." His voice held no reproach, as I might have expected, but there was no doubt about his reference. "Isn't that so?"

"Oh, I went to her house a few times. Sometimes I stayed for the evening. And we danced together, too."

I tried to make light of it, but Don Socrates was persistent.

"They say you serenaded her after a *baile* and that you spoke seriously about her."

"Did I?" Damned if I could remember what had passed between us outside of the *mosquitero.* I would have blushed for my earlier indiscretion, whatever it was, but I was too yellow and anemic. "I must have been *boracho* that night."

"Nobody saw you taking the bottle at the time," he said, without smiling, "and for once the people saw you looking happy. They thought you had become *enamorado* with the *muchacha,* and now they think you are going to marry her. I myself think this is very wise."

Although I groaned inwardly and my voice came weakly, my denial was firm. "I cannot marry." To escape further inquisition, I grasped at a straw and added, "While I am not a married man, there is someone to whom I am promised."

"Ah!" His eyebrows rose, and he looked at me with serious interest. "Where is the señorita? In La Paz, perhaps?"

"No." Committed to my line of defense now, I might as well go all the way. "She remained in Paris. She had to. A wonderful girl."

Don Socrates seemed to accept the lie for the moment, then he stiffened. "There seems to be some trouble in France from what we heard last. Of course, we have not been at the airport for several days because the radio operator is distracting himself here in the *pueblo* and refuses to interrupt his pleasures to indulge us. Yes, serious trouble in France. That is why I do not understand why this woman, to whom you have promised yourself, did not accompany you to our country, *amigo*."

You're too smart, too perceptive, I thought. Maybe I didn't quite understand why she didn't come with me either.

"There were many reasons," I hedged, searching for a plausible one to give Carlotta's doting and dutiful godfather. Oh, tell him! I looked at my questioner's honest face. "I was not in favor of her coming with me at the time," I said meekly.

Don Socrates chewed on it, he pondered my statement for the moment, as if he found it deep beyond casual interpretation, and I was ashamed for myself and Lisa, too.

"Doctor," he said, "you are a learned man, but still a young one. I am an old man and I am not learned; I have only experience to go by. But I will say that a woman, who loves a man, does not ask him whether he is in favor. No, she goes with him wherever he chooses to go. Our women, and such a one is the *niña* Carlotta, sleep with their man on straw if there is no bed; they eat *platanos* if he has no other food to offer. If the man has the luck to be wealthy, they share his wealth; if he has nothing, they share that nothing—or less than nothing even as that Indio woman does with your friend Pierre. The *mujer* goes where her husband goes, she is where he is, whenever he has need of her. And that," he went on gently, "is why I think you waste yourself on a woman who preferred the luxuries of a big city to your love."

This was the patriarch speaking from the heart, grave, sincere, well meaning, and I could not be angry with him. I did not know how to answer him— in fact, it was increasingly clear that I knew few answers to anything outside of my medical field—but I did know I wanted to have done with this uncomfortable and disquieting discussion forever.

230

"I am sorry, Don Socrates," I said brusquely, "but I cannot agree with you." Then, changing the subject abruptly, I said, "What about this bad news from France? I'd like to hear more about it. Do you think we could talk the radio operator into going back to his post? I'm so anxious to hear news of the world outside again."

"*Como no,*" said Don Socrates graciously. It was not in his gentlemanly code to pursue an unwelcome line of conversation against the will of his guest. "The operator has been courting a girl who lives in the house opposite." He grinned. "He's been hanging around there the last few days. The fellow can't stay away."

As we walked across the street, Don Socrates startled me afresh by bringing up the whipping that had so horrified me in Rojas and which I had discussed with Don Arnulfo to little point. Amazing how things got around the province, especially where the *gringo* doctor was concerned, but it was just like Don Socrates to be *au courant* of everything. He thought that my opinion was a just one, and there were others who felt the same. He told me that he had heard some of Rojas' citizens express their willingness to refrain from beating or flogging the Indios for things which were, after all, only minor offenses. They were servants, not slaves; men and not animals.

"You must have impressed the people very much," he said warmly, "and that is a real victory for you. You must see that, doctor, because it is so difficult to change old ways. But here, too, you have a reputation as a good doctor."

I was pleased, of course, but only in passing, since I was too tense to find much satisfaction in his words and, at bottom, much too skeptical. I was dying to hear the news from Europe, after being buried in the jungles for so long, and I burned with frantic impatience as the old man stopped to greet some well-wishers and then dawdled to watch a cockfight. I wanted to urge him on, but it was impossible.

Bets had been offered, taken, and the initial skirmishes were over. Another was about to begin, and people watched with glassy-eyed concentration as spurs attacked and feathers flew over the bloody heads of the cocks. The people gasped. A cock toppled over, a long red gash on his neck where his foe's spurs had cut deep, and I felt sick. But the wounded bird staggered erect and resumed battle with a pluck that I had to admire. A moment later, after a fierce struggle, he had managed to rip the eye of his opponent, who had seemed the winner earlier. I tried to press on, but Don Socrates' bony fingers bit into my arm in excitement.

I remained, an unwilling prisoner, but did not look at the cockfight until the crowd began cheering. I saw one of the birds was down, the other swarming all over his fallen enemy gouging and pecking at the limp, bloody neck and head. The umpire proclaimed the winner among more cheers, bets exchanged hands amid whoops and groans, and the lucky owner picked up his cock tenderly and began to patch up his wounds so he could fight again. The loser was dead, quits with cockfighting forever, and only fit for the stew pot unless he was too tough. More birds were brought on, sand poured over the puddles of blood staining the ring a rich red, torn-out feathers removed, and it was time for the next fight.

Enough, in this case, was too much for me. I pulled backward, hoping we could get away before the forthcoming battle began and proved another irresistible attraction to Don Socrates. He seemed to get my message either by osmosis or silent urging, since everyone was yelling so loudly I couldn't have been heard if I wanted to. But he shuffled off reluctantly, looking back over his shoulder until we had reached the house of the radio operator's lady fair. He was there, of course, and in a peculiar mood combining amorousness and half drunkenness. Our proposal appalled him, but finally he yielded to Don Socrates' pressure and persuasion. He walked back with us grudgingly to the old man's house, I mounted my horse and offered him Rudolfo's, which had just seemed to turn up next to mine. He looked sour and sulky as we rode out to the airport, refused to say a word, and I was compelled to start an apologetic conversation.

"I really appreciate this favor," I assured the man. *"Me siento mucho,* but I know you can well imagine what it means to me to hear a live radio voice after being in the jungles for almost a year."

"Como no," he said without enthusiasm.

"Why, it seems like ages and ages since I heard any real news coming directly from its source," I went on, trying again. "For me being in the jungle is like being cast into outer darkness. How I have missed not being able to hear music, the opera, a play—anything entertaining. But that's not so important compared to news, is it? I feel so terribly ignorant of world conditions after so long." I forced a laugh. "In fact, I'm excited at the thought of hearing what's going on all over."

The radio operator, still in the throes of love and alcohol, only grunted mild assent, as if he were indulging me, and I felt foolish. When we dismounted at the neat little house the airline had built for its operator, my heart began pounding. Going inside, I gawked like any provincial at the steel-gray boxes of equipment, the short-wave radio, the knobs, the dials, and the clusters of apparatus. The operator grunted again, fiddled with this, turned that, then got into his chair and glanced at his wrist watch.

"In a few minutes it will be six o'clock, and we can tune in on some of the European capitals." He yawned self-importantly. "Meanwhile, I'll try to contact La Paz. Perhaps they have something to say there."

He clamped the earphones over his head and pushed a switch. A voice, faint, urgent, and excited, apparently repeating the same message over and over again, came to me. The operator listened for a minute or so in shocked surprise, then amazed me by blushing deeply. He ticked the key lever with an embarrassed smile, listened closely, then removed the earphones.

"I'm really grateful, doctor," he blurted boyishly. "They've been trying to reach me for the last two days. Wouldn't you know it though! No action the rest of the time, but come the *fiesta* and—" His smile was sheepish. "You know they thought something was out of order here. But it seems they are ready for a flight of the *avion* tomorrow."

"*No diga.* You don't say!" I exclaimed. "*Magnífico! Magnífico!*"

The operator's remark, delivered like an awesome pronouncement, seemed to call for such enthusiasm. I faked it nicely for the young man's kindness, but I felt nothing like it. On the contrary, my throat was dry, my chest gone tight with a feeling of impending danger, a presentiment of doom. I felt just as weak as the time malaria had hit me, pulled up a stool, and slumped by the short-wave. The operator was smiling and humming to himself now, pleased with life and cleansed of all resentment of the *gringo* doctor's interruption of his wooing. I had done a good turn in alerting him back to his duties.

"Now we shall try to get Buenos Aires." He touched a dial. "You know, sometimes we can hear London and Paris just like that."

He sounded as naively pleased with himself as if he were responsible for inventing the miracle of modern communications. Another little gadget he'd dreamed up in his spare time. Ho-hum. I watched impatiently as he turned switches, moved handles, tuned and adjusted, and suddenly the small room was filled with a riotous confusion of hums and whistles, like a dance hall on New Year's Eve as the confetti is thrown into the air at midnight. The babel, so out of place, so real, lacking only drunken shouts of "Happy New Year!" was a painful reminder of times long gone by. I tried to evaluate it and my memories, calmly and objectively, but the tightness in my chest, the chilly premonition growing there were overwhelming.

Then the holiday merriment of sound was severed as if a machete had cut through the tangle of paper streamers, sliced off the shouts and cheers in every welling throat. A sharp voice spoke in perfect German, guttural, smugly pompous, insufferable, hateful, terrorizing—anything you please:

233

"Meine Damen und Herren, this is Radio Berlin! Today our great Führer, Adolf Hitler . . .

All around me, the room darkened into night. Crazy lights flickered before my eyes, the ceiling pressed down, the floor tilted, and I recoiled and shuddered like a deer mortally wounded in flight. I was back in concentration camp marching with others before the commandant. The file, one step forward, another step—then the thumb pointing to total oblivion. Huddled on my stool, Radio Berlin boomed on over my head, the words washing over me like vomit. Then panic overcame me, I lurched from the stool, overturning it, and bolted outside. The dread voice followed me, bellowing and belching excrement, but I couldn't distinguish the words. I stood there reeling, conscious of the radio operator at the door saying something urgent, which I could not hear. I lunged for the horses, snatched at the reins of one—I have no idea whether it was Rudolfo's or mine—and walked dazedly through the gate in the direction of the village, dragging the animal after me. Angry words reached me from the radio operator now, *"gringo"* and *"loco"* figuring prominently among them, but they barely registered in the upper levels of consciousness. Radio Berlin had drowned out everything else—the shout heard round the world.

I had to find someone to talk to! Someone who would listen and understand. Still pulling the horse, I wandered the back streets (if you could call grassy lanes that) of Santa Morena, avoiding the *fiesta,* and instinct brought me to the outskirts—and the squalid hut in which Pierre lived (if, again, you could call that living) with his Indio woman. At the moment I wanted to speak with him more than anything else in the world. I let go of the horse's reins, burst inside, and found him lying on a cowhide and half propped against his old trunk. He was a wreck of a man, the sight of him such as to bring pity even to one who has none. His color was bad, his breathing stertorous, and suddenly I was a doctor again. I took his pulse and pulled up an eyelid, then turned accusingly on the Indio woman, who had come up behind me.

"Three days he wait for you to come. Then he get bottle."

It was the first time I had ever heard her say more than a word or two. Her voice was flat and heavy, but, like her manner, it had admirable, stoical dignity. And her tone carried no accusation. It was in her eyes, and it hurt to look at them. Dead drunk. I sighed. There was nothing I could do— those immortal words of doctors who never know *what* to do. He'd be unconscious for hours and, in a twisted way, I briefly envied him. But I had failed him. He had awaited me feverishly and wrestled with his devil, until finally, inevitably, the agony of his thirst had overcome the agony of his need for an understanding friend. I muttered consoling words to the Indio woman, said something about coming back, and ran out. Forgetting my horse, or not seeing him. I walked back to the plaza, tried to force my way through the crowd, and found myself wedged in among those enthusiastic souls applauding the last bullfight of the day.

It had no more appeal for me than cockfighting, but it was a distraction and I wanted to lose myself in the "sport," which in this case was a cross between a rodeo and a classical Spanish Torreo. The event was held in a fenced-in area, and it made up in vigor and action what it lacked in technique and refinement. A number of men restrained the bull, whose eyes were bound. The Indian contestant mounted the bull, the church bell rang for "Go!" the animal's eyes were uncovered, and he was off, put upon, furious, and intent on unseating his rider. He raced up and down the arena, snorting, bucking, and lunging, as the spectators yelled and drunken Indios climbed over the fence, fell sprawling, then did their best to incite the bull further.

Now the bull jumped sideways, dislodged his rider, and swung back awkwardly to attack his fallen tormentor. Women screamed, men yelled, but the other Indios managed to distract the maddened animal, confuse him, and so extricate the thrown man. He was carried off, apparently not too seriously hurt, since my services were not demanded (besides, Indios were tough), the bull corralled, then another rider had a go at him, another, and still another, until the bull himself was ready to drop.

The crowd began to disperse at sunset. Two by two, the women walked home in quiet dignity, parasols folded and carried over their arms. The men collected in little groups to talk, the children hurried on ahead of everybody, and (poor, little me) it seemed that only I was alone. But not quite because, as I was passing her father's house, I saw Carlotta at the door. Unless I flattered myself, she was certainly looking for me. There were others around her not looking my way, and her message was unmistakable. She gave a little nod, her eyes flashed, and she smiled. It was better than the wireless, this *muchacha* Radio Santa Morena. I nodded back yes, but I wasn't going to see her. Not after what Don Socrates had told me, not when she so obviously sought marriage, not when I felt so damn rotten about everything.

*　*　*

Some time after night had drawn its cloak of discretion over the *pueblo,* I found myself drawn to Carlotta's home as if by invisible wires. I was cautious though, for I had already made certain that her father was in alcoholic high spirits and playing poker with his *compadres* elsewhere. Santa Morena was a small community and my spying a simple matter. Now I sat alone with Carlotta. She was lying in a hammock and I was on a stool close to her like a doctor at a patient's bedside. In the dim light I could see her black eyes shining with happiness, and she was good to look at. Her black hair, combed straight back from her forehead into a low, simple knot, gleamed like the midnight blue of a raven's wing in the moonlight, which was streaming over the garden and bathing flowers and trees in unearthly beauty.

Daguero had followed me with leisurely dignity, as if he had nothing to do and wanted to make sure I behaved myself. He lay dozing beside me, every now and then thumping the ground politely with his tail as Carlotta prodded him gently with a swinging toe. A peaceful scene, almost a domestic one, with the lovers united, the faithful dog, and romantic moonlight over everything. But it was deceptive; if Carlotta was ecstatic with happiness because of my presence, I still seethed inside. I heard her sigh and looked up.

"You are so quiet, Martin," she murmured.

Her arms were folded behind her head, stretching her silk blouse tightly over her full breasts, and the softly swinging hammock had molded itself so closely to her buttocks and thighs that it seemed part of her. She was provocative, desirable, and so compliant that any normal man would have been aroused, but I felt no emotion except the unnamed fear that had attacked me at the radio station. The awful voice of Radio Berlin still possessed me.

"Quiet?" I repeated numbly.

"Yes, so very quiet. What troubles you, Martin? Tell me. I would like to make you forget your sadness."

Her voice was so soothing, so sincere. She meant it from the heart, and a flicker of hope awoke in me. Maybe I could talk to and confide in her. Why not? I knew she loved me. She had to be receptive then.

"Life confuses me these days, Carlotta. I've always wanted to be in the middle of it, doing, acting, busy, and curious wherever I found myself, but lately—" I shrugged. "I must confess—and it is not easy—that lately I have become afraid of life. And it is the little things that make me fearful." I wanted to tell her about the radio station incident, but I was too ashamed, then sorry I'd ever begun the subject. I searched for words better to express myself, then decided to keep it abstract. "Sometimes—sometimes, Carlotta,

236

I feel like a man swimming in the ocean. He struggles hard to get free of a sinking ship, swims with all his strength, but there is a rope around the man's neck and the rope is tied to the sinking ship . . ."

I looked at her in embarrassment, uneasy, but smiling, hopeful, sure that she would understand at least a little. But her eyes were narrowed. She looked cheated, bewildered.

"Oh, you're joking with me, Dr. Martin!" she protested. "You've been talking too much philosophy with my godfather Don Socrates and that dreadful Pierre."

Her words were a blow, but I should have known. The ship I had spoken of sank now without a trace, dragging its tied swimmer to the bottom. I shut my eyes in pain and clamped my lips together. Her total lack of understanding blew over my head and heart like a glacial wind; a chasm suddenly yawned between her hammock and my stool.

"Look at the moon, Martin." I opened my eyes reluctantly, glanced at the moon, then back at her. Her face had brightened, her eyes were warm and wide again, and she seemed absolutely unaware of the unbridgeable abyss between us. "Oh, Martin, how I would love to go to Paris with you—with the man I love—some day and see all the places we read about in the *revistas*. They're more wonderful than even the magazines show, aren't they? And the big department stores, the perfumes, the dresses, the jewels, how I would love to see them. Ah, Martin, they say the French women are so lovely, so chic. Is that true?"

I stared at the ground so she could not see my face.

"And the men—they're supposed to know all about the art of love." She leaned forward as if giving herself. "Martin, are all the men in France good lovers?"

As I listened to her happy, childish chatter about love and romance, I looked back on days in Paris as a recent concentration-camp inmate, uprooted expatriate, penniless refugee, doctor without a practice, and man without a country, a cause, or anything. Remembering my unspeakable fears, my harassment by the police over necessary documents, it was all so far from her conception of the sleek, suave, practiced lover *à la* Frenchmen that I looked straight into her eyes and burst into loud, ugly laughter. Carlotta was stunned. Her face darkened just as if I'd slapped her. She gathered her skirts and jumped from the lurching hammock before I could help her. What a fool I was! It wasn't her fault that she couldn't understand what I was talking about.

237

"Carlotta, please, I—"

I hurried to intercept her as she darted for the house. Behind me Daguero yawned, jerked to his feet, and followed us sleepily.

"Carlotta, you mustn't think that—"

I grabbed her arm, but she brushed me off and scurried inside. I hastened after her, and she turned to face me at the door of her room.

"I ought to hate you!" she spat, her face contorted, each word separate and distinct. She meant exactly what she said, but it was something like a major dramatic effort that didn't quite come off, and now the disappointed little girl in her took over. Tears streamed down her face, washing rivulets down the film of white powder (her only attempt at make-up) she had put on for the *fiesta*. "I ought to hate you, do you hear?"

I started to say something—what, I don't know—then changed my mind and remained silent as she pointed to the door of her bedroom. Her extended arm wavered as she sobbed.

"I didn't hear from you since you left Santa Morena. Not a word did you send me all the endless rainy season, not a line did you write, not a message. All the same my bed under the *mosquitero* was prepared for you and me tonight. I expected you even though my father said you were not to stay here. He insists he knows what you are: a stranger to our country, who will go away one day, a man who just wants a woman for his bed, *not* a señora for his house."

She took a deep breath, tried to control herself, but could not hold back her sobs.

"I didn't care what he said. I said that it wasn't true and that I didn't care. As for his story about *El Chileno* and the money you wanted to cure him—I never spread it or told anybody. My heart wanted you, Martin, and it still does. But you laugh at me. *Laugh!* I know you have sorrows, that you are sad, but it is a sinking ship you mourn, not something real. And whatever it is that's bothering you, it is a lie, a fabrication. If it's that woman in Paris you're worried about, if it's she you want, then you're afraid because she doesn't love you. And she doesn't!" She gave a triumphant, breathy laugh that was cut off by another sob. "She didn't love you enough to come with you. She stayed in the big city, and now she laughs at you the same way you're laughing at me."

"Carlotta," I said weakly, in the face of her passionate outburst, "Carlotta, you must listen to me a little."

She shook her head. Again I reached out for her, but she retreated, crying brokenheartedly. "No! No! No!" She shrank back into her bedroom and

238

slammed the door. I stood there shaken, then walked away, tortured by the sounds of her muted sobbing. I was upset and deeply disappointed in myself. I had only half listened to her talk about the woman I'd left behind in Paris and did not at all understand what it had to do with us. A storm had broken over my head and I was unscathed somehow—only more confused. I ought never to have come here so low in mind, especially after Don Socrates' little lecture about marrying Carlotta.

Outside, I stood in the darkness for a moment wondering where I was and where I was going. I had forgotten all about Carlotta and everything she had said. I remember only going to bed, passing a sleepless and exhausting night, and getting up early, resolved to action. It was no good resisting any longer, I admitted, no good at all. I had to get out of here, breathe different air for a while and clear my head. As soon as I saw Rudolfo, I told him to go to the agent of the airline.

"If there is to be a flight today, tell him that I will be a passenger on the plane."

He stared in amazement, taking off his dark glasses and scratching his head in bewilderment. He blinked his sensitive eyes, and they seemed pink-rimmed with anxiety.

"You're—you're really leaving us, doctor?"

"Oh, not for good, of course," I said, smiling to reassure him. "I won't be gone long. There are—you see, I must find out about a few matters of importance." He looked at me, and I hastened to find a more plausible excuse. "Besides, we need many things for the *officina,* Rudolfo. I must replace all the supplies we used up during the rainy season."

He nodded, slipped on his dark glasses again, and went out. I was still pacing the room as he returned in a little while, and told me he had made the plane reservation. Then he said uncertainly, "Uh, doctor, I thought you might like to know that Señorita Carlotta has left the *pueblo* and gone to the *estancia.*"

But my thoughts were going in another direction, and I did not see how this concerned me in the least. "She has left Santa Morena then?" He nodded. "I wonder why," I mused. "The *fiesta* is not over yet. Did her parents go with her, too?"

"No," he said, putting extra meaning into his voice. "Only her personal *sirvienta* went with her."

"Hmm. That is her affair, I suppose." Rudolfo was looking at me queerly, I knew, but I was willing to let it go at that. Carlotta was free to come and go—to disappear—for all I cared at the moment. "Well, if I'm taking that plane, I better speak to Don Socrates about it, then get my things ready. I'll be back, Rudolfo, don't you worry about that. I need a breather, then there are some friends—well, you know . . ."

"Yes," he said listlessly.

"My sickness, that bout with malaria has left me weak. I need rest and change."

"Yes," he said again.

*　　*　　*

The arrival of the *avion* at this time seemed part of the *fiesta,* perhaps the high point of that particular day. A boisterous, animated crowd thronged the airport, most of the men obviously under the influence of the *aguardiente* they had been downing like water lately, the women intoxicated with the carnival spirit, and the children jumping about and frolicking like spring lambs. Nobody took any notice of the fact that I wore my dark, dress-up suit, rather than my usual shirt and riding breeches, or perhaps they thought of it as a *gringo* concession to the *fiesta.* It had been a long time since I had worn that suit. Rudolfo had put it in my suitcase when we left Rojas, more as a matter of course than because he thought I might need it, and here it was my getaway outfit. Because there was no use kidding myself; I was going and I wasn't coming back.

It was miserable of me to lie, to pretend that I was coming back, but I couldn't help myself. My conscience stung all the more because Don Socrates had been so nice about things. He had agreed so readily that it was a good idea for the doctor to visit La Paz for a fortnight to see what was new in the world, as he put it. And he did not doubt me in the least. I had worked hard, been on the go constantly, and the malaria had left me very run down. And this was just the time of year the plane could be depended on to return on its regular run in two or three weeks. So he had been pleased to grant me the favor; I was off to the capital, and he envied me the respite.

How easy it is to cheat, I thought. It was inexcusable to let Don Socrates and all of them down so shamefully, but they probably expected a *gringo* to treat them shabbily. I had no real ties here, not with Don Socrates or with anyone or anything, so I really wasn't—then I remembered my faithful Daguero and cringed inside.

"The dogs," I said to Rudolfo, as we pressed on through the crowd. "What about Daguero? Where—?"

"I tied both Daguero and Hordimales to the saddles in Don Socrates' house," Rudolfo explained. "Daguero would have been wild to go along

240

if he saw you go into the *avion*. I will take good care of him till you get back."

"Thank you, Rudolfo. Besides being a wonderful assistant, you are a good friend to me."

Someone jostled me accidentally, and I leaned heavily on Rudolfo. I felt weak and old and sick suddenly, the sensation a tangible force dragging me down, and I clutched the boy's arm for comfort as well as strength. Trying hard to concentrate, I gave Rudolfo some last-minute instructions because I *was* planning to come back. (I had been only joking with myself, hadn't I, when the idea had crossed my mind not to return from La Paz?) Let's see, let's see. Rudolfo was to stay on in Don Socrates' house, he was to wait there for me. And I'd given him enough money for his own personal expenses and to feed the dogs well—good cuts of meat now, not the cheap ones. And, remember, he was not to play the mighty doctor, he was not to accept any *curaciones* except minor cases. Rudolfo nodded and nodded and nodded. And I thought, God, how could I do this? How could I sink so low!

As I repeated my instructions to Rudolfo, like a senile old man who has forgotten everything he said earlier, minute by minute announcements issued from the window of the radio operator's house, near which we were standing with the rest of the crowd. "Yes, the *avion* is approaching the Cordillera . . . that is right, near the mountain range . . . there are strong winds blowing . . . treacherous updrafts . . . they hope they don't have to give up and go back . . . the winds are extraordinarily strong, extraordinarily strong . . ."

I kept on repeating the instructions to Rudolfo, my lips moving soundlessly in the echoing and re-echoing booming of the bulletin announcements. I felt chilled to the bone, a terrible coldness over me, the feeling of impending catastrophe engulfing me, and I would have fallen if Rudolfo had not been supporting my body. Was it really going to be a temporary stay in La Paz? Was it now, doctor? A breath of sanity, then no more back to the wall, no more headlong flight from oblivion. Come on now—be honest for once, doctor!—would I ever return? *Oh, God*, I prayed, *God! I hope they don't make it. I hope the wind is so strong the plane has to give up and go back.*

Then the voice from the radio shack again, tense, dramatic, proud, triumphant, a regular huzza for the air age: "They have crossed the Cordillera. They are over the mountain range. The plane is coming!"

I shut my eyes, trembled, tottered, and was steadied by Rudolfo. The die was cast. The Rubicon crossed. I had come, seen, and been conquered. Cowardly, weak, despicable me. The mighty doctor, eh? Doctor of what?

A loud voice to my right. An arm pointing skyward, an excited voice. *"Alli, el pajaro argento!"* The hum of faraway engines, a glittering point soaring and swaying in the distance like a silver bird. *"El avion!"* someone shouted. *"El avion! Es el avion!"* the crowd exulted in unison, every up-turned face beaming at the sight. In spite of the childish noise and hurrahs of the crowd, the roar of the engines was distinct now and increased steadily in volume, possessing all the thin, rarefied air now that the mountain ranges were passed. The airplane increased in size, the roaring seemed to shake the ground, the whole universe, and now it was overhead. The plane came in, dipped in salute to the crowd, and the big Junkers commercial plane made a fine landing.

A German plane, of course, like the one I'd come in on, perhaps the same one. There were two of them on the airline, I recalled, one called Illimani, the other Illiampu, both named after the highest mountain peaks in the Cordillera. And so what if the plane was German? I argued with myself. It was only natural, wasn't it? Germany's prestige was high, they had worked hard in exploiting South America, spent a lot of money on good will, invested in many businesses, and the Germans, who had come there (and, of course, made good) were well liked and esteemed. And hadn't I had to do business with Germans in La Paz? They said they liked Jews, that Hitler was a madman, that the Nazis were insane. And they had seemed to mean it, in spite of the embassies and consular offices, who pushed the Nazi religion. Germany had a stake in South America. They had culti-vated trade there for years, learned the language, and been genuinely interested in the people and their ways. Sure, sure, sure.

Rudolfo was saying something and I blinked at him. "What?"

"It is a beautiful thing, that *avion*."

I couldn't answer this. "You will take care of everything, Rudolfo?"

"Yes, doctor. Do not worry."

"I have to go, you understand me?" I pleaded. "I must."

"Sí, sí. Look, they are opening the little door in the side now."

The passengers, then the pilot and crew descended the little ramp ladder, and something—I didn't know exactly what—seemed all wrong and I was wretchedly disappointed. I was dazed, struggled to rouse myself, and realized that it was all because I had been counting on seeing the same pilot who had flown me down to Santa Morena on my first trip. The pilot and crew were strangers to me and, in my disturbed state of mind, I took it as a personal affront. The nerve of that airline substituting a new pilot and crew without informing me!

This man stood apart, taller than anyone on the airfield, and looking like a Nordic superman. He had ash-blond hair cut in a short Prussian style, he wore a military uniform, he held himself stiff, straight, and arrogant. All that was lacking was the swastika armband, the hand upraised in salute, and the proud *"Heil Hitler!"* I couldn't move. I was leaning harder than ever on Rudolfo, who had been joined by Don Socrates, and now the two were conferring worriedly. I stared at the pilot, making sure of my vision. The crowd was all around him, and he was laughing, smiling, and tickling the chins of the children held up to him.

They were unloading the plane hurriedly now, at the navigator's urging. It had been bad over the mountains, the weather was liable to worsen, and the wise thing would be to take off as soon as possible. The pilot agreed, taking out his handkerchief and wiping the sweat from his face and neck. It was sizzling down below, compared with in the sky, and the pilot's features were a glistening red. He grinned, he joked with the men of the village. Oh, he was a gay fellow!

"This pilot is a foreigner, an *Aleman*," Don Socrates was saying. "He is an excellent flier though. Let us move in closer and hear what he has to say." The respect and admiration in his pronouncing of *Aleman* made me wince.

I dug in my feet, made my muscles rigid, but Rudolfo was holding me, and he wanted to close in with Don Socrates. Dizzy and trembling, I was dragged along into the pilot's circle of admirers. The people were giving him the royal treatment. A *sirvienta* from the village had brought along a bowl of *chicha* to sustain the *fiesta* revelry. Now, amid laughter, she handed a glass of it to the big man, who grabbed it, held it high, and drained it in one gargantuan gulp. The crowd sighed in admiration, proud that their local beverage had found such recognition with the master of the trimotor.

Now the *alcalde* spoke to the pilot and respectfully asked questions about political events in the great world. The Nordic blue eyes twinkled, the man lifted his arm casually and pointed it toward the Cordillera, and replied in heavily accented, guttural Spanish. Even before he mentioned Hitler, I was vividly reminded of the concentration camp commandant, so big, handsome, deceptively friendly—and iron viciousness and depravity beneath the surface. My whole body began to shake. "This is not the commandant," I whispered fervently to myself. "He was much, much older." Over and over I tried to convince myself, but in vain. I felt as if the earth were giving way beneath me. "Rudolfo!" I gasped, grabbing my assistant's arm, and I was still physician enough to notice that he paled visibly as he looked at me. "Rudolfo, I can't—I don't know—take me away."

Just then the navigator came over and said something to the pilot. The tall blond man agreed, shook hands first with the mayor, then all around, stopping with an exclamation as he accepted a gift bunch of bananas from an admirer in the crowd. Nearby his co-pilot was stroking a dwarf monkey that had been given him. The little animal was clutching his shoulder, and it was awkward because his other hand was burdened with a crude cage in which huddled two, small, yellow birds. The pilots said a general good-by, the crowd responded in unison, and it was just like a *"Sieg heil!"* to a *"Heil Hitler!"*

I slumped into Rudolfo's arms as pilot and copilot ascended the ladder into the Junkers behind the navigator. The agent of the airline went up to check with them, then came out of the plane, and stood poised at the top of the steps.

"Where is the doctor?" he called out loudly, looking from left to right. "Doctor, we are waiting for you!"

I was beyond speech. Rudolfo pulled me against him with one arm and waved the other to attract the agent's attention. "The doctor has been taken ill," he shouted. "He will not make the flight this time."

The agent looked our way, the crowd turned to stare at us, and I turned my face away. I was humiliated, but so sick I hardly cared. Then the engines turned over, kicked into life, and I was ignored. A few minutes later the big plane was taxiing down the field and lifting itself into the sky with a mighty roar. People shaded their eyes with their hands to follow the silver bird until it disappeared over the horizon. All eyes were skyward except mine, and Rudolfo's, as he supported me.

"It is all right, doctor," he murmured.

I put one arm against the radio operator's house and vomited against the wall. My insides—my mind—turned inside out.

*   *   *

I can't say I remember much of the *fiesta* time at Santa Morena. I know I went back from the airport to Don Socrates' house, making a great effort to walk alone, although Rudolfo guided me all the way. He put me to bed and, fortunately, in spite of the excitement and carousing of the time, there were no accidents or sicknesses that demanded a doctor's services. Rudolfo explained to Don Socrates that I had been very ill with malaria and that I had suffered a relapse. The old man accepted this explanation, saw to it that I was comfortable and cared for, then did not bother me further as he plunged into the remaining *fiesta* activites.

I felt much stronger in mind and body, after a few days rest and sleep, and decided that the wisest thing for me would be to resume my duties in Rojas. Don Socrates, as might be expected, tried to dissuade me, insisting that I stay on in Santa Morena, but I overruled him and Rudolfo went along with my wishes. I was the doctor, I was the boss, and, for him, I made the decisions. I think he understood that I wanted to get away from the airport and its radio and, as for himself, he had enough of the *fiesta* and wanted to return to his mother at home—and probably to the *muchacha* he had left behind.

We started early and at a slow pace, stopping for our first rest period at La Laguna, close to the place we had halted on our way into Santa Morena. The early rays of the sun touched the green lake waters playfully, a mild breeze swept in from the wrinkled surface, and the sky above was a friendly blue. All around us the flat pasture land was green and fresh from the night's soothing coolness, the dew shining brilliantly in the sunlight. Our horses grazed lazily, their heads buried in the long meadow grasses. We had removed their saddles, tethered them by tying lassos to their halters, and now the long ropes slithered behind them through the grass, like thin, twisting snakes, as they moved forward.

Rudolfo was stretched out full length in the shade among our gear, his head resting comfortably on a saddle, his black hat over his face to protect his weak eyes from the sun. Below him and along the water's edge, his dog Hordimales was restlessly snuffling and searching for something along the bushes. Not far off I sat on the same log where I had shaved on the day of our arrival in Santa Morena not long before. I had just shaved there again, and I had made a small fire to heat a tin of hot water for the operation. It had died down now, the weakly glowing twigs darkening steadily and falling to ashes.

I sighed, my eyes wandering across the pastoral scene, so peaceful and serene. I could be wrong, but I felt Rudolfo had been reserved since our departure. I was probably all wrong about his accepting my decision without protest. I imagined now that he was tired from the all-night festivities and also annoyed that his chief had left the *pueblo* so suddenly, without a thought of all the pretty girls gathered in Santa Morena for the *bailes* and parties. Why had I assumed he had enough of the *fiesta* and would be anxious to go home to his mother and his girl, whoever she was? Ah, one should never assume anything about anyone, I reflected.

Daguero, lying so close to me, was not his usual self either. His big head was on his paws, his ears up, and his big eyes were fastened questioningly on his master's face. What's up? he seemed to be asking. What's this all about? As if the dog sensed my uncertainty and confused state of mind, he would not leave my side for a second. I took a deep breath. How could the morning be so beautiful, so tranquil, when I felt so rotten? I fumbled for a *cigarillo* with shaky fingers, and a slip of yellow paper fluttered to the ground. I picked it up—Santa Morena to La Paz—the airplane ticket which was to have taken me back to sanity and civilization. I studied it bitterly. Whatever was bothering me, I had to admit, was stronger than I was. I just couldn't fight it any longer. I must stop being a fool. You couldn't escape from yourself, and this was my place. Doctor in Bolivia. And there was freedom for me here in the jungles, freedom from terror and cultivated barbarism. I would just have to make myself learn to live as these people lived, to think as they thought. To learn to accept things as they were, not as I wished so longingly they might be or, even more longingly, as they used to be. Facts, reality, truth . . .

I held the paper over the almost dead fire, letting it drop reluctantly. A small flame seemed to leap from the ashes to lick the yellow ticket, snap it up voraciously, and consume it, as I clenched my fists and almost cried out. Damn it! That dead fire needn't have consumed the thing so greedily. I stamped my heel in the charred embers over and over again in anger, but the motion only caused a draft that set the whole fire blazing again, mocking me. I swore, then walked over to Daguero, who had not moved, and patted his big smooth head.

"Never give up," I admonished him. "Don't ever give up, Daguero, do you hear me? But if you do, if you have to, do it like a man with real guts. Don't run away."

He raised his honest, affectionate eyes to mine and began to lick my hands. The gesture moved me deeply. I was suddenly blinded with tears, but I chose to blame it on the sunlight, which just then hit me directly in the eye. I heard a movement and saw Rudolfo standing over me, holding the trailing end of the lassos.

"It's going to be a bad day for traveling, doctor. The sun is burning and, I thought, if we hurry we might be able to reach Don Armando's *estancia* before the heat becomes unbearable. In your condition you would suffer and the *estancia*—well, you would be welcome to rest there. I believe Señorita Carlotta is there."

246

His words were full of implications, it seemed to me, and in my touchy condition I was ready to take offense at anything. But he did not waver, he had spoken humbly and honestly, and he did not look away from my glare.

"Señorita Carlotta, eh?"

"Sí. I know she left the *fiesta* to go to the *estancia*. She would be glad to see you."

My eyes narrowed in thought. The gulf between Carlotta and myself had disappeared. Hadn't I just dedicated myself to this land, its people, and my duties? And hadn't I hurt her by laughing and sneering in her pretty face. I ought to apologize. I *should* apologize.

"Why not, Rudolfo? Let us go there and get some rest."

The suggestion was a good one. Carlotta was surprised to see me, and delighted. So delighted she brushed off my apology with a becoming blush. I was sorry, she was forgiving and loving—we were both loving. In fact, my passion for her amazed and overwhelmed me. At night a pale moon shone on the *estancia* and peeped shyly and boldly into Carlotta's room. The shutters were closed, and bedroom door left open a crack to avoid the angry little squeal the knob was apt to make during the sensitive night hours. The shafts of moonlight drifting in the shutter slits barely reached the middle of the room, and the corner where the bed—that abode of love— stood was dark, except for the ghostly mosquito net looming over it.

How we loved that night! It had been so long for both of us, and now the storm my passion had unleashed on Carlotta's body had abated. I was a strangely different man and Carlotta, warm and clinging in sleep next to me, was a different woman. Her white shoulders, bare and fragrant, and the pillow on which her dark head lay looked gray in the dim light. I turned carefully onto my back, folding my arms beneath my head, and lay stiff and straight with my eyes fixed on the encasing ceiling of the *mosquitero*. If minds could not meet and find the peace they sought, bodies could certainly do so; there had been no antagonism between Carlotta and myself tonight. We had sought release. We had found it. And now what?

Yes indeed, this was a great life, I reflected with irony. And I was a great male specimen. Oh, quite a man. Just think! Only this morning I had been tortured by unspeakable pangs, I had been racked with pain and something like near insanity at the airport a few days earlier, I had been in the throes of some soul-wrenching inner disturbance. I had no faith to support me, no belief in myself, no anchor to hold down my senses. Liquor was no help, nor could drugs soothe me, and now—look!—I slept with a girl and everything was all right, the personal hell fires quenched for good.

It was true. After hours and days of misery I was finally at peace. I had no aches and pains.

A woman had cured me—a woman who meant nothing—and I marveled. I bent over Carlotta, put my palm under her firm breast, and my loins quickened as she moaned softly in her sleep and snuggled closer. I could hardly believe that my agony of mind and soul should be blotted away so easily. Why, if an orgasm was all that was necessary to relieve my deeply felt doubts and fears, I ought to hate and despise myself. What kind of man was I, then? Yes! An ugly smile came over my lips. Perhaps I was just another of those gross, insensitive men whose minds and hearts were nothing more than appendages to their genital organs.

I groaned at the thought, unfolded my arms, and tried to draw away from Carlotta's burning body. But she moved with me, wanting to stay close, her eyes blinking and glowing in the dark as I looked at her. We were body to body now, she moved again, and her cheek touched my throat. Then she put her head down on my shoulder with a deep, contented sigh. I didn't move, stayed as one with Carlotta, listening anxiously to the beat of my heart, waiting for it to suffer and rebel as it had, for the waves of revulsion to break over me like cold sweat. But it beat on quietly. No self-disgust, no anguish, simply peace, Carlotta's hair on my cheek, her face warm against my shoulder.

All right, then, I raged—that's what I am, a man of the flesh. So be it if it means being at peace and harmony with life and myself. If I must be ruled by my loins, let my whole life be ruled by them. If my heart and brain have proved so weak and vulnerable, and my loins so strong, then let them lead me. Let them take over. The genitals forever! Let them think and act for me. My mind needn't exert its feeble gray cells any more. My loins came first, as liquor did for Pierre. Go ahead, false friend Herbert, back in La Paz, you can fight my battles for me. And you, false priest, with your iniquitous "know thyself," your preaching is a mockery. I'll take Pierre's spiritual suicide and make life easier with my testicles the master of my fate and the captain of my soul.

So vicious was my anger that it made me shake all over and communicated itself to Carlotta. A loving woman, she took my trembling for passion and turned toward me with her lips soft, open, and imploring. I drew myself up, and all the wildness of my flesh and the fury of my mind came on the woman rolling voluptuously under me . . .

248

13

I Work My New Cure Hard; I Keep Daguero "Civilized"; The Fiesta at Rojas; The Truth About Carlotta; I Meet the Extraordinary Elena

Back in Rojas again I felt I was living in a frying pan on a stove burner always set on high heat. A searing sun dominated the whole world at this season, beating down so remorselessly that one's brains seem to boil and bubble in one's skull. Rising earlier and setting later, the fiery ball stretched and lengthened the daylight hours without end. From dawn until dusk every minute of the day was red hot, red hot, red hot. The nights were welcome, but far too short, changing only the color of the heat and hardly diminishing its intensity.

It was a familiar pattern to the people of Rojas. Endless rain before, endless heat now. They sweated and suffered and lived and worked on as usual. The *gringo* doctor did the same, but not at all in the same spirit. People still got sick, he tended to them as best he could, and that was that. At the moment things were fairly quiet in the village. Most of the *estancieros* had gone with their cattle to the Brazilian border. The few men who stayed behind in the *pueblo* slumbered through their days and lived through the nights, surviving as always, and leaving the women to their housewifely duties, heat or no heat.

Where there had at one time been broad puddles, murky pools, and stretches of mud (Had it *really* rained that hard?) in the streets of Rojas, the ground was now covered with a fine dry dust that no breeze ever stirred or disturbed. Time mixed with the heat and pressed heavily, achingly, bakingly, on Rojas. Most of the mosquitoes had disappeared. People still used their mosquito nettings at night, however, not so much out of force of

249

habit as a means of securing bedtime privacy. Few houses in the village provided separate rooms for each adult or even married couples in the family. The bedrooms were small, packed to capacity with cumbersome, piano-legged beds that left only a narrow space between them, something like a small army barracks.

During the day, the side curtains of each *mosquitero* were flung back over the top of its framework, shielding the bed with a canopy. At night the sides of the white netting were pulled down, the ends tucked tight under the mattress, and the occupants then considered their beds a private sanctuary. And so they were. Parents respected them as such—with reservations. Remembering their own hot-blooded youth, they were well aware of the adventurous temptations that have so much appeal to the young. So they took the precaution of putting a family chaperone in another bed in the same room with their nubile, eligible, and perhaps available daughters.

Lucinda was a lively and attractive brunette *muchacha*. Her father was fairly prosperous, his house spacious compared to most, and he could easily have provided his daughter with a room of her own. But he knew better, as Lucinda herself confided to me in loving frankness, so he had seen to it that she shared a room with an elderly aunt as her guardian. This would have clamped the lid on some girls for good, but not Lucinda. If her father was prepared to make adventure difficult, then she would accept the dare and outwit him. She studied her aunt's sleeping habits. She listened carefully to her *tía's* breathing and was able to gauge precisely the exact moment when the older woman's soft snores signaled complete unconsciousness.

Then Lucinda smiled, pushed aside her already loosened *mosquitero*, and quietly tiptoed past her aunt's bed to the door. Her firm fingers grasped the knob, turned it with breath-taking slowness until it would go no farther, then she pushed the door open a tiny, almost unnoticeable slit. Grinning with anticipation, she hopped back into bed and lay back watching the door through the untucked opening in the mosquito netting. By this time I had learned that the preparatory technique was the same for all girls expecting gentlemen callers. And all those planning to slip under a *muchacha's mosquitero* followed a similar strategy.

My eyes were keen enough now to have seen Lucinda's door open. For an eternal hour I had been standing outside the house in the shadows close to a huge tree trunk, which offered excellent concealment. It was dark, the moon would be late, but—damn it!—there was still a light on in another room in the house. I had made certain that Lucinda's father was away. It must be that her mother was still up, or perhaps a guest. I waited im-

250

patiently, wishing I could smoke, until the light went out and darkness swallowed everything except the promise of delights to come, my sure cure for everything these days.

Another few minutes to be on the safe side, then I removed my shoes, having already untied the laces so as not to lose time. Moving ahead cautiously, I went over the corral fence, jumped to the wall, stopped to look around, then went ahead cautiously along the wall to the door of the house. I stopped again and waited. There was still time to give up. Discretion was vital, and once in the bedroom anything could happen, but nothing had thus far in my many previous encounters, and Lucinda's burning glance on the plaza had assured me she would be passionate and accommodating. I felt for the door slit, forced it open a foot, squeezed through, and paused to listen. Even though this was old business to me now, my heart was pounding and the blood tingling in my face. Not a sound, the aunt's breathing continued undisturbed. Good. I sighed and gently pushed the door shut, leaving only a slit for an easy exit. A few more steps, quietly, quietly now, and I was by Lucinda's bed.

"Oh, Martin," she said, lifting the white mosquito net and murmuring in my ear, "you come so late."

"Shh!"

I put my hand over her mouth before she could protest further, put my shoes at the head of the bed—I must remember that place!—and dropped down beside the girl, bracing myself so the bed wouldn't squeak. When the palpitations of my heart had quieted, I undressed silently and expertly. A brief pause in which the *muchacha* and I reached for each other almost simultaneously, then not a word, not a sound, as I came over her.

Different places, different customs—even in love. Because they might be surprised or interrupted at any moment, I had long since learned that jungle lovers could not waste time on preliminaries and loveplay. They came quickly to the point, as Lucinda and I did. The massive bed betrayed no movement and, inside the *mosquitero,* we clamped on each other mouth to mouth so that no moan, no loving sigh, no unconscious endearment might alert the sleeping aunt. The houses here made perfect sounding boards, the partitioning walls going up only as high as the outside walls, and all the rooms communicating with each other through the triangular hollow beneath the thatched roof.

When I lay on my back again, shaken and spent, the *muchacha* turned on her side, rippling her hands over my hips as if in gratitude, and put her lips to my ear.

251

"I had the door open for you last night, too. And you did not come."

No use in answering that, since it was clearly better late than never. I turned my face to her so that my mouth was over her ear now. An easy lie would fix everything.

"The light in your father's *sala* did not go out at all."

"Papa left the village at noon yesterday." She paused for the fatal thrust. "And that night you slipped into Melitta's house and stayed there until late."

Ouch! I sat up with a start. "That's not true." How the devil did people find out about such things so quickly? "Really, Lucinda—"

She put her hand on my shoulder and pressed me back on the bed. Then she lay quiet, as if considering her next move, and approached my ear again.

"I could not believe it myself, *querido*. But it made me feel badly." She waited for further reaction, but I said nothing, and she went on. "They also say that you are *enamorado* with Carlotta in Santa Morena, and that she refused your love."

"I am not *enamorado* with Carlotta," I whispered in Lucinda's ear, sure I was telling her the truth. "Nothing like that."

As Lucinda turned this over, I leaned back and recalled with detachment the time I had stayed with Carlotta at her father's *estancia*. We had both slept late, and the morning was well advanced as I left her room. Rudolfo, who was pacing the veranda, came up to me immediately. He pointed to a horse in full harness hitched to a beam.

"That horse belongs to Señorita Carlotta's brother," he informed me. "He has just arrived." I looked at him blankly, and he went on the same serious vein. "It is quite possible he came to see his future brother-in-law."

I was still not wide awake, and it took a little time for his meaning to penetrate. "Are you joking, Rudolfo?"

"No, doctor. He is here and probably for a reason."

I winced. Carlotta was wily enough to have planned all this. She had left for the *estancia* knowing I would follow her, then she had alerted her brother, and—oh, no! I made a face, and Rudolfo smiled.

"There is a way out, I think. During breakfast, while all of us are sitting around the table, you can look surprised suddenly and say you have just remembered we must continue our journey to Rojas right away. That it is important for you to leave. It will work because, in the presence of her brother, the señorita cannot say anything to stop you, you see?" I nodded and he added, "I have already saddled the horses."

And that was just what I had done. Carlotta had been startled, but had not protested before her brother, as Rudolfo had predicted. At the time I had felt like a sneak thief, but there was neither remorse nor shame left in me. Nor, now that I thought about it, did I feel any particular satisfaction either. Why should I? A cure was cure, wasn't it? As I had promised myself, my emotions had become more primitive, my needs basic, and I was right down to the earthy fundamentals. Plain and simple spiritual suicide. Pitiful, amoral, contemptible—anything you want, but how it eased the heart and mind into blessed insensibility, a numb state without pain, sentiment, or any second thoughts.

So here I was lying beside Lucinda in the darkness ("At night all cats are gray . . ."), telling her cheap, glib lies, pouring on all the little *mosquitero* tricks I had learned from Rudolfo, my assistant—or was tutor the better word? Now Lucinda sighed, burrowed her face into my shoulder, and bile suddenly rose in my throat to choke me. I swallowed it down and sighed. I'd made my bed and, not only was I lying in it, but I was wallowing as well. I stared grimly into the darkness, my mind mercifully wandered and, as if looking through the wrong end of a telescope, I examined my last "grand affair" in the town where I was born.

This was no Lucinda, but a rare beauty with an ultrarefined background, a woman to set on a pedestal. I had been lucky that night. I had gone up to her, been accepted, and just like that had led the apparently unapproachable belle of the ball to the dance floor. How I had rejoiced in the almost imperceptible straightening of her neck, the trembling of her body, her flushed face as my fingers exerted a light pressure on her back and my knee touched her thigh for a meaningful second. Could I be dreaming? Could I be! Was I *the one* then? Unbelievable, I reflected, shrinking away from Lucinda's amorous embrace, that it was only a few short years ago. Why, looking back, it was another man in another life, not me.

Later on that evening, over the rim of a glittering wineglass, my eyes had put a question to my proud, susceptible beauty. I had no trouble reading my answer in her radiant glance. Yes and yes again. Oh, joy! And yet, getting up in the sobering hours of the morning, I had looked at her in the dim gray light and found a question in *her* eyes. I was worried now. Like Carlotta, she wanted a permanent attachment—something I dreaded. I could not declare a love I did not feel. We had both had a moment of divine, exquisite happiness. Why spoil it? To continue our affair, I explained, would only be trying to stretch a beautiful dream *ad absurdum*. One must know the right moment to say good-by then. She blinked back tears, and I quickly kissed her on the lips.

"This is the only way," I murmured with false humility, "that we will keep green the memory of our beautiful hours together, unshadowed by flaws and free of the recriminations that come to all lovers."

Oh, God! Just remembering those words turned my stomach. Lucinda clasped me again, and I could no longer retreat without falling off the bed. I was still a fool. Romantic memories of beautiful hours together with this one or that one had never helped me when I was most depressed. How often would I have thrown them all in the refuse heap, where they belonged, for a few minutes of real friendship, a companion that meant something. The hell with all of it! It was time to go. I sat up, but Lucinda pulled me down. She would have me again.

I had little left to give, and it did not take long. Lucinda seemed pleased, replete, and fortunately unaware of my exhaustion.

"The moon will soon be out," I whispered. "I must go."

Lucinda said nothing, then sighed. "Papa will be away from the *pueblo* for a few days. I will have the door open tomorrow night, *querido*."

I opened my mouth to speak, but thought better of it. What could I say? So I kissed her, dressed hurriedly, picked up my shoes, slid off the bed through the mosquito netting, and started out. Before I could stop her, Lucinda crossed with me silently to the door. She embraced me passionately, then flitted away. I took a deep breath, reached for the knob, and a shoe in my hand went clunk against the door frame! Damn! I stood motionless, holding my breath, ready to jump and run at the first move from the aunt's bed. But the old lady's snores continued unchanged and undiminished, the house was as quiet as before, and the only sound I could detect was a muted giggle from the direction of Lucinda's *mosquitero*.

Walking slowly on tiptoe, I edged myself through the door. Outside, I immediately cowered against the wall—the sneak thief again—and stooping low slid through the grass and under the fence. A dog barked from the patio, I tried to hurry, bumped my head, and almost cursed aloud. The dog came closer, barking his head off, and I jumped the corral and fled. I slowed my pace only after I had gained the middle of the street, and went another block before putting on my shoes. Back in my own house, I straightened out my clothes, adjusted my belt so it went through all the trouser loops, washed my face, and combed my hair.

I unlocked one of my suitcases, took out some money, jammed my black hat on my head, and grabbed my flashlight. I stopped at the window to look at the pale moon just climbing up from the edge of the night. There was still a fever to burn out of my system, and all the time to do it in.

Something jumped at me, made happy whimpering noises, and licked my hand.

"*Buenas noches,* you *ladrón.*" I patted Daguero's big head. "Where have you been? Not calling on girl friends, I hope," I said mockingly. "Do you want to go to Rojas' night club with me." He barked and wagged his tail. "Come on then! We'll see how our luck is."

Together we walked to the gambling house. Here, as I had counted on, some men sat around a lone table engaged in a noisy poker game as a number of younger men looked on.

"Ah, doctor!" said Don Bonaparte in cordial greeting. "We have been waiting the champion. Now we can begin."

I threw my money on the table, a stool was pulled up for me, and the cards dealt. Instantly I was absorbed in the game, Lucinda, my cure, everything else forgotten in the fascination of the cards and beating these old goats. Things went well for me right away. I managed to bluff Don Bonaparte out of a big pot and hauled the money in with loud laughter at his discomfiture. A little while later, however, I attempted the same trick, the tables were turned on me, and Don Bonaparte's booming shouts of laughter infuriated me. As we played on, he kept riding me, and I sat there tensely, biting my lip and struggling to hold in my anger. Sensing my mood perhaps, Daguero, between roaming the establishment, came back from time to time to put his head in my lap. But I pushed him away.

The stakes went higher—and so did my temper. I grabbed my cards greedily, and was guilty of all the faults I had found in other gamblers. My hands shook. I was waspish. I could hardly wait to outwit my fellow players.

"I raise you!" I declared defiantly. "See me. I have nothing in my hand."

"You don't fool me this time and I have you." The *alcalde* threw his on the table. "Doctor, your eyelids were twitching. They have all night every time you've held good cards." He raked in the pot. "You have the fever as never before, it seems, but you must do more than bluff."

By the time the game had ended, I had lost most of my money. I was furious at losing, and furious at myself for being such a poor loser. This was not my night. They never were any more. Nor the days either, I thought bitterly, as I left. The sky was gray now. I walked home with my head down, ignoring Daguero scampering ahead of me. I stopped at the door of the house. What was that? Oh, the horses. Already? It didn't seem possible, but the night was gone, used up in whoring and gambling. I went over to pet the horses. They passed the nights on the pampas and trotted in, always at the same time, for their morning feeding. I gave them some corn, hesitated, and looked at the sky. Might as well finish the night—or what was left of it—and ride off into the dawn, or perhaps infinity. It hardly mattered which. I saddled the smaller horse, looked around for Daguero, but hadn't the patience to wait for him. I jerked the reins and started out for the pampas.

It was still coldly moist and clammy, as the nights usually were, and I shivered in the saddle. I was lightly dressed and felt the cold, but not so much as my inner loneliness and the external loneliness of the limitless flatlands. How to describe the pampas which depended so much on one's mood wandering across them? Barren, parched, achingly sterile in the dry season; at other times a sea of grass as tall as a man, with beautiful, sharp blades, all with round, graceful stems. The pampas at sunset so wild, so exciting, so encompassing of all horizons north, south, east, and west. A region of endless fantasy, melancholy, or ecstasy, whatever the case might be. The pampas by moonlight a dream scene, the pampas in dawn's early light wide, awesome, frightening, and yet peaceful.

I rode out in the middle of the grasslands, pulled up my horse, and sat there for I don't know how long trying to sort out my emotions. Then I turned back toward Rojas, feeling better, and keenly aware of my surroundings. Back in the village I passed some women making their way toward a house before which was suspended a big, bloody side of meat as an advertisement for today's butcher. They nodded cordially, we exchanged greetings, and I rode on, my attention suddenly attracted by the disturbing sounds of loud and violent barking coming from behind that particular house. I circled around and came on a pack of dogs fighting savagely. Back hairs on end, lips curled in fearful snarls, teeth flashing, they leaped and lunged and had at each other ferociously. I watched them, startled and appalled, stiffening as I noticed my own generous, good-natured Daguero taking part.

It hurt to see him among that bestial pack, his mouth gruesomely agape, screams issuing from his distended throat as he battled his enemies alongside his friend Hordimales. Furious at his behavior, I lunged off my horse, catching my foot in the stirrup, and falling flat on my face. The horse shied away, but I was so intent on the dogfight I hardly noticed. I waded in among the animals frantically, yelling and kicking out right and left, finally succeeding in cutting off Daguero and Hordimales from the others. I was sweating all over and beside myself, blood in my eyes, as it were, and my brain in tumult. I slashed, yelled, and scolded. Hordimales slunk off to

Rudolfo's house, Daguero cringed before me, and I chased him back to the house.

He cowered on the doorstep before me, whimpering and scraping the ground with his belly, but I had no mercy. I dragged him inside by the scruff of the neck, lifted the horsewhip, which always dangled from my wrist on a loop when I went riding, and began to beat him. I was in a frenzy. Daguero howled only once, more in surprise than pain, as the whip bit into him repeatedly until I was covered with sweat and my arm limp.

"You stupid son of a bitch!" I yelled, blinded by my tears. "Can't you be civilized? Haven't I spent hours training you? Don't I give you everything you need? Goddamn you, I'm not going to have you behaving like those other brutes!"

Then I flung the whip across the room and struggled for breath. Daguero lay there stunned, then he crawled over to lick my hand, and I kicked him—kicked him so hard in the muzzle that his jaws clicked. I'm not sure what happened afterward, but I do know that Daguero disappeared and was gone for two days. The house was emptier than it had ever been, and I had plenty of time to reflect on my inhumanity. And yet—damn it!—he deserved the beating. How else would he learn? I didn't want a *gassenbub* of a dog. That awful word. I had heard it on my own mother's lips. It was what she had called me once with devastating effect, and the memory still filled me with horror. But no more than the whipping I had given my good Daguero. How I missed him!

I said nothing when Rudolfo told me that Daguero had come over to his place. He had gone under the bed there, stubbornly refusing to come out for food. Rudolfo expected some reaction on my part, but I kept my emotions under tight rein with an effort and only shrugged. On the evening of the second day, I could stand it no longer. I went over to Rudolfo's house, stood by the bed, and called the dog's name. He came part way out and stared up at me with so much love and hurt pride in his gaze that I was moved to apologize. Quickly I suppressed the feeling and refrained from touching him. Mustn't go soft in my discipline.

"*Venga*, Daguero," I said sternly. "Let's go home."

He came along meekly, and I was sure he had learned his lesson. For a whole week he was the model of obedience, coming to heel whenever I went out, and obeying every command as if he were my shadow. Then it happened. Rudolfo and I had had an emergency call outside the village. We were returning on horseback and were passing the shack of the *pueblo's* idiot. This pathetic mental defective had a wild brute of a dog, who was

257

touchingly loyal to his unfortunate master. The slack-eyed, drooling-lip man watched us go by, then, grinning foolishly, sicked his dog on us. Snarling, he went for Daguero and Hordimales, who flanked our horses. Both dogs eagerly accepted the challenge and advanced on the brute. Again I saw red, yanked my horse around, and spurred him between the two dogs and their attacker.

"Back, Daguero!" I shouted. My horse's momentum knocked Daguero head over heels, stopped Hordimales in his tracks, and even the idiot's dog backed away as I lifted my threatening whip. "Again?" I screamed at Daguero as he scrambled to his feet. "You dare do this again! Have you forgotten the last beating?"

"Doctor," said Rudolfo sharply, reining in at my side. "You must not do that." It was the first time he had ever raised his voice to me, and his vehemence shocked me. "A dog must fight, doctor. It is his nature."

"Not *my* dog," I snapped. "When I want your advice, I'll ask for it. Otherwise do me the favor of minding your own business!"

After this I curbed Daguero at every opportunity, jumping on him, and bringing him quickly to heel whenever a clash with other dogs seemed imminent. I broke his wild spirit with scolding and sarcasm; I made him behave and respond like a gentleman. I felt a savage thrill just standing at my door and watching Daguero prepare to mix it up with other dogs. I had only to put my fingers in my mouth, whistle shrilly, and he came trotting back docilely to the house. It gave me a curious sense of power with overtones of lust. As he obeyed my whistle so promptly, I could feel it emanating from my loins and ascending to my chest. Why, I was aroused as I would be with a desirable woman. The sensation would have made me smile, except that it frightened and horrified me. Over it all was the same disgusting pride I used to feel at the thought of a new conquest, wringing from a *muchacha* not only the exact location of her bed, but also her sub-missive promise to keep her *mosquitero* open.

Who was brutalized now? I wondered. I had better not let such feelings enter my professional life or I would become a most unethical doctor. And yet I had to have my way, it seemed, or perish. How carefully I observed Daguero as he slunk home one night to crouch in shame in the farthest corner of the room. A few minutes later Hordimales dragged himself inside panting heavily, covered with dust, and bleeding from several cuts about the head and neck. As he lay trembling on the floor, Daguero edged over and began to lick Hordimales' wounds lovingly. Hordimales submitted to Daguero's ministrations only until he had recovered enough to take care of himself. Then he bit and snapped at Daguero, and my dog retired to his corner with a beaten expression in his eyes. Apparently Hordimales had been ambushed by the pack, and Daguero, without whistling or threat on my part, had remembered his training. He had deserted his friend in dire need, and Hordimales had suffered in consequence. Strange, though, that both dogs seemed to know who was at fault.

My feelings of lust and power were overshadowed by discontent at this, but I quickly shrugged it off. What did I care about Hordimales so long as Daguero obeyed me? Perhaps something was wrong in my reasoning, but I wasn't going to dwell on it. That would mean going back on myself, all sorts of self-recriminations, and—no, that was out. If Hordimales was to be victimized, well, that was just too bad. Life was that way always. And certainly no one had ever taken any pains to bother about what happened to me.

*   *   *

Every Bolivian village had to have its own festival. Now the approach of its own long-awaited *Fiesta del Pueblo* transformed sleepy Rojas into an anthill of industry. The occasion had to have a reason, a theme, something to celebrate, an anniversary. Nobody seemed to know exactly when his village had been founded, but it was decided to make the *fiesta* a centenary commemoration.

In the few houses boasting foot-treadle sewing machines, women gathered around the ancient machines to stitch fancy silk dresses and mend costumes. Wives and mothers cleaned and pressed the suits and dark ties of their men; stores put on display merchandise that had been long stored away or recently delivered on urgent summons, and, bit by bit, the whole village quivered and awakened from an age-old sleep. Besides fun and good times, a *Fiesta del Pueblo* meant good business at higher prices and coveted cash on the line. It was a time when everyone demanded as his right things he had gone without all year. People from far and near suddenly wanted hardware, yard goods, and luxuries which were no part of daily living on distant *estancias*.

Barrels of potent *aguardiente* were set up to be tapped conveniently as the carnival spirit took over. Big bottles of brightly colored sweet soda came by *carreton* from the Brazilian border to be on hand for the villagers eager to spend their few, hoarded Bolivian *pesos*. Accumulating much-prized beer called for enterprise and secrecy. A number of shrewd citizens had succeeded in their efforts, a few cases of the cherished beverage had been delivered, and they had taken great pains to hide them from their neighbors. It was a matter of personal greed. Beer was a special way of celebrating the *fiesta,*

259

and it took a smart operator to get it. Once the festivities got under way, the smart ones broke open their cache, tenderly dusted off each bottle, satisfied their own palates—then down to business. In the heat of the carnival days, each bottle brought at least six or seven times its original purchase price, not counting a considerable fee for air freight.

"It is like liquid gold, this beer," Rudolfo explained solemnly. "No cattle are accepted in exchange. It has to be paid for in hard cash."

"Do you really like beer so much that you will pay a ransom for it?"

"Without it there is no *fiesta*, doctor. You will see."

I found myself involved in the preparations simply because the patio of my house was the largest in the village. I had been asked for permission to use it and could hardly refuse. Between a round of routine medical examinations and calls at Don Hector's house, where the uncomplaining señora waited to die, I gladly helped the school director and the teachers put up a big, rough stage back of my house. Now the play was the thing. In school the children concentrated on learning their lines, and outside they spent their time getting in the way of the workmen.

Even Rudolfo had a part. He became closemouthed, spending his time studying a few sheets of paper, and mumbling to himself as he cleaned syringes in the *officina* and, using a wooden spoon, worked the mixture of vaseline and lanolin which served us as a valuable ointment. Once I came on him looking at himself in the little shaving mirror that hung from the bamboo rod over my window. He had attached a frizzy white beard to his cheeks and looked like a juvenile Santa Claus.

"You must not see me, doctor," he said, hurrying off. "This is to be a surprise."

"It is," I assured him. "It is, Rudolfo."

How childish these people were in their enthusiasms. I felt quite detached from the *fiesta* at the beginning, but, as the stage began to take form in my backyard, I found myself caring and caught in the local contagion. Rojas buzzed and hummed. On the eve of the *fiesta's* official opening, the *pueblo* was thronged and more and more *carretons* were arriving. It was Santa Morena all over again as riders on mules, oxen, and horses streamed in. Standing in the open door of my house, Hordimales and Daguero on either side, Rudolfo and I watched the new arrivals. I knew many of them by name, and it was startling to watch men, known to be bitter enemies, embrace each other with a warm *"Querido hermano, amigo!"* Those who were close and fond of each other embraced in silence. They had looked forward for months to this meeting, and words were unnecessary.

260

"Aquí!" Rudolfo exclaimed. "Here come the men from Santa Morena."

The riders paraded by at a trot, waving and calling out greetings. Among them I was pleased to see Don Socrates, ever the imposing patriarch, and he came straight toward where I stood. He saluted and dismounted, thus indicating his wish to stay with me during the *fiesta.* I recognized this as a signal honor and appreciated the gesture. We embraced as father and son. It was as if we had never been separated. The old man was full of talk. The long, exhausting trip seemed not to have touched him. He was tough, leathery, and born to hard riding. He stretched himself out in the hammock and, typically, plunged into a discussion of the world at large and its relation to the province, what had been going on in Santa Morena since I left, and, particularly, the problem of *mal de caderas,* the pest that had lately attacked his horses.

As we chatted, the Indio woman who cooked my meals and kept house for me served us small cups of steaming, freshly distilled coffee. Silent, stone-faced, and uncommunicative, she slept in a hut in the patio and did her job well. I knew little about her. She was unobtrusive, she came, she went, she worked, and that was all. Now she held out the sugar bowl for Don Socrates. As I watched him automatically stroke with his spoon to clear away the dark, crawling crust over the sugar itself, I was amazed to realize how acclimated I had become to things that would have horrified most Westerners. That dark crust was alive. It consisted of hundreds of ants that had gathered on the sugar since the bowl had last been used. The ants had been spooned off then, returned en masse as always, and that was the nature of things. When Don Socrates had finished scraping off the writhing crust, there were still plenty of ants on the sugar. But they were small and nobody cared; the ants were black and so was the coffee.

"Have you seen Pierre lately?" I asked.

"A few times, yes. *Pobre diablo,* how he goes on living I don't know. Ever since he found out that he missed seeing you when you were last in Santa Morena, he has been worse. He told me to tell you that he is coming down to Rojas one of these days for a talk."

"I would like to see him, but I hope he doesn't try it again. He's in no condition to travel."

We talked on into the dusk under the flickering light of a kerosene lamp; it was a pleasant time, and it was good to be with my friend. But things have never been the same between us since he had brought up the question of Carlotta. Don Socrates kept looking around the house and fretting, and I was hardly surprised when he harked back to the old subject.

"*Hijo,* you still have no señora in your house, have you?" A thought struck him, and he beamed. "Then perhaps things will change since Señorita Elena is on her way here. *Si Dios quiere*—she will be the right one for you."

"And who is this Señorita Elena?"

"You will see for yourself, but, *hijo,* after my mistake in Santa Morena when I recommended Carlotta, I should not urge you. That one was a great disappointment. Still," he mused, "a man like you without a señora to take care of your house and represent you—no, I do not understand."

"Then I won't explain it again," I said with a smile. "But what's this about Carlotta? Why are you disappointed in her?" I was afraid I knew, and I put the question casually to disarm him.

"Ah, women!" Don Socrates made a face and threw his arms outward. "Doctor, as you know, I am Carlotta's godfather and her father is my *compadre* and dear *amigo.* But it is only in the last months that this *muchacha* has shown her true colors. Take just now, for instance." His thick eyebrows marched up and down on his forehead. "She insisted on coming to the *fiesta* in Rojas while her sister, the postmistress, is very sick. It is Carlotta's duty to stay behind to take care of the *officina,* as she has done in the past, but no, this time she absolutely refused. And there is no one else in Santa Morena who has the experience to act as substitute."

He stopped and clapped his big hands together in annoyance.

"I tell you this *muchacha* has nothing on her mind except men and pleasure. And, *por Dios,* doctor, I advise you not to confide in her any more. Why, during the whole trip Carlotta did nothing but talk about you and that woman in Paris. It shames me to say it, but Carlotta is no longer worthy of your confidence."

I was puzzled for a few seconds, then I unhappily recalled the little lie concerning the "other woman" that I'd fallen back on to evade Don Socrates' matchmaking in Santa Morena.

"Uh," I began hesitatingly, not wishing to make the old man any unhappier, "I have not confided in the *muchacha,* Don Socrates. You are the only person I have ever told about the woman in Paris."

"So?" he said seriously. "*Hijo,* I hope you do not believe for a single moment that one word you have ever told me has escaped my lips. I swear it! I give you my *palabra de honor* . . ." His eyes darkened and he passed a shaky hand over his weathered face. "Although it is possible I may have made some chance remark to Don Armando—*hijo,* you must forgive me."

The matter greatly upset him. I had to use effort and persuasion to calm him down.

262

"I'm sure you said nothing. I am sure of it. But what was that you said about Carlotta helping with the mail?" I said conversationally, struggling to get things back on a less emotional level.

"Ah, *sí, hijo*. You see, her sister has been sick off and on for the last year, and Carlotta has had to substitute at the *officina*."

I barely listened, then it hit me, and I sat up straight. Missing mail, the mystery of my expected letters that never came. By God, what I was thinking was pure melodrama, the case of the purloined letters, and yet it made sense. All the same, it was too late to make any difference. Still, for my own peace of mind, it would be well to ask. Don Socrates talked on, and I listened with half an ear as I wondered where Don Armando and his devious daughter might be staying in Rojas.

I had no need to go looking for Carlotta. Early in the morning, soon after Don Socrates and the son who had accompanied him set out for the *riña de gallos,* the inevitable cockfights, I was cleaning up as she came in. It had been bloody work extracting a splinter, deeply and inexplicably imbedded in an Indio rump, and there she came, swaying and undulating in a way to make the eyes pop. She was dressed with exaggerated elegance, probably in a manner she conceived fit to kill, but to my mind more like a little girl playing grown-up. Over her head, with its wide-brimmed, high-crowned hat, she balanced a bright parasol, and her smile was a smirk of self-satisfaction at the undoubted impact of her appearance. I finished drying my hands and Rudolfo, with a quick glance at her, shut the door of the consultation room behind us.

"Martin, *querido*," she said in a shrill, fluty voice.

How affected she was! That tone, the pose, the clothes. She was so changed that I was ready to forget my suspicions about the mail.

"Why, Carlotta, what's happened to you?"

"*Por qué?*" She batted her heavily mascaraed eyelids.

"Well—" I must watch my words—"you act so differently. That walk, the way you speak, everything. What's come over you?"

For an instant the false smile left her face, then again she was all oversweetness and light. "Nothing has happened to me, *querido*—nothing—*verdad*." She gave a brittle laugh. "What an interesting office you have here. May I look around?"

She tripped about the room on high heels, examining my drugs, bottles, instruments, and supplies with bright looks, giggles, and cries of feigned interest, which wouldn't have fooled Rojas' village idiot. With calculated suddenness she pirouetted so that her skirt whooshed about her and looked at me coyly.

"What is it, *querido?* Don't you like me to look like the great ladies of Paris—those ladies of whom you are so fond?"

She swept in close to me, trusting that I would find her irresistible, and it was then that her perfume assailed my nostrils. It was suffocating, in fact, so strong that it quenched my rising anger as water does fire. But that miserable mail business . . .

"Listen, Carlotta. I understand you've been accustomed to helping your sister with the mail in Santa Morena—is that true?"

She pouted, her expression turned sullen. She seemed to slump, and her four-square posture brought back the Carlotta that I knew.

"Yes, I have. It is true."

"All right," I said crisply. "Then have you ever had the occasion to handle letters I have written, or letters addressed to me?"

"I have," she said mockingly.

It was melodrama, I told myself, and we were doing the courtroom scene with me as the domineering prosecutor and Carlotta the stubborn, knowing witness. My job was to break her down; hers to resist.

"Do you mean that there actually have been letters for me?" She only stared at me. "Carlotta, you might as well tell me: what happened to my mail?"

"*Your* mail, eh?" She moved back of a table filled with medicines and turned on me, her smile changing to something like mirthless laughter, half hysterical, half childish triumph. She was Carmen at her worst, lacking only the rose between her teeth, only then she wouldn't have been able to spit her wrath at me. "So you want revenge. *Venga,* take your whip then and beat me, because I tore your love letters to bits. Hit me because I burned your precious mail. That woman," she said scornfully. "Why didn't she come with you? A *mujer* who lets her man go away by himself loses her claims on him, all her rights to him. You shared my bed and I was happy. During the rainy months, while you were gone, I suffered miserably, sustained only by the dream that I was in your arms. You were mine! It was only right that I destroy your letters and hers. In—"

"Carlotta," I interrupted.

"In Santa Morena, during the *fiesta,* I was so happy when you came. You were hard with me, cruel. I wept, ran away to *estancia,* then, then you followed me and I was happy again."

She paused to get her breath, her face flushed, her eyes stony, her chest heaving. It was a scene from a melodrama, all right—a bad melodrama with myself unwillingly cast as the heavy and Carlotta the ingénue. Again I

264

tried to interrupt, but Carlotta indicated she was not finished by brandishing her parasol like a spear.

"You shared my bed at the *estancia,* and I was at peace. Then the next morning you left me so coldly, you abandoned me without a tender word. And I could say nothing because my brother was there. All the while I thought it was because—because—" She couldn't find the words. "But you never came back!"

Affected, hysterical, melodramatic she might well be, but her accusations stung because they were damningly, humiliatingly true. Somehow I had to justify myself.

"I know, Carlotta. You see, I meant—that is, I didn't mean to—" I stammered and stumbled for a riposte. "All the same, y–y–you had no right to cut me off from the world, to destroy my letters like that. The mail is—"

"I had the right!" she screamed at me. "I did! *I did.* It was just and God Himself showed me so. Did he not kill the *mozo* who carried the mail? Was this not proof that God never meant for you to receive her letters?"

The business of proof and the mail carrier's death were beyond me, but I had to make her understand.

"If I have hurt you, I am truly sorry. It is not easy to say this, but, don't you see, Carlotta? It's not really the woman in Paris that keeps us apart, it's just that . . ."

My words trailed off because I couldn't bring myself to say that I did not love her. What could I say under the circumstances then? Shocked disbelief was reflected in her face, as if I had flung a pail of icy water at her or hurled her against the wall. She broke into wild sobbing, rushed around the table, and held out her arms beseechingly to me, the parasol dangling from her wrist.

"Martin, *querido.* Take me, for I am yours. I don't care about a wedding —I don't care if you do not want to marry me. And I am not afraid of my father. Let me be yours, let me stay, let me share your house, I beg of you."

The love she had for me, the magnitude of her offer stunned me. Carlotta, the daughter of a prominent citizen, a well-brought-up girl, was generously giving herself to me without benefit of clergy, security, or any guarantee. Mistress, living in sin, call it what you will, she was giving everything, and I could not have thought less of myself or my motives.

"Carlotta, I cannot express my appreciation, tell you how grateful and flattered I am, but, please, you must understand," I pleaded. "I am a *gringo* doctor, a stranger who does not belong here, who is only passing through. I am not worthy of you and—"

"No!" she protested. "It is *I* who am not worthy of *you*. Anyway, I don't care, do you hear?" A sob shook her, but she did not bother to dry the tears streaming down her contorted face. "I don't care about anything except being with you forever."

"You must listen." It was so hard to explain, and I felt lower than a crawling mongrel. "People like me live only a transitory life. Attachments of any kind are intolerable to us. And if there should be a child—"

"That is of no moment." Sniffling, she held up her head with pathetic dignity. "No woman of our region has yet urged a child upon a father who does not wish to be bothered."

She had me at every turn, set down, beaten—degraded. It was obvious, so terribly obvious, she must know it and still not care. It struck me then I did not know what love was, that I had never known and—shocking revelation!—that I was more of an incomplete man and unfulfilled person than I had ever imagined in my worst moments.

"That is very possible," I said dully, "and it is good of you to say so. But, all the same, for me, it would be quite a problem. I must be free, Carlotta. It seems to me that I have been trapped and behind bars all my life, and now I must be able to move at any time to any place in order to breathe." She eyed me blankly. It was all beyond her, and I tried again. "It is not your fault, Carlotta. It is all so unforgivably mine because I am a refugee and, yes, a wandering Jew who—" I broke off.

Carlotta stared at me, a little girl with a smeared face, a rejected child.

"Es una mentira," she said in a trembling voice. "You lie! You lie! You lie! That woman is still on your mind."

Crying pitifully, she snatched up her parasol, fumbled for the knob, and wrenched open the door. It opened so easily she all but fell over backward, then she stumbled over the threshold and fled. I stood there paralyzed for a full minute. Then I walked over stiffly to my supply cabinet, reached back of the big bottles for the whisky I knew was there, and swigged some straight from the bottle. It burned my throat, spilled down my chin, and slopped down the front of my shirt. I drank until tears came into my own eyes, but it didn't help and I felt nothing.

How could a man of stone have emotions?

* * *

I drank more than usual in the next few days. Not enough to get drunk or to affect my work, but enough to encase myself in a dull protective film. The *fiesta* had begun, although it was not yet in full swing, and at the

266

moment Rudolfo and I were idle between patients. He was slouching by the door and, behind him, I was checking over the medical kit I took with me on outside calls.

"I wonder," I heard him say to himself. "Can it be?"

"You wonder what?" I echoed him. "Can what be?"

A man and a woman on muleback were passing the house, and Rudolfo was straining his neck to follow their passage.

"I think that man is Don Ambrosio, Don Arnulfo's brother-in-law. If he is, then the woman must be Señorita Elena."

"Really." Having put Carlotta forcibly out of mind, I felt a little stirring of curiosity about this Señorita Elena. She was Don Socrates' latest candidate as my wife, and I might as well have a look at her. "I didn't know Don Arnulfo had a brother-in-law in the province," I said carelessly, coming over to join my assistant.

"They live in San Marequo, which is in another province. During the dry season, it's about a six or seven days' trip from here. The *muchacha* is supposed to be the most *bonita* in her *pueblo,* the prettiest girl in the village."

"Is she now?" I looked hard at the girl, who had stopped her mule just beyond to exchange greetings with a friend, and grinned at Rudolfo. "Go on! That woman in dark glasses with the painted lips and the dirty overalls? No, Rudolfo, one woman looks much like another."

"If that is the one, then she is beautiful." Rudolfo was not going to argue; he knew what he knew. "The señorita has been to school in the big city. Don Ambrosio is a rich man, and for many years his daughter has been educated in La Paz and in Cochabamba. I wonder if she . . ."

He left off as his interest was drawn to a little boy running hard directly toward our house. People gathered in knots in the street moved aside to let him pass, and I quickly recognized him as Don Hector's youngster. I picked up the emergency kit I had been working on.

"Trouble at Don Hector's house," I said to Rudolfo. "Get the big bag and follow me."

I clapped my sombrero on my head and, kit in hand, met the boy at the door.

"*Mamita!*" he gasped, fear and horror in his wide eyes. "Come quickly!"

I nodded, he darted off, and I followed with Rudolfo a few steps behind me. Daguero broke trail for us as we made our slow way across the crowded *pueblo* toward Don Hector's house, which was at the other end of Rojas. Don Ambrosio and his daughter reined in their mules to let us by, and I fancied that Elena was staring at me. She had no doubt heard of the *gringo* doctor, the bag I was carrying would make her certain of my identity, and I pretended to be unaware of her glance. A close-up view of her face, partly hidden by the dark glasses she wore, did nothing to change my original impression. Her hair was covered, and all I saw were reddened lips and dirty overalls. It pleased me to think her ugly, and I discarded the thought to concentrate on the emergency.

Undoubtedly the señora was dying—a wonder she had held out this long—and there would be little I could do, yet I had to go through the medical motions. Odd that the youngster had said *Mamita*. The chances were that he didn't know or hadn't been told that the sick woman was not his mother. She was much too old for that. According to local gossips, it was really her grandson. It seemed that a number of years ago Don Hector's daughter had fallen in love with a man who had a family in another province. She had died giving birth to their child, and Don Hector and his wife had then brought up the boy as their own. It happened often enough down here.

The house was on the outskirts of the village, where, fortunately, the *fiesta* spirit was not so evident as in the main part of Rojas. I ordered Daguero to wait outside, pushed the bamboo door open, and went in with Rudolfo. We found the poor woman lying on a big strip of cowhide, holding a piece of bloodstained linen to her mouth. As she struggled to restrain the cough that would only make her spit more of her life's blood, the wasted muscles of her face and neck stood out like cords. Under her faded yellow hair her skin was a pasty white with two spots of pink marking each cheekbone like bruises.

Don Hector was so preoccupied that he hadn't heard us come in. He was bent over, trying to clear away some of the blood his wife had spit up. But he was so excited that the cloth he was using shuddered in his shaky grasp, and all he was doing was smearing the blood all over her. As I hurried forward, he turned and straightened, relief flooding his face.

"Doctor—*gracias a Dios!*" He stumbled over to a stool, flopped down on it, and absent-mindedly began rubbing his thick curly hair with the blood-drenched rag he had been using. "You must help her," he pleaded, his eyes fluttering with exhaustion. "You must do something, doctor."

The hypodermic syringe was already in my hand. I took the woman's almost fleshless arm, and the limp, folded skin ballooned over the injected fluid as I thrust in the needle. The señora moaned in pain, mutely apologizing for her weakness with her expressive eyes. A few minutes passed,

268

Don Hector blinking intently to stay awake, and soon the señora's face relaxed. Slowly now, her hand fell away from her mouth, the bloody rag slipping away from her fingers. I motioned to Rudolfo. I eased my hands under her armpits, and Rudolfo picked up her legs. She seemed to weigh nothing at all, a hollow woman. We placed her gently on the wooden bed that lay along the wall, adjusting the hard pillow, and pulling the sheet over her inert body on the straw-filled mattress. I watched her closely. Rudolfo, well trained, began to clean up the blood. From a corner the little boy, who had reached the house before us, twitched and stared with enormous, worried eyes. On his stool Don Hector blinked on, his eyes never leaving his wife.

Now the old lady fell asleep, utter collapse evident in every gray contour of her face. I had seen death many times, but I would never become used to or hardened to it; the same with birth, except that was usually a happy occasion. So many times I had wondered what to do when there was nothing to do. She was beyond medical help, beyond prayer, and now in God's hands. Death was a mercy in her case, and yet . . . I looked around. The room was a grimly poor one, but spotlessly clean. These were good people who had little and made the most of what little they had. What better epitaph would anyone want? I would never deserve such. I looked at the old lady, then back at Don Hector. There was nothing else I could do to make the lot of either any easier. I hoped that the woman would not wake up, that she would die peacefully in her sleep.

I sighed, got up, and moved over to Don Hector. I put a gentle hand on his arm, feeling the tremor that went through his old body. His bony fingers closed over mine, and we looked at each other and let our eyes speak for us. Nobody moved as we left, the señora on the bed, Don Hector back on his stool, the little boy in his corner, all three were quiet and still. Somberly and silently, doctor and assistant walked back through the crowded, noisy *pueblo* to my house. What we had just seen and what we now felt clashed so achingly with the *fiesta*.

"She will not last long," said Rudolfo at the door.

"Yes," I said.

"It is just as well, I think, doctor."

"Yes," I said.

We sat around inside, not talking, not looking out the windows. I was tempted to have a stiff whisky, but I put it off and was glad, because soon we had some patients at the door. We worked on together as a team, speaking only when it was necessary, the noise of the carnival far removed from

269

us. It was in the middle of the afternoon that we had a caller who was not a patient. She was a *sirvienta* from Don Arnulfo's house with a personal message. Rudolfo called me over, the woman remained in the doorway, then in a singsong voice she delivered what she had so painfully memorized.

"The patron has taken the liberty to invite the doctor and his assistant, Don Rudolfo, for the *merienda* tonight."

"Very nice of the patron," I said, in no mood for a dinner invitation, "but I don't think I—"

"Of course, you will go," Rudolfo broke in. "We thank your patron and will be there."

The maid scurried off, and Rudolfo started to go back to my room.

"Now what are you up to?" I grumbled.

"I'm going to get your black suit ready, then I'll run home and see after my own clothes."

"I don't want to go, Rudolfo. I don't feel like it."

"Ah, doctor, you feel badly now, but tonight you will feel better. Where there is death, there is also life, and that is what we must explore. Besides, it is always pleasant at Don Arnulfo's and an honor to be invited to share a meal with his guests."

For the moment Rudolfo was the doctor, and I the patient. But I was glad I followed his prescription. When we arrived at Don Arnulfo's house, he, his señora, and his two sons were gathered in the *sala,* sitting around Don Ambrosio, who was in the hammock. Everyone stood as Rudolfo and I entered, introductions made, and two chairs brought for us. I had barely been seated before Elena's entrance jolted me to my feet again. She was enchanting to look at—so enchanting that I was nearly floored, and Rudolfo turned to me, as we were introduced, with a triumphant I-told-you-so gleam in his eye.

Nothing was left of the girl I had seen in worn, dusty travel clothes riding a mule. This was a strikingly dressed, tall, beautiful young girl of twenty-two, as I learned later. Her long, swept-back hair was coal-black, her eyes had a sparkling bluish sheen, and her lovely features combined sweetness, intelligence, character, and vivacity. All this was startling enough, considering the other young women I had met in and around the province, but it was her poise and *savoir-faire* that made me gulp as nervously as a schoolboy.

Dinner was served on the broad veranda that ran along the house on the patio side. The table was a big one, it was covered by a thick damask cloth, and at either end there were ancient, elaborate candelabra providing illumination. Truly a gala occasion for Rojas, and I was particularly flattered in

270

that Don Ambrosio and I, as the two guests of honor, were seated at the narrow ends of the table opposite each other. I wondered why Don Socrates was not present, and I heard that he had been invited, but had regretfully declined because of a previous engagement. Which was quite plausible inasmuch as he was a prominent man and much sought after.

Don Ambrosio, as was his right, dominated the conversation all through the soup and the delicious roast duck that followed. It was the best meal I had ever had in Rojas and, from time to time, I managed to interpose an admiring word to the hostess in praise of the perfection of her *assado*. Invariably, and with regal dignity, she countered my eulogy with excuses for the poverty of the meal. Custom demanded extravagant compliments. Good, bad, indifferent, or execrable, one always praised the food and hospitality one received, and the reply was always diffident and apologetic. So much so that I was often tempted to begin by saying everything was terrible, just to see how my host or hostess would react, but I had never had the nerve. So I said my piece, caught myself ogling the fair Elena, and was only brought back to reality by Don Ambrosio repeating something for the second time.

"I beg your pardon?" I said.

"It occurred to me, doctor, that you must often long for news of the outside world. If you wish some newspapers, I have some in my *maleta*."

To my annoyance Don Arnulfo undertook to answer for me.

"We have some newspapers only three weeks old. I have offered them to the good doctor, but he has shown no interest."

"Well, ours date only from last week," said Don Ambrosio. "Isn't that right, Elena?"

"*Sí*. You see," she explained for all the company, "San Marequo lies on the main route of the airplane to Brazil. Once a week the *avion* stops at our town."

"And what about during the rainy season?" asked our host.

"There is no difficulty. None at all." Don Ambrosio spread his hands, pleased as if he were responsible for the arrangement. "This *avion* is not dependent on the moods of the fickle Cordillera. It takes a route over the lower mountains, and the only time the pilot doesn't land is when our airstrip is flooded. That rarely happens. Very, very rarely."

I had heard of this main-line, lower-mountain route before. Ah, yes, I recalled it now. According to the false priest, it was on this run that Carlotta's father had given his warped version, to all who would listen apparently, of my fee for taking care of the late *El Chileno*.

"Elena has just come back from La Paz over Cochabamba with the *avion*," said Don Arnulfo, wiping his fingers on his napkin. "She is studying to be a nurse, doctor. What do you think of nursing as a career for our young woman?"

"A wise, an excellent choice," I said, disliking the man more and more. "I can't think of a better one."

"*Sí*, but not better than being a wife to a good man certainly." He chuckled and turned to his niece. "*Hija*, how much longer must you study at the hospital."

"Half a year, *tío*."

"Ah, so. You see, doctor, if you need an *enfermera*, an excellent nurse, here she is."

Elena looked down at her plate, blushed, and seemed all the more lovely to me. Our hostess tactfully changed the subject, spoke of the *fiesta*, then dropped her little bombshell.

"There is going to be a special surprise tonight," she announced with pardonable complacency. "We are going to open a can of fruit."

Since canned fruit was as much a gold find as beer in the area, this was greeted by exclamations of astonishment and delight in which I shared. The can itself was brought to the table with considerable flourish and pomp, and the señora produced an heirloom silver ladle to dip up a smooth, golden, peach half, dripping with syrup, for each guest. At one time I would never have imagined myself thinking such a simple dessert a delicacy, but now, like the others, I ate mine slowly in order to savor that delectable sweetness as long as possible.

The can was a large one and now our hostess, greatly daring in her generosity, asked if anyone desired another half. No one said anything, and the señora looked eagerly at each face around the table. Alas, none of us had the temerity to flout convention and be truthful. I was bursting for more of that sweet goodness, and my expression must have given me away.

"What about you, doctor?"

"No indeed, señora," I said with polite deprecation. "Who could indulge further after so magnificent a meal?"

The señora dropped her exquisite pretense and breathed again. After all, one could not always trust foreigners not to abuse one's hospitality. I knew exactly what she was thinking and, again, I wished I had the nerve to cross her up. We moved on to tea, *cigarillos*, and the superb meal was over. Automatically I launched into the expected compliments, a flattering finale at the excellence of my hostess' banquet and the superiority of her table.

Flattered as she was, she fielded my compliments as automatically as I had given them, murmuring the customary apologies for the inferior fare and the well-known faults of cooks these days. It was a form of ping-pong etiquette with each of us giving little attention to the way the ball bounced.

After we left the table, Don Ambrosio resumed his place of honor—this time in the hammock spanning the veranda—while the others pulled up stools and formed the usual half-circle around him like pupils at the feet of the maestro. The talk, as always, was about towns, villages, personalities, and politics within the province, which I had begun to think of as "the world," and everything was local, the community, what this one said, what that one did. The exchanges flew back and forth between the firefly tips of cigarettes glowing in the darkness, and over all the voice of Don Ambrosio, the oracle and the sage.

I felt restless, out of things, and out of sorts. I joined in the men's discussions, but it was Elena I wanted to talk to, and I found myself listening to the chatter of Elena and her aunt. I had liked and been drawn to the girl on sight, and I wanted her to like me because I was "different" as she was "different." And I wanted her to be impressed. But the few times I tried to converse with her, it went flat, never lasting more than a sentence or two. I was surprised, then, at the ease with which Rudolfo, who had said little during the meal, made conversation with her. Soon they were deeply involved in nursing problems and the hopeless case of Don Hector's wife. I was jealous, of course, but refused to admit it.

The evening wore and droned on. I took less and less part and interest in the proceedings and, finally, I jumped brusquely to my feet and said I had to go, giving work as my excuse. I thanked my host and hostess again and said how delighted I had been to meet Don Ambrosio and his charming daughter. Rudolfo got to his feet, wavered, and—damn him!—quickly obeyed me when I urged him to stay on. I hurried away, lonely, discontented, and angry with myself. It was only natural for me to be attracted to someone like Elena (and unnatural for her not to be attracted to me, of course), but I didn't like it. It was weakness. I was safe with the other muchachas because the attraction was only a sexual one. With Elena it was that, very much so, and also much, much more. All in all, let's say it was just as well that she didn't seem to like me.

As I went into my house, Daguero lunged at me with his usual noisy devotion, but I brushed him off, went into the consulting room, and threw my hat on the table.

"All right, all right, you love me. That's because you're an animal and

273

don't know any better, old boy. Don't you know that people like me are only strong so long as they don't care about anyone or anything? That's a fact, Daguero. When they are touched, reached, moved—put it any way you wish—they become weak and restless. So nothing, no one must touch me too closely, old fellow, not even you. The weakness is one thing, but I know just the thing to cure this restlessness of mine."

I removed the jacket of my good suit, pulled my belt from my trouser loops, and mechanically began to wind it up. I extracted all the jingling coins from a pocket, slipped in the belt, took off my shoes and socks, then put my bare feet back into my unlaced shoes. All set now? No, one last, important thing. I changed my white, dressy shirt for a dark one. I had to be just as gray as all the gray cats wandering in the night. Daguero whimpered and pawed at the door. He wanted to go out; he was restless, too, and had his needs. Perhaps he knew of a bitch in heat. The thought made me wince, but what was a thought? It came, lingered briefly, and went. Or did it?

"Not you, Daguero. You stay home like a gentleman. As for your master, he better hurry. The moon will be out soon, and he might miss his cure. You wouldn't want that now, would you?" I opened the door cautiously, grabbed his collar before he could break out, and threw him back into the room. "And you know what his cure is, don't you, Daguero? It's Melitta or Lucinda. They're the only cures for a 'mosquiteer.' All for one, and one for all—and all that." I patted him, shut the door on his whimpering, and started for the cure-house. "What a life, eh? What a life!"

14

*Elena Is Understanding—Too Understanding; I See
Pierre for the Last Time; Daguero Dies—and Part
of Myself; I Retreat to Santa Morena*

I regarded the *fiesta* as a disinterested onlooker, until it came to my house
and all but overwhelmed me. A crowd milled around the place and jammed
my patio for the opening night of the great show. The actors were tradition-
ally nervous and fidgety, frantically adding last-minute touches to their
costumes and make-up, worrying over their lines, staring into space, and
moving their lips in anguish. No footlights or spotlights were available, of
course, but one of the schoolteachers brought over Rojas' only gasoline
lantern. Gleaming like a meteor, it hung from the middle of the rafter that
also served as a rod for the makeshift curtain, illuminating the stage to a
degree, as it cast patches of harsh brightness and black shadow, but actually
blinding both actors and audience.

Mozos had hauled benches and stools from nearly every house in the village, placed them in uneven rows before the stage, but there were not nearly
enough, and standing room was at a premium. The waiting audience was
more excited than a select, sophisticated assembly in a big-city theater at the
première of a glamorous play by a renowned author. This excitement was an
electric, tangible thing. Everyone buzzed with anticipation. Since, almost to
a man, every spectator was related to at least one of the actors, much more
was involved than mere local pride in the big show. The onlookers all had
a personal stake in its success; they were like a group of parents, cozy,
intimate, and self-important, watching their children perform before the
public.

The lively scene so fascinated me that, for the time, I nearly forgot my own troubles. I leaned against a post on my veranda, smiling as a mother tried to get her sobbing child into costume, laughing as two racing dogs bumped into a bench, overturned it, and sent its occupants head over heels, and musing as two lovers walked apart, trying to pretend that neither cared a whit for the other. The women in the audience wore their best clothes, with fine black shawls over their heads and shoulders. Their male escorts walked beside them in heavy dignity, showing how uncomfortable they were in their good clothes and on their best behavior. At the far end of the patio, enterprising citizens sat behind little tables under the trees hawking soft drinks with a base of *essencia de grosella.* (This currant juice was mixed with water from the *currichi.* It was a popular drink, but I had sampled it and found it palatable, but too sweet for my taste.)

The men of the village, bathed, shaved, pomaded, and slickly dressed, were almost unrecognizable to me. They laughed at and teased their friends just in from the roads and pampas, who hadn't had time to scratch off their beards, change clothes, or even wash their grimy faces. These rugged fellows joked right back. It was *fiesta* time, and nobody cared. Scraggly mustaches bristled; deep-set, hooded eyes gleamed with *alegría;* here shining white teeth shone in wide grins, there pitifully toothless gums gaped in merriment, and everywhere joy and mirth bubbled over.

The minute I saw Elena arrive with her uncle and aunt, I dashed over to greet them, inquiring politely about her father. It seemed that Don Ambrosio did not care to watch the show; he was at a poker game somewhere. I hurried to offer stools from my house, since most of the seats had been taken, but the uncle and aunt had already gone on, and Elena, refusing to meet my eyes, didn't seem to hear me. The hell with her! I thought. Miss Know-It-All. Here I go out of my way to be courteous and considerate . . . Give me Melitta any day in preference to this touch-me-not ice queen.

A bell jangled, tinny and timid, and an expectant hush came over the crowd. Nervous hands jerked futilely at the curtain, it finally stuttered open, and schoolchildren, standing in ragged rows on the stage, broke into the national anthem to the accompaniment of two *guitarras.* The audience jumped to its feet and stood at grim attention. The participation of the smaller schoolchildren ended with the singing of the anthem. As soon as it was over, they scampered off stage like a herd of young calves seeking their mothers.

Just as Rudolfo came out of my house, white cotton beard in hand, to take his part in the play, the school director took up a position on stage directly under the hissing gasoline lamp. He was a smug, stuffy young man, who

276

knew he was far too good for the likes of a dump like Rojas, and being sent out to the jungle, as a federal employee, to "organize and improve" the hopelessly primitive school system, had soured him. Now he duly waved the flag. *Patriotismo* and *Dinamismo* were the words that figured most prominently in his dull, platitudinous speech, emphasizing them each time by sawing the air with his arms. It was patriotic propaganda, nationalism rampant again, even if in a small way, and I was glad to note the crowd's increasing restlessness and resentful impatience.

They knew they were being imposed on and patronized, and I felt like applauding these people. The spirit of rebellion, muttering, and shifting about on the benches, crept forward from the back rows, become more pronounced and articulate as it traveled, and I wondered if they would boo the man and shout him down. The school director was no fool, however. He was doing his job and, determined to give his party-line speech, as it were, in full, he promptly accelerated his delivery until his words were all but unintelligible. As he finished, he was duly applauded for hurrying official matters painlessly along.

The little bell raised its thin, tinny note again, and the crowd quieted. Again the curtain p-p-parted and, after startled silence, laughter rang out. Rudolfo had been caught unprepared. He was in the middle of the stage, struggling with his recalcitrant beard and staring at the audience in horror. I was laughing as hard as the others, when someone plucked my sleeve and whispered urgently in my ear. Wedged in as I was on both sides, I could hardly move.

"*No diga*," I said in apology, pushing through the rows of stools and benches. "There is work for me at Don Hector's."

No one paid any attention. I heard shouts of laughter as I went into the house, and I assumed Rudolfo was still trapped on stage. This time, at least if it was what I expected, I wouldn't need my trusty assistant. I got out my small emergency kit and hurried off through the village, coming on the frightened *muchacho* who had just alerted me, worriedly returning to summon me a second time. He ran back as he saw me, and I followed at a run. I was breathless when I reached Don Hector's house and, as I had feared, I was too late. (Who can race certain death?) The señora's waxy face was a fleshless skull on the pillow; her hands, gaunt bundles of thin bones, were folded on the blanket over her chest, peaceful at last. Candles burned at each side of the bed, and the room was as solemn and quiet as a church.

I turned away from the dead woman just as Don Hector came forward, his tear-stained face working in a heartbreaking attempt to smile the usual polite greeting.

"Doctor, in spite of all your labors and all my prayers, she is gone. She has left her old husband *solito* with nobody but the little *muchacho* she always loved as her own." He took a deep, rasping breath. "After fifty years in my house, she has left her *viejo*, her ancient one."

He went on in this vein for a while. Then he tottered across the room for something, and I sat in the corner in compassionate silence watching him gulp from a bottle. Don Hector was known as a good man who took everything just as it came. Death was making him do things he had never done before—drinking *aguardiente*, complaining about his hard life, giving up because he had lost what he loved best. Liquor helped a little when desperation gnawed one's soul, but for this good man to—I stiffened as a dark presence filled the bamboo doorway. Malvenido! Death's harbinger was a little late this time.

He posed in the entrance and I noticed that, in spite of this being the hot dry season, he still wore his sleeveless fur jacket. A strange, bloodless man, this Dr. Malvenido, who seemed to feel the heat no more than the cold. Now the *curandero* moved slowly across the room to the dead woman's side, paused, crossed himself, then went to lay a gentle hand on the shoulder of the stricken husband.

"*Amigo,*" he said, "it was the will of God, and no man could have changed it."

He spoke in the same hair-raising, crackling voice, but without resentment or curiosity. Although he did not once look my way, he held no brief that the *gringo* doctor had been called in rather than himself. I could do nothing further. Don Hector seemed to find relief in the *curandero's* soothing words, and I slipped out. Just beyond the door, I found the little boy sobbing against the wall of the house. I murmured my sympathy and reached out for him, but he shrank from my touch and ran inside.

Foolish to let this thing bother me so. She never had a chance, and I knew it—everybody knew it. But what good was that to poor old Don Hector, abandoned, alone, and now finished with nothing to live for? What had the great, experienced *gringo* doctor done for him that Dr. Malvenido couldn't have done? Nothing! It was the will of God, and no man could have changed it. I walked slowly through the empty village, so low that I felt unable to face the festivities in my own patio. If I could just find a quiet place and sit awhile . . . My steps turned to Don Arnulfo's house, I went up on the dark veranda, over to the beckoning hammock, and sank down gratefully. As my eyes became accustomed to the darkness, I saw a gray figure at the table.

"*Quién es?*" I said irritably, preparing to go.

"Don Hector's wife—did she die?"

It was Elena's soft, cultured voice, and I jumped to my feet.

"Señorita, what on earth are you doing here? They'll miss you at the *fiesta*."

I saw her shrug carelessly.

"Did Don Hector's wife die?" she persisted.

"Yes. Yes, she died."

Neither of us spoke for a few minutes. Then, almost in a whisper, she said, "Would you like to talk about it?" I said nothing. "Please, doctor. I am interested. I want you to talk about it."

"What is there to say? The señora never complained, neither did Don Hector. When the disease ate up one of her lungs and the blood came vomiting out of her mouth, she still managed to smile in gratitude for my efforts, sympathy, and friendliness. The señora tried never to give any trouble. An exemplary patient always—the kind that breaks a doctor's heart and makes him realize his own futility."

I stopped, afraid I had said too much, but it was good to have someone like Elena to talk to. In spite of myself, I went on

"A doctor studies so long and thinks he has learned and knows so much. But he knows next to nothing. The irony of it is that I worry about the quacks, who are so certain they know everything and can work miracles. But what good am I? What was I able to do for this woman? And what can I do to make life easier for the poor old man who is so alone now. Doctor! What a title," I sneered. "It's at times like these that I want to chuck the whole practice of medicine, throw everything away, and go hide in the woods like an animal."

Elena waited a little while before speaking.

"I understand that Don Hector's wife knew her end was near. And she was not unhappy; she never was. Why should she be? She and the *viejo* lived long, happy, fruitful lives together, so long as God permitted. Now God has taken her, and her husband will finish his time in her memory until he, too, goes to Paradise and joins her. That is life, doctor. It has always been life; it will always be life."

Her words fell on me like a blessing. I had to hear more.

"Please go on, Señorita Elena. Talk to me. It is good to listen."

"But you know all these things."

279

"Maybe, but I need to be reminded of them again. Talk to me."

"What can a simple *muchacha* say to you?" she said, suddenly hesitant and shy. "You are learned, well educated, and have seen the world. Still, if you will let me, I would like to speak of these quacks. My countrymen know the limitations of these *curanderos*, and these so-called doctors know them just as well. If we call them in, it is not really for their medical opinion. After all, in the case of a sick child or whatever, more often than not the mother or the grandmother knows what to do as well, or perhaps better, than any *curandero*. So it is not for that that they are needed. It is because the *curanderos* have learned to face death calmly. They are less frightened of it. And so the weak ones among us—and who is not weak where death lurks?—call on them in order to have someone to lean on in times of desperation and despair."

Her words, her cool, clear logic astonished me. "My God!" I exclaimed. "Did I have to come to the wilderness to find a wise, intelligent woman?"

Elena's answer astonished me even more. "As a *muchacha*," she said, "your words have pleased me. But, as a *hija* of my land, I consider myself insulted!"

"I am sorry. That was not my intention. Far from it. But you are so different, Elena. Why, you think, have thoughts, use your mind."

"All *muchachas* think, doctor," she said firmly. "Perhaps you have been misled because you have never given the ones you know an opportunity to speak their thoughts." Her bluntness seemed to embarrass her, and she turned and called over her shoulder to a *sirvienta* sitting in a dark corner. "*Hija*, come; let us go back. My shawl, please." She took it from the maid, put it around her, and they started down the steps. "It has been interesting to talk with you, doctor. Good night."

*   *   *

I found Elena both troubling and enlightening. On the evenings that followed, I made it a habit to appear at Don Arnulfo's house after dinner. Elena was always sitting on the veranda and, ever so casually, I went up to sit by her and talk. It meant more to me than I realized. I wanted to be careful not to spoil it. Above all, I wanted Elena to like me.

"You know," I began, one night toward the end of the *fiesta,* "yours is a wonderful country. I've been living here now more than a year and, except for inquiring whether I was married, not a single person has ever asked me a personal question. I wonder if it's because the people are apathetic or just not interested. What's your opinion, Elena?"

"I think you must know the answer. The people are not apathetic and they *are* interested. They know you. Even I know things about you, Martin. And I don't live here."

It was the first time she had called me by my first name since we had met. I was pleased.

"What do you know about me, Elena?"

"Enough. How you treated *El Trimotor* and the story of *El Chileno*'s fee, according to Don Armando, Carlotta's father."

The mention of Carlotta's name seemed to trouble her. She had been about to add more, but now she held back. But how would she have heard about *El Trimotor,* I wondered, unless . . .

"The priest. You have spoken to the priest perhaps?"

"*Sí.* I have talked with *El Cura.*" She waited for me to ask further, but I held my tongue, and she went on. "Out here news spread like ripples after a stone is thrown in the water. My uncle wrote to me when you helped cure his facial palsy. And they discussed it all over the province after you examined the schoolchildren—it was a fine thing and not only because it made both teachers and pupils feel more important. I also heard that you worked over and stayed with the carpenter's only child all night until—until it closed its eyes forever. And the woman in Paris, I have heard about her. And Melitta, too, on the night of my arrival."

All this was startling, bewildering, and, the last, acutely embarrassing. "I can't get over it, Elena. How can you people know everything so quickly while I hear nothing?"

"Ah, Martin, it is not hard to explain. There are few of us out here and we know each other so very, very well because, because—well, we are all so much alike."

"You are wrong. I have met no one else like you."

"I have had certain advantages, that is all."

A gleaming stripe of white light on the horizon caught my eye. The moon was rising, such a beautiful moon . . .

"It is much more than that, but I was thinking about Europe when I brought up your wonderful country before. It is so different there, the very atmosphere, the air one breathes—you cannot imagine. In the Old World, such as it is, a man no sooner goes some place than he needs a permit to stay, a permit to walk, a permit to eat, to sleep, to—oh, for everything! He is constantly being forced to give some vicious minor official his life's history, religion—it's all so complicated and horrible. And to think that only last month I was permitted to vote in the elections here when I'm not even a citizen."

"Why not?" said Elena warmly. "You're a member of the community,

281

aren't you, and an important one? And you must have paid the road-building tax, or you wouldn't have been allowed to vote."

"I did indeed," I acknowledged. "But what really intrigues me is the question of religion. In Europe millions of people—most of them Jews like myself—are being persecuted because of their religion, and many will be killed for the same reason. Here, nobody has ever mentioned religion to me, although I suppose some people probably have behind my back. But only my poor friend, Pierre, has ever said anything openly and, typically, he is a European."

"What is there to say about religion?" said Elena. "Tell me, Martin, do you believe in God?"

"Why do you ask?" I said stubbornly.

"Because here we feel there are only two kinds of religion. There are those who believe in God, and there are those other unfortunates who cannot believe in God."

"Put that way it sounds so simple. Like last Easter when *El Cura* asked me to accept the honor of being a standard-bearer in the procession. I told him I wasn't a Catholic, and he replied that it made no difference."

Elena's silence led me to believe that she agreed with the priest. I was about to ask what she thought of his being a so-called "false priest," but I could guess what her answer would be and had no wish to sour our conversation.

"When did you last see *El Cura?*" I said now.

"A few weeks ago. He usually stays at our house when he is near San Marequo."

"I miss him," I said. "He hasn't come to Rojas for months now, and I wondered why."

"Probably because smallpox broke out on an *estancia,* and he stayed there with the people. Insisted on it."

"Smallpox? A real outbreak? My God, here I am health officer of the province and I never even heard a thing about it."

"It's impossible for you to know everything that goes on in these vast regions," she said gently. "Besides, you are bound to the *pueblo*—your duty is there—while the priest is at liberty to go wherever the spirit moves him."

"A remarkable man," I said thoughtfully. "Brave, fearless, and selfless. I wonder what made him, well, come to this country, live the life he lives, and dedicate all his waking hours to others."

"He *is* an admirable man and a wonderful one," she said warmly. "He's been all over the world, but as to why he came here—it's hard to say. But he did say something to me once. I could only sense what he meant, but perhaps you will understand. I remember his words well. 'There was a time,' he said, '—and I was a young man then—when the world had no frontier left for me to dream about crossing. But here, in these regions, I make my own frontiers every day.'"

She paused, and I did not know what to say. I understood the priest— and I didn't.

"*El Cura* has breadth, vision, and humanity. It was he who persuaded Papa to let me go to the city and study to become an *enfermera*. He knew what it would mean for the people—and to me—to be a nurse, to be useful. You may not know it, Martin, but *El Padre* is very fond of you, Martin. And not just because you helped save his life. He says that you are like him, that somehow he recognizes part of himself in you." Again Elena paused, this time taking a deep breath as if to fill herself with courage for what she was about to say next. "He is so very much concerned about everything people say about you. Lately he has heard about this program you have for disciplining your dog, making him a gentleman, not allowing him to fight as dogs will. And he said to me: 'Poor dog, poor doctor . . .'"

Damn it! Why didn't people mind their own business? What I did with Daguero was a matter that concerned only dog and master.

"Come with me for a few minutes," I said, brusque and cold. "Let's walk in the moonlight."

"If you wish, Martin."

As we walked through the patio, we heard the twanging of a guitar and the shrill wail of a lilting flute from somewhere.

"Ah, the *baile* in the subprefect's house has begun," I said. "Would you like to go?"

"Not particularly. I don't feel like dancing."

She was so patient, so understanding, so proper that I was annoyed.

"Won't there be talk if you're not there?" I said sarcastically. "Since the people here seem to know everything, they must know you are with the *gringo* doctor."

"I don't know what people will say. I know I do enjoy more freedom from gossip than most. That is because I have lived for years in the city, and I am no longer so well-known to them as they are to me. But, yes," she said bitingly, "some will no doubt say what you are implying: that Don Ambrosio's daughter has added herself to the string of women who open their doors and lift their *mosquiteros* so eagerly to the doctor . . ."

Now she infuriated me for being so all-wise, so all-seeing, so innocently ruthless in exposing my weaknesses.

"There isn't the smallest chance of their being right, is there?" I sneered.

283

"Martin, Martin." Elena sighed. "Why do you try to hurt yourself in my eyes so much when it is only yourself you hurt? You know there is not the smallest chance."

"I wish there were," I said apologetically.

"Perhaps I would, too, in different circumstances. But I do not give myself or my love lightly. You are too hard on yourself, and you are hard on us here because of that. What did you expect to find when you came to Bolivia, doctor? A second Europe, cultured people, the same degree of civilization you were accustomed to in your former home."

"Elena, please—I do not want to discuss it."

"But I do, Martin. I know you have suffered as a Jew and a refugee. I know that you have had to stand and watch as your life, your career, your future were smashed to bits. But people suffer here, too. You have seen them living in hovels, poor, illiterate, badly cared for, and with no future— not even a present—to speak of. It must be that your problems have been so personal, so great, so overwhelming that you could see nothing else. You have worked hard here, saved lives, done much good. But you have not given of yourself. You have met our people at your level, not theirs. Oh, it is not your fault—and maybe it is true that you do not belong here— but who is to say where one belongs? I wish I could—I'm sorry, Martin, if I've been rude. But I do like you and—do you understand what I've been trying to say?"

"Yes," I said thickly and then, because I saw everything with a sickeningly terrible clarity, I added, "no."

We were at my house now. We circled around to the garden and came on two chairs close to the trunk of a big palm tree, back of which were shadowy shrubs. As we sat down, I heard a pattering of feet and a shadow, blacker than the darkness, hurried down the path.

"Daguero," I said. "Good dog. Good friend."

"Come over here, Daguero," called Elena. He put his great head on her lap, and she scratched him between the ears. "Such a big dog." She sighed again as she scratched. "Poor dog," she said sadly. "Poor doctor."

Again her sympathy irritated me. I wanted to say something bright, ironic, and cynical, but this girl was so fine, so brave, so warm, so worthy of a good man, which—let's face it!—I was not. Her sad tone touched me, as I let flippancy go hang, and, for all that lay unspoken between us, I felt reassured and a little more buoyant. We were kindred spirits.

The bright moon climbing high over the flaming horizon and up into the heavens, until silvery light flooded the patio and gardens, splashed grass, trees, flowers, everything with a ghostly loveliness daylight could never approach. The slender palms cast long shadows on the earth, and I shuddered. It was an unearthly beauty, indescribable.

Suddenly Elena leaned forward tensely, her arms out toward the moon.

"Look, Martin," she said in an awed, hushed voice. "This is what drove me back here. When the men in the city asked to stay there, when the *muchachas* begged me to stay on, I wanted to tell them about this moon and our pampas—about this." She waved her arms, eloquently, ecstatically. "But I couldn't find the words to express it." Now her words were a faint whisper. "And I can't now."

"No one could find words for this," I murmured.

The moonlight blinded me, the cool, clear, sweet air exhilarated me. Suddenly I wanted to cry.

*   *   *

It seemed that no sooner than I had said hello to Elena than I was saying good-by, though, regrettably, I was not to deliver my good-by personally. Knowing her, talking with her, being with her was an invaluable experience. The days she was among us slipped by. Other people were interested in our budding friendship, and no one more than Don Socrates, who might have hatched the whole infertile egg, but he never prodded, never said anything, but looked at me with inquiring eyes. Then one morning I learned indirectly that Don Ambrosio and his daughter had left Rojas. Just like that! It took my breath away. I missed Elena. She had taught me so much, and I couldn't help wondering what kind of impression of me she had taken with her. But it didn't bear thinking about.

When I remembered some of the things I said—especially my proposition so smug, so crude, so bald!—I felt ashamed of myself. She was a girl in a million, and I was a species of clod. But I'd never had a chance with her; I'd been sure of that from the moment I saw her, the instant she opened her mouth. The game was over, and so was the *fiesta*. The men from Santa Morena stayed yet another day to gird for the trip back. This time my good-by to Don Socrates was painful.

"Did you not like Elena, then? Forgive me for asking, doctor, but it means much to me. You were with her every night, you seem to have so much to talk about, so much in common, then pouf! she is gone, you remain, and nothing." He looked unhappy and perplexed. "I cannot understand it."

"Then you must ask Señorita Elena."

"How can I when she is gone? Is it that—could it be—no, I must not ask."

"Say it, *amigo*," I prodded.

"It is not possible then that she is not woman enough for you?"

"On the contrary," I said as honestly as I could, "I am afraid I am not man enough for her."

Don Socrates eyed me unbelievingly, shrugged in his inimitable way, and trotted off. Then again I was back in reality and routine. The old medical round and everything as usual, except for a certain lack of enthusiasm for my cure and gambling now, and the rainy season fast approaching again. Rojas was bustling with preparations, but the spirit was different than for the *fiesta*. This was a battening down, a digging in. The *estancieros* worked their *mozos* frantically to wind up the tasks of the *campo;* there were furious comings and goings, mending of houses, roofs, and gutters, and the village buzzed at the forthcoming seasonal influx of its "suburban" citizens.

The coming rainy season, endless, miserable, and confining as it could be, filled me with neither the apprehension and irritation I might have expected. Ever since knowing Elena, it seemed that I saw things differently; my mood had changed from one of quiet desperation; I accepted everything with an equanimity I had never imagined myself to possess. Things no longer upset me so much and, when they did, I no longer had immediate recourse to the bottle, my cure, or the gambling house.

I marveled at my calm the morning I found a saddle ox hitched to a fence post by my house. It was a portent. I feared the worst, for some reason, but I looked the animal over unexcitedly. Its eyes bulged, its hide dripped with sweat, and I knew it had been driven hard, which meant someone was badly in need of me. But who? I saw a dark Indio boy cowering by the wall, but Indio faces had a way of looking uniformly alike. And yet . . . I squinted, and it was perhaps thirty seconds before I recognized the young Indio was one of the two boys, the sons, of the woman who shared Pierre's hut. Pierre must have sent me a message.

"*Qué tal, joven?*" I called amiably. "What's the news?"

The boy's eyes flickered nervously. "Señor Pierre sick. He say countryman come."

"I would like to go. I want to help him, but you must understand that I cannot leave for Santa Morena at a moment's notice."

"Oh, not Santa Morena," he said hastily. "Señor Pierre he come here. He try to come, but he very sick now. Lie down on the road."

286

God! Sick as he was, I never thought Pierre would carry out his threat to make the hard trip to Rojas once again just to see me.

"Where on the road, my boy? Where is he? How far did you get?"

"Only to *El Cementerio*. Then he fail, fall down . . ."

I groaned. A whole day's ride, no, more than that. It would mean closing the office for a day, being away that night, and probably all the next day as well. But there was no alternative. Pierre was my friend and—oh, what the hell! I was going out to get him and bring him back to Rojas.

"Rudolfo!" I called into the house. "Saddle up the horses quickly!"

He came out of the house shading his eyes. "Where are we going?"

"*El Cementerio*. Now get ready!"

"*El Cementerio?*" he said incredulously, looking from the boy to me.

"You heard me. It's an emergency."

The indomitable boy took the lead and held it. He set a fast pace. It was late afternoon as we rode up to the door of the hut at *El Cementerio* where I had first met the priest and treated *El Trimotor*. Now Pierre was lying on the same worn cowhide in what seemed even worse condition. His lined, bulging face was bluish, his eyes opened wide. He struggled to lift his arm in greeting as I came in, but barely raised it an inch from the floor.

"Ah, countryman, you! I thought I could make it, but—"

"Why didn't you send word for me, Pierre? I would gladly have come to take care of you."

"Would you now, my good friend? That is good to hear, but I was so sure, so very sure, you wouldn't linger long in Rojas. You're not made for these damned jungles any more than I am. Civilized men like us . . . I waited and waited for you to come back to the airfield to take the *avion*. I thought you would want to be near so you could leave any time you had enough. I do know that you nearly took the *avion* that time during the *fiesta*, but—"

A violent spasm of coughing wracked his ravaged body. It was as frightening as a dog barking in an empty ruin. I motioned for Rudolfo to bring my bag, and took Pierre's pulse. Thin, irregular, missing beats. I reached for my syringe, but Pierre gestured weakly in protest.

"No hope, Martin, none at all. You know it, I know, so let's not waste time. I am dying. Let me die then, but first listen to me. For me it is too late, but maybe I can open your eyes. You don't know what it means—"

He choked, his eyes darted to the side, and from the shadows glided his Indio woman, more tattered and haggard than ever. She bent her head in silent greeting, and held a tin of water to Pierre's lips. He drank with effort, licked his lips, and water slobbered down his chin and front.

"Martin, did I ever tell you about my child? About my lovely wife and my best friend who became her lover when I got to be—the way I am now?"

"Of course, you have, Pierre. Many times. I know all about it, so please don't try to talk now. I'm going to give you an injection and then perhaps later . . ."

"There is no later for me." A sudden change came over him. A victory smile, repulsive and frightening, crossed his troll's features. "The priest was in Santa Morena just now. Praying and saving souls. So he came to me as usual." He laughed at the thought, hacking, coughing, jittering with laughter. "I told him! Oh, yes, I told him off. I said the doctor didn't fall for your leather book, for your 'know thyself' dung. No, Martin, my coun-tryman did not either, any more than I did. Ah, if you had seen him then." He whooped and fought to get out his laughter, but he could not. "Oh, Martin, that priest . . ."

I said nothing. I listened and, bit by bit, his ramblings became incoherent. He stopped, seemed to sleep, then his lips were moving again.

"Twelve years here in hell. I couldn't stand it any more. So I went with the cattle drive across the Andes. I wanted to get back to La Paz, had to, but after two weeks on the road I caught malaria. I was so sick, Martin, like now. And it weakened me. I was as frightened of the world outside as I had been when I first came. So I couldn't go back, and I couldn't go on living as I . . . So then this woman—she lived in the mountains with her two little children—she nursed me, cared for me. I took her to Rojas first—she had no good life there—they hated her—us. So I went back to—nothing —oh, nothing." He became confused again, and I understood no more until he said, "But not for you, Martin. This is no life for you. When you go back to La Paz, take her along there. The boys—the boys—"

Pierre did not speak again. I gave him an injection and, as doctors say when they can do next to nothing, "did what I could." The Indio gave us something to eat, which tasted much better than it looked, and we bedded down in the hut, the living, the dying, and the resigned. I was awakened by Pierre's terrible coughing spell. There was just light enough to see that it was four in the morning. I hurried to him. Foam coated his bulbous lips. He seemed at once to fight to see and to talk. Then his chin dropped, and he was dead. Rudolfo came to me, shaking his head, and we looked up to see the Indio woman and her two boys already with shovels in their hands.

288

By the time it was light enough to see clearly, Pierre's skin was the deep yellow of a diseased liver, and he had the look of a great, collapsed balloon lying in folds on himself. Rudolfo and I shut his eyes, composed his limbs, then wrapped him gently in the faded, worn, and inadequate cowhide. It was like trying to cover a ham with a paper napkin. We carried his body, which was surprisingly light considering his bulk, to a clearing within an island of trees, where there were several old graves. It was this that gave the place the name *El Cementerio*. Near the old graves, I saw a freshly dug one. The woman and her sons had been busy taking care of Pierre in death as in life. It was much more than I, or anyone else, had done.

I muttered a few words, although it was not expected of me. The woman had walked behind us to the grave, silent as always. She had watched as her sons filled it in, her hands folded across her breast, her head erect, a simple dignity and serenity about her that greatly moved me. Indios seemed to know how to accept life, whatever it might bring, and, just as easily, death, however it might come. I held out my hand to her, and she took it. Her palm was callused and hard, her grip warm and firm.

"What will you do now?" I asked. "Where will you go?"

She turned to the horizon, where the Cordillera formed a thin blue line, and pointed. I wondered whether I ought to give her the little money I had with me, then decided not to. Certainly Pierre hadn't left her money, nor had he given her any when he was alive, and she had made out all right. People like her usually did—far better than those like Pierre or myself. I shook her hand again, wished her well, said good-by to the two boys, then mounted my horse.

We said little on the trip back to Rojas. Tactful and understanding, Rudolfo rode well behind me, and the burning sun did its best to bake every thought out of my brain. All that coming and going of Pierre seeking me out. At first he had wanted me to leave Santa Morena and go back where I came from. When I moved to Rojas, he had forced *El Trimotor* to bring him to me to make sure of what? That I was getting acclimated, that I was getting used to things, that, possibly, I might be happy in my work and life? Well, he needn't have worried, and now he was dead. Still, what had he been so fearful of? Since he had cast me in his image, I was expected to react in kind. What if I had managed to solve my problems and been content to stay on in the jungles?

But I hadn't solved any problems. He had solved them for me with his spiritual suicide, together with liquor and my cure. Poor Pierre had had

289

only liquor. *Pobre diablo,* in addition to all his misery and heartache, he also had to contend with a humiliating physical handicap. I would long remember him, but the memory of Elena burned much brighter.

Yes, poor Pierre, innocent victim of God and man, misfit, defeatist, unbeliever. Today there were thousands like him wandering around the world. Thousands of Martins and Pierres and Herberts. Where did they belong? Who cared, for that matter?

I looked around me, and my mind was like the pampas—vast, indecisive, and resigned to fate. Let the wind blow, let the rains come, let the sun beat down. Nothing would stop them anyway.

*　　*　　*

One more rainy season had come over the land and passed. Life for the men in Rojas went on with a little work now and then, endless discussion about cattle and politics, women, of course, and cards. I'm afraid I was no exception. I felt like Noah on his ark, and I endured. I will say, however, that I did more work than the others except the *mozos,* whose duty it was to do the dirty, arduous labor. I still had many medical calls outside, my *officina* was filled during office hours, and I even did some veterinary work on cattle.

It seemed intelligent for me to get to know cows. They represented fees and my herd, which was getting bigger all the time, still grazed with Don Arnulfo's. I checked them one by one periodically and was so successful— or lucky—in ridding or keeping them free of disease that others soon approached me and asked that I examine their cattle. Now and again I considered setting up my own *estancia,* but I always put aside the idea. The main thing was laziness, I suppose, and then there was all the troublesome business of getting involved in such a venture. After all, I was a doctor and not a ranch owner. Yet I thought about it every time I saw my herd and felt a thrill of pride and ownership.

Elena had left her mark, but I was lonely—and so human. Where women were concerned I followed the routine of the younger men, taking my fun when and where I could find it within the limits of discretion. The field was a limited one, the rounds circumscribed, and it's a wonder that we didn't get our signals mixed and end up three or four under one *mosquitero* or, worse, all come down with venereal disease. The young men rarely gambled. Their nights were spent in love-making, while I combined two games and always joined the older men at the card table after a night out.

I had status now. I was a respected doctor, I had a growing herd, women liked me, and I was good at cards. I took life calmly now; there was only one thing that bothered me, and that was Daguero, ever my faithful and obedient companion. My new Spanish pride—acquired from others by contagion more than from any personal convictions—was constantly outraged by those who called my dog a coward. Oh, true, Daguero used to turn and run, tail between his legs, as soon as other dogs made unfriendly advances. And this attracted attention because he was big and strong. No use explaining that he was no coward, that what seemed to be craven behavior was simply obedience to his master's will. If I had ordered him to attack—and I wouldn't—I was certain he would charge into battle like that. But they saw only what they saw, these people. *"Es cobarde!"* they sneered. And it was the worst thing they could say about man or dog.

Don Arnulfo incensed me one day by bringing up the subject in my own house.

"My dog is no coward!" I shouted, turning on him.

He shrugged. "I only say what the people say."

"Damn the people! I'll show you whether my dog is a coward."

The day before I had treated a hunter, and he had given me a tiger skin in payment for treatment. The hide was in a corner, a big, stiff, rolled-up bundle. I flung it on the floor, unrolled it, and was not surprised to see clots of ants writhing where flesh still adhered. I dragged it outside, fuming, and spread it on the grass. My horses had been grazing nearby, but as soon as they caught the fresh scent of the terrifying animal, they snorted, whinnied, and bolted as if the Devil himself were after them with a fiery pitchfork. Hordimales, who had come running to the scene, sniffed the air and stopped dead in his tracks some distance off, hair bristling on his back, claws digging into the soil. He wasn't moving, and he wouldn't be moved. Not Daguero. He saw me next to the tiger skin, and he came on merrily. He sniffed it, walked on it, pawed it. Then he lay down and rolled happily all over it.

"Aquí!" I called out angrily to Don Arnulfo. I noticed that Rudolfo was standing by quietly, but I ignored him. "Is this your coward?" I pointed to Daguero romping where others feared to tread. *"Aquí está su perro cobarde!"*

Don Arnulfo only smiled politely. Later, when we were alone, I called Daguero to me and petted him.

"Let these ignorant people call you a coward," I said affectionately. "What do we care, you and I, when we know better. You be just as I want you to be. One of us must be a gentleman out here."

Apprehension stirred deep within me as Daguero licked my hand, his tail between his legs, his ears drooping. Spirit mattered, not appearances, I tried to convince myself. Hadn't Daguero proved himself fearless? On our medical calls away from Rojas, we often came to rivers. Daguero always plunged in without ceremony, while Hordimales ran up and down the bank whining and on the lookout for the deadly predators that so often lurked in the water. Once a snake slithered across our path. The horses shied violently, Hordimales bounded off in fright, but Daguero only stepped calmly up near the coiled snake, looking back at me with one ear up, the other down, as if questioning the danger involved here.

Making my rounds in the village, Daguero often preceded me into the houses of the sick to announce the doctor's arrival. Some might call him coward, but most people liked the big black dog with intelligent eyes and gentle ways. Wherever I may have been until late, going home nights, Daguero always went ahead of me as guide and guardian. Once inside, he settled down tentatively on his sackcloth, not relaxing or shutting an eye until I had tucked the ends of my *mosquitero* under the mattress and prepared for sleep. He was a good dog, and I don't know any higher praise. I loved him.

One night I played poker for hours at the subprefect's house. We were in the host's *sala* with the *alcalde* and three other prominent citizens. It had been rather boring for me. No sensational hands. I had won a little, lost a little, and was about where I had started. Daguero had come with me and left. He sat in a corner for a time then, as the hours wore on, he would visit around town a little, go over to the house to make sure everything was all right, and soon come back. I noticed now that he was still away, had been for a long time.

As we played on, I heard a wild frenzy of barking in the distance. The others hardly noticed it, but I was worried. I said nothing, so as not to disturb the game, and I had heard too much comment about Daguero anyway. How it was a sin the way the foreign doctor spoiled and pampered his dog, buying him the choicest cuts of meat, letting him sleep in his own room, and all that coward business. It was a little later that I noticed an Indio boy hovering by the door. The Indios were trained never to intrude on or to bother their masters—and superiors—and they never spoke unless spoken to. No one paid any attention to the lad, and we all happened to be concentrating on our cards. But the boy stayed by the door, scratching the back of his head and picking his nose. Finally, when the subprefect was out of the game, he turned to the boy.

"What is it you want, *hijo?*" he said offhandedly. The boy mumbled something in a singsong voice, and the official looked at me. "Doctor, this *chico* says that something bad has happened to your dog."

If I had jumped up to leave as I wished, they would have said the *gringo* was *loco* or, at best, had bad manners. I damned myself for having to consider the amenities—what did I care what they thought?—and played my hand out as was expected of me. Then I got up, apologized formally, and was excused. I thanked my host, gathered up my money, and secured my flashlight. There was no need for it, as there had been earlier. A big round moon spread silver light over the village. The palm trees stood like statues, slim and elegant, against the star-studded sky, and twisted heaps of rubble, which had been handsome, well-kept buildings during the legendary rubber-boom era, looked like romantic pyramids in the soft moonlight.

All this beauty struck me in passing as I hurried after the Indio boy. He stopped for a minute—no, much less than that—at the edge of a field. I looked out, back at him, and he had disappeared. But this must be the place where all the barking had come from. Disregarding the ever-present danger of snakes, I ran out into the wet, high-grass field. I wore no protective boots. My sandals and thin linen trousers would not stop the fangs of a rattler, but I hardly cared or worried about the threat. Halfway through the field, I found where the grass was trampled, a little farther on was a place where the stalks were flattened, and it was there I saw a patch of something black and wet in the moonlight. I knew what it was, but I put my hand in it all the same. Blood. More blood leading off through the grass. He must have tried to make it home.

I began to run, tripping once and falling before I cleared the field, then down the street at a gallop to my house. I saw more blood on the way. The trail led to the house, around it, to the back door, and inside. There I found Daguero in a pool of his own blood. It still gushed from two gaping wounds on his back and hind leg. His face was untouched, his mouth and teeth clean of blood. He had been caught from behind by that wolf pack, and all but torn to pieces.

"Daguero!" I cried. "Daguero, what have they done to you?"

I knelt at his side, took his great head in my hands, and he looked up at me weakly in recognition, pain and love in his glazed eyes. His tail beat feebly, he struggled to lick my hand, his legs kicked out, he gave a convulsive jerk—then he was dead. I pushed myself erect, blood on the knees of both trousers, both hands, in my eyes, heart, and soul. For the moment I felt nothing. I got a shovel, wrapped the dog's body in the sackcloth that had been his bed, and staggered out with my load. I carried him deep into the banana garden, back of the patio where the trees stood in rows like columns and large leaves formed a lofty roof. Thinking of nothing, I began to dig mechanically in the moonlight.

As I dug, pattering steps sounded through the quiet night, and Hordimales, sleek and black, slipped out of the grass, restlessly searching and sniffing, a curious whine coming from his throat. His nose bumped Daguero's covered body, and he fell back as if hit in the head, his whining now high-pitched and mournful. Then he slumped to the ground and began howling miserably. The ululating seemed to clutch at my throat like so many fingers. Putting my shovel down, I reached over to console the grieving Hordimales, but the dog snapped at my hand. Hurt, I resumed working, finished the trench, and fumbled with Daguero's body.

I tried to do it gently, but I had to bend over, the trench was narrow, and his body fell heavily with an almost audible "Unh!" into the grave. I filled it in, shovelful by shovelful, dirt and stones trickling into the grave in mournful cacophony. Then I stood motionless by the grave, leaning on the shovel, covered with sweat, my faded khaki shirt sticking to my clammy chest, my bloody, dew-soaked trousers slopping coldly around my ankles. My head felt dull, my throat burned, and my heart was empty. I was lonelier than I had ever been in my whole life. My only friend was gone— and I had killed him.

All the night sounds of the jungle began to attack my ears—sounds which I was usually hardly aware of, which I had learned to live with. Now they all cried out at once. The steady chirping of crickets, the deep croak of frogs, the roar of bulls out on the pampas, the shrieks of wild parrots, and all the rest. They were all screaming at once, raising their voices in accusation and protest, saying the same damning thing.

"You killed him, killed him, killed him, killed him, killed him."

I fled from the grave and into the house, followed by the inexorable moonlight. A bat, chased out of his haunts, flapped through the air, clapping awkwardly against the wall with its ugly body. Giant cockroaches marched in hurrying ranks across the dirty floor; golden-winged chafers sat motionless on the drapes of the mosquito netting. In the corner my saddles had a desolate, forbidding appearance and, to their front, the hammock hung empty and lifeless.

"Killed him," screamed the voices from outside. *"Killed him."*

I was dazed and numb. A small burning spot in the pit of my stomach spread into a searing white-hot filament of pain from the top of my skull to my toes. My torment stiffened my body in spastic cramps, and from

294

every side I seemed to see Daguero's loyal, loving eyes looking at me in pitiful accusation. *Et tu, Brute!*

I slumped into a chair and began sobbing—for Daguero, myself, for the whole world. The moonlight was fading to gray dawn as I recovered consciousness and was able to recognize my surroundings. I knew what I had to do: finish the job. I walked over to my suitcase slowly, opened it, and from the bottom yanked the picture I had hidden there—the picture of the little boy in the starched white collar. I went outside and looked up and down the streets at sleeping Rojas. The village was gray, indifferent, beyond emotion.

Like a pallbearer, I walked back to the banana garden and the grave. Here I knelt on the ground, scrabbling into the earth until I'd made a little hole. I jammed the hard cardboard into it, pushed back the dirt, smoothed it down, then got up as if my joints had rusted. My hands came to my side and I straightened like a soldier at the grave of a fallen comrade, which was exactly what Daguero had proved to be. He had given his life for me, died so that I might live. The poor, loyal, betrayed son of a bitch . . .

"*Adiós,* Daguero," I said aloud. "*Adiós, amigo,* and thank you."

*　　*　　*

In physics there is a law that says that every action is followed by an equal and opposite reaction. It is debatable whether such a law can be applied to human emotions, but Daguero's death, following hard on Pierre's and all the more bitter and personal, changed my habits. I was no longer seen at the card tables. Poker had become as unimportant as my cure. The *mosquiteros* were ready to welcome me as always, but my lust had withered and died, at least for the time. Nor did I find any need to seek relief in alcohol.

I spent my evenings and free time lying in my hammock, staring wide-eyed at the gaping, rat-infested ceiling overhead. I slept badly, my nights a jangle of nightmares, all of them centering on Daguero and Pierre, with myself involved with them in some haunting and horrible manner. It was then that a plan took root in my mind. I told my patients and friends that I was going to move back to Santa Morena. It was no whim, but an irrevocable decision although no one chose to take me seriously at first.

The sensation that my announcement caused in Rojas would have been flattering in any other circumstances. I should have been pleased that I was such an important citizen and not taken for granted, as I so often felt, but I just wanted to get going. Rudolfo was upset, but he never had questioned my decisions or motives, and that was one of the reasons we teamed so well together. But he did say that everyone was shocked at the thought of my leaving. Why, the subprefect no longer strolled about cackling to himself, but looked grave and stricken. And, said Rudolfo excitedly, Don Arturo was going to pay a call on me.

It was the first time, so far as I could recall, that the man with the gap in his bridgework had entered my house. He sat down ceremoniously, looking rather ill at ease in the holiday suit and necktie he wore in honor of the occasion. After the painfully conventional—and obligatory—phrases concerning the weather, the price of cattle, and the latest political events, he came to the point. Speaking for the others, as well as himself, he would greatly appreciate it if the doctor reconsidered his decision and stayed on in Rojas. Or, if that were not possible at the moment, he respectfully requested that the doctor return after visiting Santa Morena. Even Dr. Malvenido had heard of the doctor's impending departure and, Don Arturo insisted, the news had left him disconsolate. I doubted that, from what I had seen of the man, Malvenido would be such a hypocrite, but I smiled politely. Everybody meant well and so, I was sure, did I.

Since Don Arturo had been anti-*gringo*-doctor since my arrival, how much of his about-face might be due to pressure from his fellow citizens remained a matter of conjecture. Still, his coming to plead with me, when only two short years ago I had been the object of his open enmity, was a triumph of sorts for the foreign doctor, the *gringo*, the *judio*. Had it come earlier I might have been gratified and elated, but now I felt next to nothing. I had hated this man for opposing me and trying to arouse the town, and here he was calling me friend and irreplaceable. The wheel swung full turn —and so what? You can't get even with people, I told myself. Either you don't catch up with them, or you do and don't care any more.

Outside of my medical practice, my time was taken up with preparations for departure, which continued far into the night. Then one morning, just at dawn, a *mozo* drove a *carreton* up to my patio door. It was a total move. I had told myself I was going to Santa Morena with bag, baggage, and everything, and it was dark as we finished loading the big clumsy wagon. It seemed to me that I had accumulated a lot of possessions in the time I had been here. The *carreton* was full, a few crates of drugs, medical supplies, and some chairs and tables piled on top and lashed down with lassos. The barefooted *mozo* swung his whip and the cart, pulled by two teams of oxen, started the long haul for Santa Morena. The big sullen animals were paired to the pole by yokes fixed hard against their bony heads, and they clumped, waddled, and huffed powerfully along. They moved sluggishly and set their own pace. Greased leather cords were wound tightly round their horns and in tight, unyielding knots around the carved wooden yokes.

The *carreton* went in slow motion. The oxen stamped their hoofs into the soft earth with each step, turning the big clumsy wheels at a veritable snail's progress which would surely have driven anyone but a phlegmatic Indio *mozo* to distraction. Rudolfo and I stood together watching the vehicle until it was out of sight. He looked sad and depressed, and I was annoyed.

"We're next," I said. "I'm going to get some sleep so we can get an early start."

"Are you still glad you are doing this thing, doctor?" Rudolfo asked. "You have no regrets?"

"I've decided and I'm on the move," I said curtly.

"Surely you are the least bit sorry, though?"

"Who knows, Rudolfo? All of us have regrets about everything, but it is better to have them before than afterward."

"The thing is then to be sure, eh?"

"I would say so." I squeezed his shoulder. "Yes. Now go over and get ready to go."

He came back in half an hour wearing his oldest trousers and leather gaiters, and carrying a bundle wrapped in a clean linen towel.

"Two fried chickens, white bread, and salt," he reported. "Good eating on our journey."

"I should say. I must say good-by to your mother before we go, and thank her for her many kindnesses."

We talked on a little while, then both went to sleep. I slept fitfully because I had so much on my mind, and I envied Rudolfo's deep sleep and easygoing nature. He may have had worries, but he never let them worry him. I dozed on and off, awaking early as I heard the horses coming to the house on their own. They trotted through the patio to the back door and stopped. Then I grinned, waiting in anticipation for the knock. The smaller of the horses had taught himself a trick, always announcing his arrival and his hunger by banging a forefoot against the wooden door. The banging came like a rifle shot, cutting off Rudolfo's sleep in mid-snore.

"What is it?" he said, sitting up and rubbing his eyes.

"Just the horses."

"So soon?" He yawned. "I was having the most pleasant dream."

We poured corn into two containers as the horses, delighted to have

297

awakened us, galloped playfully about the patio, ready to be coaxed back for their breakfast. We called them and, still shy, they were hesitant about approaching their feedboxes. But their greed soon overcame their timidity, and presently they were both grinding the yellow kernels of corn with their chisel-like teeth.

My horse was a clean feeder. Rudolfo's was not, invariably scattering corn far and wide as he munched. The chickens of the neighborhood had soon discovered this daily windfall, and now a good three dozen rushed up as usual from all directions, cackling with excitement and darting about pecking at the ground. Once again the big rooster, who was bigger than all the others and a tyrant by nature, mercilessly attacked the chickens so he could get all the grain. I had grown to detest him as a symbol, but had learned that there was little I could do about his brutal bullying. Whenever I tried to chase him away, all the others took fright and fled. I had to let him get fat just so the others could get a few kernels, and his savage gluttony didn't bother them half so much as my police action.

I watched the familiar scene with a smile, until I caught Rudolfo watching me. The horses coming in by themselves at dawn, the peremptory knock at the door, the feeding of the corn, the arrival of the chickens for the feast, the cock laying about so he could eat at will—yes, I would miss it. But what the hell? I thought. I had missed a lot of other things I had to give up voluntarily or involuntarily.

"What will these chickens do without their free meal?" said Rudolfo. "They will not know what to do mornings when you are gone."

"Oh, they will get on. Never worry."

While the chickens were feeding excitedly as the horses ate their corn, Rudolfo now came from behind and slipped bridles over the horses' heads. The rooster attacked here, attacked there, gobbled his fill, but already the chickens had returned to peck up what he had overlooked and couldn't reach. I happened to look toward the corner of the house and saw a rotund man peer into the patio.

"*Buenos días,* Don Arnulfo!" I called. "You're up early today. Come in, my friend."

"*Muchas gracias.*"

Don Arnulfo carried a cane, not so much because he needed support as because he thought it gave him dignity; he wore a black hat, and his antique pince-nez was perched on his nose. It was the only optical accouterment of that fashion in the whole region, and Don Arnulfo was fond of it. That it no longer helped his vision—if indeed it ever had—was of no concern.

298

The pince-nez, the black hat, and the fancy necktie he wore were strictly for formal occasions. I was touched.

"*Qué tal?*" I greeted him cordially at the door. "How did you arise this morning?"

"Thank you, doctor, well. And how have you arisen?"

"Very well, thank you. Come in, Don Arnulfo. My house is more humble than usual this morning. I cannot even offer you a cup of coffee. But do me the favor and sit in the hammock."

After the mildest of protests, Don Arnulfo sat in the hammock, one ankle crossed over a knee, the other foot pushing against the earthen floor and swinging the hammock gently.

"Please don't preoccupy yourself with the thought of serving me coffee," he begged in his scratchy voice. "Even if you had twenty cooks, you couldn't serve anything at this hour of the morning—not the way these Indios cook these days anyways. They're all so lazy!"

I hid an amused smile at this eternal complaint so reminiscent of Old World matrons knocking their servants. I knew he had gotten up early, made a special trip to see me, and I wanted to show my appreciation. I reached into my saddlebag, which was still on the floor, and took out my last bottle of whisky. I poured a stiff drink into a tumbler and handed it to Don Arnulfo, now all smiles.

"Well, doctor, to your health!" He gulped down the golden liquid and wiped his mouth with a sigh of pleasure. "Ah, that is good."

"Thank you. I feel very honored that you came to say good-by."

Don Arnulfo made a little bow and leaned back in the hammock.

"Ever since they installed the new radio station at Santa Morena, I have expected you to move back there, doctor. I imagine the radio station is for you what *aguardiente* is for me. If there is none, why, I can do without it well enough, but, frankly, I am *loco* when it comes within reach." He smiled apologetically. "I must say I was surprised that you came back to Rojas last year at all. But we have been grateful, doctor, really grateful to have had you with us all these last months."

Although I told myself I no longer cared one way or the other, praise is always gratifying and I was about to murmur a polite disclaimer, but Don Arnulfo gave me no opportunity.

"Ah, señor," he went on, "some of the others were sure you would be able to resist it for long here, but, no, not me. I never believed that. Though," he added with a wry smile, "it would have been more to my liking to believe just as they did. You see I am being honest with you. And you seemed contented for a while, so contented that I almost convinced myself I had been mistaken in judging you. So now, after the citizens were so certain they had a good hold on you in Rojas, off you go."

He shook his head, little grimaces flickering across the left side of his face. His old paralysis had almost disappeared. It was only when Don Arnulfo became tense, as now, that his face pulled off to the right of his nose.

"Nobody will miss me here. Besides, I'll only be gone a short time, then I'll come back."

Don Arnulfo shook his head. I picked up the bottle, and he held out his glass without looking at it, trusting my judgment in filling it. He drank it in two gulps.

"You say one thing, but perhaps you think another without knowing. Naturally, it's your right to choose any location in the province you like in which to discharge your duties. But, I still say, you have changed. *Amigo,* you have become a different man in a very few months. And it makes me think. You see, we are familiar with the two types of *gringos.* The first consists of the men who come and stay with us all their lives. They become accustomed to our ways, our thinking, our voices, our vices, our diseases. And after a while they forget the big cities from which they come. I had hoped you would become such a one, but you do not belong with them.

"You belong to the smaller group—to the *gringos* who come to us from time to time, live with us, drink, play, work, and love with us. Then one day they are gone. What brought them here? What?" He looked at me. "We do not ask questions. What is it that makes them go?" He shrugged. "We do not know, but we have our opinions." He studied his empty glass as if it were a crystal ball. "Some leave women with broken hearts. Some leave children. The women forget in time, and the children grow up not even knowing what kind of father they had at the beginning of their lives."

Don Arnulfo looked up and smiled. Pulled to the right as they were, his features still betrayed a winning charm.

"So far as is known, you have no children at present, eh, doctor, either born or unborn? And about broken hearts, I shall not talk."

My laugh was short and dry. "Not that I haven't tried to be one of you. But I will have to consider all this as mere flattery."

"*Vaya se,* doctor," he said simply. "What woman wouldn't like you!"

This time I was honestly astonished. I couldn't think of a thing to say, but Don Arnulfo didn't expect an answer. He put his glass down carefully on the floor and straightened up to speak face to face.

300

"I came to say good-by because I think you are on the go," he said unhesitatingly. "I do not believe you will ever come back to Rojas. I do not believe you will stay in Santa Morena, radio station or no radio station. You are on your way to the world where you belong. *Claro,* very clearly, you are leaving us for good. You have become quiet and full of purpose. You are young and you have wings. You are not old enough to resign yourself to our life. And I'm not sure that I can blame you. As you know, I yearn to see the big cities myself."

"I wish you'd believe me when I say I have not thought of giving up my position here."

Don Arnulfo chuckled. "It is working on you though. It is."

Then he got up and put his foot squarely on the glass he had so carefully set down. He stumbled, recovered, and we both laughed.

"May it be for luck," he said, then instantly turned serious again. "Doctor, never forget that this region is part of America. Here, a man's father may be rich or poor, the man himself may be *vivo* or *sonso,* clever or stupid, no matter; the man himself counts only for as much as he accomplishes, for —for what he is. That is why we will always have room for you and people like you!"

It was an important declaration, the meat of his conversation, and his face relaxed when it was done. Now he pulled a letter from his pocket.

"This is my excuse for intruding on you at this hour of the morning. Will you do me the favor of giving it to our *amigo,* my *compadre* Don Socrates? *Muchas gracias.*"

I blinked at the letter and searched for words to tell this good man what was in my mind. There was so much I wanted to say.

"Give my best regards to Señorita Elena, if you see her," I said at last. "Tell her I will not forget our talks—that I will never forget them."

"I will. A fine young woman. Just now she has left the city to come back to her home in San Marequo. You do almost the opposite and so—"

At that moment Rudolfo came in and greeted my guest with a polite, "*Buenos días,* señor."

Don Arnulfo had badly wanted to say something more to me, something I was particularly anxious to hear, but he turned to my assistant and spoke in the same grave tone he might have intended for me.

"*Buenos días, joven.* Ah, how have you arisen so early in the morning? Well, eh? Good! It is a long, tiring trip. Now do not forget to give my regards to your *tío,* Don Socrates, who is my *compadre.*" Now he laughed and poked a finger in Rudolfo's side. "And stay away from his daughter."

301

Because he had just brought up the subject, it struck me that Rudolfo's blond hair and weak blue eyes might well have their origin in one of those *gringos* who came, stayed awhile, and left behind brokenhearted women— and children. But I had no time to consider it. The horses were pawing the ground, we were shaking hands again, and it was time to be off to beat the sun. Hordimales was running about excitedly, as he always did before a trip, and mechanically I looked for Daguero to come trotting up before I remembered. A lump formed in my throat, the house seemed to blur before my eyes, I hastened to mount my horse.

"*Adiós,*" I called as the horse bounded off eagerly.

"Go with God!" I heard Don Arnulfo say, and I waved.

15

Back to Santa Morena; I Pull a Tooth and Visit Pierre's Grave; Good-by to Don Socrates and the Jungle; The Marvels of Civilization; I Am a Hero to My Friends; I Come to Terms—at Last

Our horses were fresh and frisky, and we galloped out into the main street of the still sleeping *pueblo* past the houses of the subprefect, the *alcalde,* and the tax collector. Following the deep tracks of the *carreton* that had gone before us with our supplies, we reached the end of Rojas' principal thoroughfare, turned left, and let our horses slow to an even trot, which would take them farthest with the least exertion.

Where I had been wide awake before, I now felt drugged with sleep and lethargic. We were on the pampas now, flat space all around us and wide open vistas. Perhaps it was this panorama of endless green pastures stretching to the horizon that had this strange effect on me. Perhaps it was the monotonous trot that went on hour after hour, or perhaps it was the pitiless sun which released a man from all his inhibitions. I had learned that it made a solitary rider daydream or talk to himself; in company he talked aloud, speaking a mixture of truth and fantasy, wishful thinking and reality.

It was too early in the morning for the sun—already hot, but not yet burning—to have loosened our tongues. So Rudolfo and I rode in silence, each deep in his own thoughts, and only Hordimales active, noisy, and tireless. I couldn't watch him without being reminded of—and missing—Daguero, and I found it easier to stare fixedly at my horse's neck as we went along. But the mood passed, my mind cleared and had done with inner thoughts, and I found pleasure in looking at the grimly beautiful countryside around us.

Our path circled an island of trees standing out from the pampas. Beyond the field of vision expanded again, and our way led straight ahead. On the right the high grass seemed rigid in sleep as far as the eye could see; on the left, where the land was barren and swampy, thousands of birds had settled on mud, water, and patches of oozing green. Some were as tall as a man. While these balanced on one leg and dozed, their smaller brethren crouched in the shade under them, beaks tucked under their wings. Not a bird moved as we passed. Not a flutter. Not a chirp. They seemed at complete harmony with themselves and nature.

How peaceful it was here! How beautiful! I looked all around me in humble gratitude. If only human beings could live together as serenely as these wild creatures. Large beaks and small beaks, straight ones and bent ones. Long legs and short legs—there was room for all and welcome. Neither was variation in color, species, and temperament an apparent reason for avian discrimination. All of them belonged, each had a place in this great natural symphony.

The tranquil morning air had a delightful fragrance all its own. I breathed deeply and looked at the squadrons, battalions, and regiments of brightly colored birds ranging from deep black over purple and burning red to silver gray and snow white. Packed together in rippling, uneven ranks, they were like a series of frozen rainbows. Now one of the huge birds spread its wings wide and effortlessly climbed into the air. It swung fearlessly toward our horse, passing low over our heads. I watched it breathlessly, marveling at this easy conquest of space, the graceful long neck and thin legs outstretched in a straight line with the streamlined body. The bird's disdain for gravity was complete; its fluid, flapping motions did nothing to break the silence.

"We should travel to Santa Morena that way," said Rudolfo, smiling. "Like the *avion*."

"Better than the *avion* by far. He can fly. Man has to pull himself through the air with a machine."

"Birds only do what God intended for them to do. With God's help and his own brain, man has taught himself to do things that are not natural to him. And that is a fine thing, too."

"Yes," I admitted grudgingly.

It was burning hot now, and we pulled our wide sombreros far down over our faces. It was close to the noon hour. The sweltering heat had weighed down the slightest breeze, engulfed the faintest breath of air. It was hard to breathe, sweat was pushing through our clothes, the horses were wet and putting one foot painfully before the other in the slowest of labored walks. I looked up and saw that Rudolfo had reined in up ahead at a crossroad.

"*Qué dice,* doctor?" he said, as I came up to him. "What about spending the hot midday hours at Don Victoriano's *estancia.* It is miserable traveling for man and beast in this heat, and the cattle ranch is only half a mile from here. When the heat lessens, we can continue and cross the Yucoma River in the late afternoon."

"A good idea, Rudolfo," I said, wiping the sweat from my face on my sleeve. "I am melting."

He laughed. "So are the horses! And Hordimales' tongue is touching the ground."

Don Victoriano was a big, amiable, older man. He was a *compadre* of Rudolfo's, and we were warmly received. I was glad we had come. That last half mile had left me limp. Our host entertained us while his wife bustled about the kitchen directing the *sirvienta.* Soon the aroma of frying meat filled the patio, and I felt my mouth watering. I had revived in the shade, and I was starving.

We took our ease, awaiting lunch, Don Victoriano lounging on a chair on the shaded porch, Rudolfo stretched out on a bench, and I lazing in the hammock. As we talked, an elderly Indio approached the *estanciero* and stood by his chair. He shifted feet, scratched the back of his head, and looked at the ground. Finally, after Don Victoriano asked what he wanted, he bent over and murmured a few sentences in a low voice.

"*Sí, sí,*" said Don Victoriano and turned to me. "Doctor, this *hombre* believes that God has brought you here today. His wife has had a bad toothache for nearly a week. We would all be very grateful if you could do something for her."

"Gladly," I said. "I'll see to it right now."

The old Indio went to get his wife, Rudolfo to fetch the emergency kit from my saddlebag, and I arranged a chair for my dental patient. I had just prepared the instruments as the old Indio came out of a hut in the patio, followed by a surprisingly young Indio woman. One of her hands was pressed against her swollen right cheek, the other was stuffed into her mouth, nursing her embarrassment. But her shyness quickly gave way to stark, unreasoning terror the instant she spotted the menacing forceps shining on the towel I had set on a low table by the chair. She stood frozen with fear, and I had to press firmly on her shoulders to seat her.

As usual, I picked up an audience. Half a dozen Indios had closed in

to watch, giant turkeys perambulated the patio with absurd self-importance, and tiny yellow ducklings waddled and quacked around my feet.
I had managed to get the woman's hands down once to locate the tooth,
but now they were back in the way, and she was still paralyzed with fear.
I smiled, patted her shoulder, and told her not to worry. I had the forceps
in hand, keeping them hidden, and now I approached her from behind.
Now just once more, would she show me the right tooth? We didn't want
to make a mistake, eh? We had to be sure, wasn't that right?

Which one? A little wider, please, and point to it. Ah, that one! I put
two fingers of my left hand on the gum on either side of the aching tooth,
then I whipped my right hand from behind my back and shot the forceps
into her gaping mouth. Quickly and coldly, I dug the edges of the forceps
deep into the gum below the root line. A flash and a yank, and the next
instant I was dangling the diseased tooth before the young Indio woman's
popping eyes. She had been so taken in by the ancient trick of distraction
that she could hardly believe her ordeal was over. Rudolfo handed her a
glass of water, she shook her head incredulously, and in another minute
walked away all smiles.

Rudolfo began to clean the forceps so we could close shop. Just then I
saw another Indio, servilely scratching his head, approach Don Victoriano,
who had been watching the proceedings from the porch. He looked at me,
and I nodded and prepared for more dental work. In the course of the next
hour or so, I must have extracted at least a dozen teeth, and Rudolfo had
been kept busy, too. The turkeys were still circling the patio loftily, their
noses in the air, and the ducklings were falling over one another to paddle
in the rivulet of rinsing water running from the dentist's chair.

We enjoyed a good meal, a quiet *siesta,* and it was time to be on our way.
The sun's rays were waning and had lost their malignant sting. I thanked
the señora and we set off, escorted by Don Victoriano as far as the next
estancia, a quarter of a mile or so. The patron pulled up his horse to ride
beside me, while Rudolfo and an *estancia mozo* followed.

"Do you plan staying long in Santa Morena, doctor?" said Don Victoriano, sucking on the stump of a *cigarillo.*

"*Quién sabe?*"

I didn't like being pinned down, and it was the only reply to that
troubling question that I had found.

"Then do you plan going on to La Paz?"

"I hadn't thought of it particularly. But, staying at a *pueblo* where there
is an airfield, one of these days I might well be tempted to have a look at
what is going on in the capital."

306

Don Victoriano pursed his lips. "Doctor, I've heard that you haven't been the same man lately. I watched while you were pulling teeth just now, and you know what I think? I think you are going to leave us. *Sí.* And I say that because I detect a cold purpose about you that I have seen before in other *gringos.* It comes over them when they carry a problem too long in their minds and are finally ready to make their decision."

Ah, these amazing people, I thought. They knew everything. But they were wrong. I was going to Santa Morena and not beyond.

"I'm afraid you're wrong. I assure you that I have not even considered giving up my job here."

"All right." He smiled and blew out a cloud of smoke. "Remind me, doctor, to embrace you for a final good-by when we reach the river."

Don Victoriano had mentioned accompanying us to the next *estancia,* not the river. I appreciated his courtesy, but I resented his knowing what I was going to do better than I did myself. It was another hour before we got there, and no one said a word all that way.

"Here is the Yucoma," he said, standing up in his stirrups. "I am turning to the left. You go straight, doctor. *Adiós,* and good luck."

"Thank you for everything then. And *hasta la vista,*" I said defiantly. "You will see me again."

But Don Victoriano only smiled and went his way, taking the *mozo* with him. Damn the man anyway! How could these people be so sure I was leaving? Don Arnulfo, and now Don Victoriano. These men seemed to know me, my motives, and my objectives, when I didn't know anything about myself. I fell to brooding again, giving my horse his head, and paying little attention where I was going. When I looked up, the setting sun was golden on the horizon, and Rudolfo was not in sight. I saw a familiar hut a little way ahead and an island of trees beyond. *El Cementerio,* the place where Pierre was buried. There were no grazing oxen this time, there was no *carreton.* Not a sign of life.

I dismounted. Leading my horse, I walked to the trees, then through them to the hidden clearing. Here I stopped in surprise. Tall grass was growing on all the hillocks, but the spaces between the graves had been painstakingly cleared, and a wooden fence, strong enough to keep out trampling cattle and other marauders, had been built around them. Coming closer, I noticed a new cross on Pierre's grave, the wood still whitely fresh, and I remembered his wish. All that was needed was a shaft of purple light for the grave and cross he had talked so longingly of finding. Poor Pierre, I thought affectionately, he *must* be happy now.

But who could have done all this work, this arduous caretaking? Certainly no one else except Pierre's swarthy Indio woman and her sons. She must have come all the way down from the mountains to tend his grave. A hard trip, but she was capable of such loyalty and fidelity. Why, there was a garland of flowers hanging on Pierre's cross. The blossoms were faded, the leaves shriveled, but there was still some green in them. Only one of the other crosses had been decorated with a wreath; it must have been long ago because all that remained was a papery residue of flowers and leaves. For Pierre's wreath to be so well preserved under that fiery sun, it must mean the woman had been here as recently as yesterday. Perhaps she was still around.

I stood bareheaded, holding a horse whose noble head was also bowed in weariness. The sky was darker now, the sun drowning in clouds on the horizon, and a tiny breeze whispering in the leaves of the trees around me. A grave meant finality, the end of the road, but, surely, not the end of everything. I knew that. And in this small, jungle cemetery, death did not seem irrevocable, but more a peaceful continuation of life in another form. The people in these graves had been conceived, born, had lived, and now they were dead. Just like Pierre, those who lay on either side of him had experienced joys and sorrows as deeply as their capabilities permitted them. Then, *llegó la hora,* the hour had struck, the game was over, and everything else, including such vitally important things as politics and dictators, supply and demand, race and religion, plus the other ills flesh is heir to.

Graves and graveyards give many people the creeps. They are uneasy and can't wait to get away; their unreasoning fear of the inevitable unknown gets the better of them. It has always seemed to me that standing before a grave, men become children again. Their defenses are down, the crust of pretense that life grows over their hearts melts away. Before a grave, as I was now before Pierre's, a man can be his true self and, facing what will be the final truth of his own life, as with all the millions that preceded him, he can battle for the truths in the time that remains to him.

Looking at the cross on Pierre's grave, I seemed to see a series of crosses and tombs and myself grief-stricken beside every one of them. And with each it had been a time of crisis going far beyond the death of the loved one. Pierre's grave had been dug in a time of heartbreaking confusion for me, and on top of that, when I was still lower, there came Daguero's violent death—I still thought of it as murder. And looking back I saw myself beside my mother's grave in Europe, the cross, the flowers, and the dead, drab feeling in my heart. That, too, had been the end of an epoch for me, and the beginning of another. The beginning of a terrible period of persecution, a time of jails, concentration camps, and the stealthy life of the fugitive for all Jews. Driven from my home, through Europe, and finally across the sea as a refugee and displaced person, I was far more fortunate than most of my kind.

I was alive in a free land, on my own in the New World, and what had I done with my priceless opportunity? Next to nothing, I accused myself bitterly. I was self-infected. The past and all I had lost had crushed me. Here in the New World my corroded, ironclad links with the Old had driven me into the jungles and, as I saw it now, personal defeat after personal defeat ending with the loss of Daguero, a symbol, my only true friend, the only thing I had ever really loved outside of—it couldn't be true!—*myself*. I hated the thought, wanted to throw it aside, but it kept intruding as the truth will.

It seemed to me then that I could see Elena's brilliant, expressive eyes and her cool beauty, that I could hear her telling words. ". . . You have worked hard here, saved lives, done much good. But you have not given of yourself. You have met our people at your level, not theirs. Oh, it is not your fault—and maybe it is true that you do not belong here—but who is to say where one belongs? . . ." Ah, but it was my fault, so much my fault. And I remembered her story of the priest, who had dreamed of crossing frontiers and had come to the jungles of Bolivia because ". . . here, in these regions, I make my own frontiers every day." How did the man do it, false priest that he was? How did he face himself and go on in spite of his fears? Because of the message in the leather-covered book, that was the answer. "Know thyself." It was time I did. About time before it was forever too late.

I was in a free land, free to breathe the free air as deeply as I liked, free to come and go wherever I pleased, free to carry a gun in defense against man or animal. I was my own man, completely free, but only so long as I could free myself from a warped and bruised mind, dismal, self-pitying thoughts, and an almost criminal lack of faith in life, men, myself, and, finally, *everything*.

I took a deep breath. The light evening breeze moved across the pampas. The green leaves whispered overhead, and the wreath on Pierre's cross bobbed gently like a buoy on a peaceful ocean. I looked up through the branches at the sky, where the sun had burned away another day. My eyes swung off over the illimitable pampas to the far graying horizon. It was all of a piece and, at last, I fervently hoped, so was I. I looked at Pierre's cross with serenity and compassion.

"I'm all right, Pierre," I said, my words shockingly loud in the silence. "I tore off my starched collar and buried it for good. It cost me Daguero, but I'm free now—and whole. God bless you, *amigo!*"

Before leaving *El Cementerio,* I looked in on the hut where the priest had attended to *El Trimotor* and I had treated the man's malaria. It was empty and forbidding. *El Cura,* the false priest, where might he be right now? Probably risking his life again to do good, to bring peace, love, and understanding. Pierre was dead. So was Daguero. And Elena was not for me, nor Rojas, nor Santa Morena, nor, I was afraid, all Bolivia or South America. Loneliness overcame me and suddenly I felt a great yearning to see my friends in La Paz, Karl, Herbert, and the others. But, of course, I wouldn't go. I couldn't stand seeing them as a failure. They would say Martin has run off again, and their I-told-you-so's would only torture me.

I got on my horse and started off after Rudolfo in the direction of the river. It was only a short ride to the little landing by the water. There I found Rudolfo with Pierre's Indio woman and her two sons. I was delighted to see her and wished to compliment her on what she had done with the graves at *El Cementerio.* But she didn't give me the chance. She and her sons had bundles of lumber on their backs, and the boys were hauling a small tree trunk as well. They were in a hurry to be off, and the woman knew what she wanted to say and obviously didn't want to linger.

"Don Pierre dead one year," she said, her eyes flashing. "Me and my sons build house at *El Cementerio,* take care of graves, help other people on the road . . ."

She rattled it off as if she had rehearsed it as an emergency measure. And with her last word she turned, hitched up her burden, and marched off, followed by her sons, as if she feared that I might not let her go unless she took and kept the initiative. I watched them go, my heart going with them as they plodded deeper and deeper into the high pampas grass until the stalks reached their shoulders and covered them completely. What a woman! What guts, fortitude, and godliness. Pierre was fortunate. Even after his death she kept her loyalty to him, and now she and her sons had created a living monument in his memory to keep it forever green by helping travelers and wayfarers passing by way of *El Cementerio.* My eyes were misty, my throat working and, for once, I didn't give a damn. This magnificent woman deserved everything that was good.

Somebody plucked at my sleeve and, such was my reverie, that I was startled to see that it was Rudolfo.

"We must be getting on, doctor. And, worse luck, the canoe is on the other bank. I'll have to swim for it."

He went discreetly behind a tree, as I stood looking at the river, and returned a few minutes later wearing nothing except his precious dark glasses. He took the saddles off the horses, jumped on the bare back of his own horse, and grabbed its mane firmly in his fist. Then, whipping the air with the slack of his reins and kicking hard with his heels, he started to drive the animal into the river. The horse was reluctant. His nostrils flared, he tossed his head, he reared, but Rudolfo held to his work and eased the animal into the water, flailing, yelling, encouraging. Once in the river, he slid off the horse's back and, side by side, they struck out together for the opposite bank.

My mind still on the devoted Indio woman and her sons, I had been watching man and horse idly. Rudolfo and the horse were close to mid-stream now, and my attention was drawn to a big branch floating down-stream some distance above them. The leaves were altogether and strung out moplike on the water, and I suddenly straightened and stared hard as I thought I detected some unnatural movement under the protective cover-ing of green leaves. No doubt about it and it was—it was—an alligator! Now I could distinctly see the scaly head and the enormous jaw emerging from the floating branch, and striking out in the direction of Rudolfo and his horse.

"*Cuidado, el caiman!*" I yelled frantically. "He's back of the branch and coming for you, a big one. Get out of there, Rudolfo. Hurry!"

My voice, urgent and shrill, echoed over the river. Rudolfo cursed, hauled himself up on the horse's back, and looked back coolly at the oncoming alli-gator as my heart thumped and I broke into a cold sweat. Rudolfo had always communicated well with animals, and the horse responded by redoubling his efforts. The alligator was coming on fast, but the man and the horse had a good start. It would be close, but they would make it. Filthy damn beast! They got their quota every year. That was probably what had happened to the missing mail carrier I had been told about. No doubt letters addressed to me, except for those that Carlotta hadn't willfully destroyed, were resting somewhere on the bottom of this miserable river right now. And to think I'd been so wrapped up in my own thoughts that it had only been sheer luck that I'd seen the killer at all.

I wiped my face with my handkerchief and sighed in relief. Rudolfo was on the opposite bank now. He was off his horse by the edge of the water,

311

an angry avenger, cursing and throwing rocks at the alligator, who, seeing himself outwitted, had lunged back to his leafy concealment in the branch that was still swirling downstream. Rudolfo hurled a last rock, tied his horse to a tree, and went down to the canoe. After he paddled it back, he came up to meet me and we shook hands on his narrow escape.

"*Caramba!* What a cunning beast," he said, laughing. "He might have had me, doctor, if you hadn't spotted him and called a warning."

I wanted to tell him how close I had come not to seeing the damn alligator at all, but decided not to. I helped him load the saddles and saddlebags and other equipment into the canoe. He took them across, came back and left me the canoe, then forced the other horse to swim over. He rode the horse bareback, while I paddled alongside, both of us keeping a sharp eye out for alligators, and with Hordimales tied down and lying in the bottom of the canoe. We rested a few minutes and Rudolfo dried off. Then he put on his clothes, which I had brought over in the canoe, we saddled the horses, got everything set, and continued our journey.

Evening darkness had fallen softly over the pampas. They were gray and purple and black, limitless and enchanting or awesome and frightening, depending on one's point of view, but certainly the stuff that both dreams and nightmares are made of. But now my thoughts had crystallized. With every mile I was more and more certain of my decision. Don Arnulfo and Don Victoriano had been unquestionably right from the beginning. I *was* on my way to the big city. And there, regardless of everything, I would have to face my friends. The prospect rather distressed me, but I had already faced myself and, certainly, whatever lay ahead could not be that unpleasant. Suffice it to say that I had served my time and had enough of the jungle, that it was interesting, revealing, and all that, but not for me. And, if they assumed that I had failed, well, well—well, let them.

The dangers of the river passed, the trip was familiar, routine, and uneventful. We made camp, slept in our blankets, cooked our meals, and rode in the cool dawn, the baking noon, the endless simmering afternoon, and on into the refreshing haze of evening. Two days later, late in the afternoon as we neared Santa Morena, Rudolfo stood up in his stirrups and peered intently ahead, as if he were trying to identify landmarks.

"In a quarter of an hour we shall be at La Laguna," he announced.

I nodded. His tone carried some special significance, but I was tired and not inclined to look for it anyway. We rode on in silence until we reached a crossroad. Here Rudolfo stopped, drew up his right leg so it rested on his

312

horse's shoulder, and sighed with what seemed to me exaggerated weariness.

"What is it?" I said testily.

Damn it! Why was he dallying so much? Didn't he see I was tired? Didn't he know I wanted to get in to Santa Morena as soon as possible. It was close to dark now and, at this rate, we—

"Oh, nothing really, doctor," he said casually. Then he motioned with his head. "But Señorita Carlotta's *estancia* lies over that way." I tightened my lips and said nothing. "You know, she might be there. As a matter of fact, I believe she is. And I know her father and brother have gone to the Brazilian border with their cattle. We might stay there overnight. It is late now."

I looked straight at Rudolfo. The boy was wearing his dark glasses, but a telltale red crept up his cheeks to his hairline, so marked that it was easily visible in the half-light.

"Thanks for the information," I said, smiling. "But I think it is better for us to head directly for Santa Morena."

My answer was so startling, so fantastic evidently, that Rudolfo lost his balance. His leg slid down the horse's shoulder, and he would have pitched off if he hadn't hurriedly caught himself. Finally he straightened himself and stared at me with frank disbelief.

"But there are only a few *sirvientas* there—and no one else except the señorita herself."

"It is better for us to go on to Santa Morena all the same."

Rudolfo's mouth opened. For a minute he forgot to close it. I found his inability to understand my change of heart, mind, call it what you will, far from flattering. Then I reflected how much easier it is for a man to gain a reputation than to lose one. I could almost hear the wheels turning in his brain. My God, she's waiting there for him. Her *mosquitero's* wide open and she's palpitating and he says it is better for us to go on!

"*Parece imposible!*" he exclaimed with a chuckle. "It doesn't seem possible." He turned to me with his most winning smile. "I thought—I was sure that—"

"I know what you thought." He reddened more deeply, if that were possible, and I laughed. "It's all right, Rudolfo, and I don't blame you. But Carlotta is safe alone at her *estancia,* and I am safer here with you. Let's go!"

He kicked his horse, and we went the last few miles at a slow trot. The late moon had come up behind us as we reached the outskirts of Santa Morena. We passed a few huts and followed the trail that led us through the *currichi*. From the rise beyond we saw the roof of the church and could make out the slender tower of the radio station in the distance. The sight of the tall mast filled me with elation in which there were overtones of sadness.

"You like to be back in Santa Morena?" Rudolfo said.

"Yes and no. How about you?"

"Oh, I like it here, but Rojas is my home."

"That's it," I said heavily.

"Forgive me, doctor, but your home—it was destroyed?"

"For me, yes. You see, I had to leave Austria. A lot of others like myself had to do the same thing."

Rudolfo turned this over. "You are looking for a home then?"

"That's one way of putting it, I suppose."

"It is strange," he mused. "A home is a thing a man has. He is almost born with it. It is there and he is there. I wouldn't know how to look for a home if I had to do so."

I was tempted to chime in with "Neither do I." Instead I said, "Oh, it can be done. Lots of men have had to do it."

"I don't know," Rudolfo went on dubiously. "Bolivia is my country and Rojas is my home. I cannot think of other places to live. Doctor, is it true that you are leaving us?"

"Yes." I don't know why, but my voice shook as I said it. "Yes, it's true, Rudolfo. I didn't know it myself for sure till the other day by the river, where we saw the Indio woman and her sons, and the alligator tried to get you. Not till then."

"I knew it," he said, his voice very low, his face turned away from me. "I think I have known it for a long time."

*   *   *

When it comes to burning one's bridges, the instructions never specify whether it should be done slowly or with dispatch, the essential business being the total destruction of these personal lines of defense. At the moment I favored speed and, painful as it was, with my mind finally made up I forced myself to be as blunt as possible. Even then Don Socrates would not take my words at face value.

"It is good to go to La Paz. But how soon will you return?"

I had made my little speech twice; I wasn't up to it a third time. So I avoided his eyes and shrugged for an answer. Then my meaning seemed

314

to sink in, and he looked heartbroken, pacing the *sala,* shaking his head from side to side, gnawing on the ends of his mustache, and throwing his arms into the air.

"Ah, *hijo,* this is terrible. Terrible! You are leaving, the priest has gone to the border—in a village in Peru where there is yellow fever—and God knows when he will be back. What will become of us?"

"You will be all right, Don Socrates. You are a strong, intelligent people."

"Perhaps, perhaps. But this is such a terrible thing. I thought you would be happy here with us, settle down, and find a wife. Still, it is up to you. After all, it is your life and your decision to come or to go. And, as I have learned, a man must do what he thinks he must do."

Hurt and disappointed as he was, it was typical of Don Socrates that he made no attempt to dissuade me. Rather, more practically, he began an immediate discussion of my financial status.

"You have done well and you have Rudolfo to thank for making sure you were paid in livestock. But this is not a good time to sell your cattle. Too much hoof and mouth disease. But you will need some money to carry out your plans, and it is only right that I advance you the price of several dozen head."

"No," I protested. "That can wait until you sell them. Then you can send me the money."

"It is better to give you the advance because you are sure to need money," he explained. "And this way you will still have about two hundred oxen left, not counting the cows. Next season I shall make it the first order of business to sell them for you and send you the money—wherever you are."

Two hundred oxen plus cows. Just visualizing such a sizable herd staggered me. In a material sense I had done very well in the jungle. Few people in the province ever accumulated so many animals. But there was more I wanted to say.

"Don Socrates, you have been wonderful to me since I have been here, but I have a few more favors to ask."

"Anything, *hijo,*" he said, bright-eyed. "Ask anything."

"I will accept the advance. That I can use, but the money for the remainder of my stock I want to put in your hands for very definite reasons. First, the woman who lived with Pierre—no, let me finish. She is a good woman with a heart. She is building a house at *El Cementerio,* taking care of Pierre's grave there, and planning to help travelers passing through. I want to give her twelve cows, twelve young steers, and two teams of oxen

315

with a *carreton.*" Again he began to object. "This is my firm wish," I stressed. "Will you see to this and also give her some money for her needs?"

"You have my word that I will do as you say."

He promised it, but he was quite unmoved. I would simply have to take him at his word then.

"And now—just a minute." I went to the window. "Rudolfo," I called, "will you come in, please?" He came in, greeted and embraced Don Socrates, then both men turned expectantly to me. "Rudolfo, have you liked being my assistant? Have you enjoyed the work? Did you find looking after the sick and diseased interesting?"

"*Sí,*" he said sincerely. "That is why I miss your going so much. It is selfish of me, but never again will I find work I like so much."

"Then how would you like to be a doctor?"

He was struck dumb for an instant. "But I couldn't be. I have no education, no background, no training. Besides, I am poor, and people like me never get to be doctors or lawyers—or anything. Ah, doctor, you must not play with me."

"I am not playing with you!" I said heatedly.

Rudolfo was speechless. There was an inexpressible yearning in his eyes, he was seeing a vision that would be snatched away from him any second.

"Surely, you are not serious, *hijo,*" said Don Socrates. "Such a thing is not possible."

"Why not?"

"It is a dream for a boy like Rudolfo."

"No, Don Socrates. The money you get from selling the rest of my stock I want used for Rudolfo's training and education as a doctor. I do not know how to go about this, but there must be a way. Surely Elena will know what to do. And, Rudolfo, let her be your example. She is going to nurse her people; you must doctor them. You can do it if you want."

"Why, this is *magnífico!*" said Don Socrates, beaming and clapping a stunned Rudolfo on the shoulder. "We will have our own doctor from our own people." He crossed and embraced me warmly. "*Hijo,* you will never be forgotten here. Your memory will live on and on. Well?" he said now to Rudolfo, who had not regained his powers of speech. "Have you nothing to say?"

"It is too much," he said, close to tears. "I cannot do it. I do not have the brains nor the ability."

"How do you know unless you try? I have seen you work with me and you have always been calm, efficient, and skillful. Talk to Elena first. You

316

will not fail, Rudolfo. The training is long, hard, and exhausting, but there is no reason for you not to graduate if you really want to. And they need you badly here, remember that."

"Doctor, doctor." He was crying openly now. "I don't know what to say."

"Then don't say anything," I said, struggling to make light of the huskiness that had come into my voice. "If you go back to Rojas for a while, look after the house for me. I will take the emergency kit with me, but everything else, all the medical supplies, I leave in your hands. You don't have to thank me, Rudolfo," I went on, squeezing his shoulder. "The best thanks I can have will be for you to become the doctor that I know you can."

"Amen to that," said Don Socrates. "And now let us drink on it."

He wanted to give a party for me before I left. So did others. I was touched and rather amazed that I was so popular, but I wouldn't let them because I couldn't help feeling what—and I'm glad it did—seemed to escape them. I had failed and was running away again. I had let them down and let myself down. But I did know that wherever I went next, there I would stick and stick and succeed. (And how many times had I promised myself that in my brief lifetime?)

*　*　*

A crowd assembled at the airport to see me leave on the *avion* the next day. I was conspicuous in my black suit, black hat, and my suitcases around me, Don Socrates on my right, and a crushed Rudolfo on my left. We had said our good-bys, we had embraced, and the departed traveler felt uncomfortable and spent. I was glad when the big Junkers landed, and I didn't give a damn who the pilot and crew were, or what they looked like. When I remembered balking at taking the plane earlier, vomiting against the radio station wall, and running off hysterically because the pilot looked like a carbon copy of a Hitler youth, I couldn't recognize myself. Why, I must have been crazy!

I went aboard, and the crowd quieted as the *avion* prepared to take off. I walked back to the door and waved to all of them for a last time.

"Send us more *gringos* like you!" Don Socrates called for all of them.

"I will do it," Rudolfo shouted suddenly. "Count on me, doctor, and pray for me."

A few moments remained, but I had to go inside. Then we fastened our seat belts, the motors roared, the plane picked up its skirts, and gradually, the narrow, sun-blighted airstrip dropped away below. As we circled the area before heading for the mountains, I saw Santa Morena spread out like

3¹7

a magical picture-book village below—the thatched houses, the huts, the shacks, the rutted mud and grass streets, and the *currichi,* just a half-moon-shaped puddle to someone who didn't know. Past the village now and over great trees, their green crowns like the fleece of giant, emerald-colored sheep. Farther on gray woolen clouds enveloped the plane, the altitude gauge needle in the passenger compartment went up and up as we climbed, I shut my eyes, and time passed. Time? I had to remind myself that it was only two years since I had arrived at the same airstrip in the same *avion.* It seemed a lifetime—and it was. Oh, it was!

I looked forward apprehensively to my arrival at La Paz. Why hadn't I had the sense to send a radio message to either Herbert or Karl. Simply to turn up without warning was childish of me, but then, I rationalized, it was only because no man likes to herald his return from the battlefield where he has met defeat. I dozed for a while, but was awakened by icy cold air filtering into the plane, and sat up shivering in spite of my overcoat. The mountains were clear and sharp. Beneath us, the snow-capped peaks of the Cordillera raised their heads, and a passenger pointed to the majesty of Illimani, the highest summit, on our right, awesomely beautiful and forbidding. From the tropical jungle to the Arctic. Such a big country with the people, especially like me, so small. Well, the bridges were all burned. No retreat. It was onward and upward with the medical arts in some other location until—what? The next fiasco? The next retreat? Oh, shut up! Leave me alone, brain. Who cared? I was just going to wait and see. Then, relaxed, I slept . . .

I awoke just as we circled La Paz. I got my things together, put on my hat, and straightened my clothes. Now I felt like a deserter about to go before a military tribunal, a court-martial. We landed, filed out of the plane, and I blinked in the bright sunlight of civilization. Somehow, because I felt low and changed, I expected everything to be changed. But nothing had changed at all. And there, waiting at the end of the ramp, stood a familiar figure. A big man, slightly stooped, with a pipe in his mouth. Herbert.

I hurried to greet him. We threw our arms around each other and said the usual, hearty, welcoming things, but meaning them.

"I never expected anyone to meet me, Herbert. How did you know I was coming on this plane?"

Herbert explained to me as we drove into the city in the airport station wagon.

"I heard it from the representative of your province. You remember I went along with you for your first interview. Well, a few months after you left,

318

I met him on the street, and he told me you were doing wonderfully. Later on he said you were on your way to owning an *estancia,* a house, and"—here he grinned—"that all the women were after you. Same old Martin, eh? And then in the dry season he had reports concerning you every few weeks. They came from a man with a Greek name, Socrates, I believe. Maybe I'm mistaken about the name, but . . ."

Doing wonderfully, an *estancia,* a house, all the women after me. My God, if I were to tell him the truth about myself, the beating I took, the miserable times I had, the bitter loneliness, he would speak differently. All the same, hearing these third-hand reports about myself was breath-taking. What I had conceived as two whole tragic years of isolation had been unceremoniously reduced to an absurdity in these few minutes. I had thought of myself imprisoned in a steel chamber—and there had always been a door. And the door was never locked. More than that, while I had seen myself cut off from the world with my walls impervious from within, people had been looking through them from the outside all the time.

"So you know all about me, Herbert. But you never wrote."

"I did, Martin! For months all of us wrote to you every week. I took all the mail to the airline to make sure. Except for one letter shortly after you left, we heard nothing from you. After a while, we thought—we couldn't help thinking that you had become a rich man and that you no longer belonged to us." He looked embarrassed. "You know, migration and resettlement often do things to people."

He sounded disillusioned and discouraged. But his dull, lackluster eyes, the heavy sadness in his voice were even more heartbreaking. What had happened to this good friend who had always been the strong, buoyant one among us?

"Herbert, I assure you that that was not true. It wasn't my fault. You see, there was a girl—oh, what's the use?" How could I possibly explain the lovely, devious, lovelorn Carlotta? "Whatever happened, I thought—" If I put it as I had intended to, it would sound far too blunt. "Well, I thought just the opposite."

"That we no longer belonged to you because we stayed behind where life was easy?"

"Not exactly," I said gently. "More that you people didn't want anything more to do with a fellow who ran away and left you flat."

"I don't see how you could think that," he said, not looking at me.

And I couldn't see how they could think me so heartless as to have abandoned them. My God, this failure to communicate. But then—odd that I should remember it so vividly—Herbert had spoken of the line of least resistance and leaving others to fight one's battles right at this very place the car was passing right now. I could see the buildings as they had looked, hear the intonation of his voice, recall the expression of his face as he said it like an accusation. And here I was back in La Paz again, wavering, unsure, and no more fit to fight the common battle than I had been before leaving for the jungle. Better to change the subject. I looked around at the bustling city outside the glass.

"Are the llamas still roaming the streets and do the Indios still wander about chewing coca leaves?"

Herbert smiled, a tired, weak smile. And again I was uneasy and let down. What *had* happened to the tower of strength I had left behind?

"Yes, the llamas still roam the streets, the Indios still chew their coca, and everything is the same." He sighed. "Only we have changed—you and I." He coughed apologetically, then roused himself. "Where are you planning to stay in La Paz, Martin?"

"Why, I don't know. I hadn't given it a thought. Perhaps at that big hotel at the Prado, whatever it's called. I'm afraid I've forgotten the name. But have you got any other suggestions?"

"Yes. I have a nice big room along the Prado. It has another bed, and you're welcome to use it. Besides, you won't be alone in the evenings. You can't know how long they can be here."

So he, too, knew about the lonely evenings and seemed to believe that loneliness was foreign to me. I ought to enlighten him, I suppose. But what about his wife? Hadn't she joined him yet? Was she coming over? There was so much I wanted to ask Herbert. The station wagon was passing the railway station, and my eye was caught by an Indio woman at the curb wearing a peculiar stiff high hat and many skirts. She was selling newspapers, and they were arranged on a wooden box before her. Newspapers! I jumped from my seat and tapped our driver on the shoulder.

"Stop here for a minute, *por favor!* I'll be right back."

He was surprised, but he pulled up as everybody in the car stared at me. I hopped out and ran to the newsstand.

"Give me this one, the *Diario,* the *Razon*—oh, and this one, too." I gave her some money and didn't bother to count my change as I ran back to the waiting car. *"Gracias!"* I called back to the Indio woman.

I climbed into the car holding my bundle of papers tenderly. The pilot of my plane, who was riding with us gave me a supercilious smile, but it bounced right off. Stinking goose-stepping Nazi bastard! What did I care what he thought.

320

"Look, Herbert," I whispered. "My God, they've got today's date. They're not six or seven weeks old. Today's date!"

"They're just newspapers," said Herbert sourly.

Surely he must understand what news fresh off the presses must mean to me. Or was the gulf yawning between us so much wider than I had guessed? I pressed the newspapers to my chest, as if they were a baby who might cry at any minute, and stared at the stores, the restaurants, the big buildings, the smartly dressed passers-by, the traffic so heavy in both directions. We passed the motion picture theater with its shiny marquee and glittering announcements of its current attraction, and I thought, "Tonight, tomorrow night, and every night I'm here, I'll go to the movies." The idea so thrilled and delighted me that I shivered in anticipation of the delights to come. There was so much to do in La Paz, so much that I had missed, longed, and ached for.

Just walking into Herbert's room excited me. It was so large, so well appointed, with comfortable furniture, pictures on the walls, two spring beds with mattresses, and a wash basin, which I ran over to immediately.

"Look, Herbert, it's like magic. Running water. And it's really hot!"

"Sometimes that even surprises me," he said. "And I live here."

It was meant to be funny, but his tone was so bitterly vitriolic that all the humor inherent in the remark was eaten away. It was totally unlike the man I had known, and I could contain myself no longer.

"Herbert, old friend, for heaven's sake, what's the matter with you? You're not yourself at all. You look down at the mouth, you hardly smile, and you're so bitter. It strikes me especially because, in my mind, you've always been a tower of strength. Whenever I was low and miserable in the jungle—and that was often enough, let me tell you—I thought of you and how strong and resourceful you were. Of course," I went on, wanting to be completely honest, "that only seemed to make me more miserable, but still it was good to know that you—"

"Tower of strength! Agh!" Herbert's laugh was dry and ironic. He clamped his teeth on the stem of his pipe, struck a match, then tossed it away before the tobacco was lighted. "I'm anything but that, Martin. As you can see, Martin, I am alone. Is that not strange?"

"Yes, I wondered—"

"You wondered what had become of my wife, and you were discreet enough not to ask. Well, I'll tell you: I no longer have a wife. My wife—I should say my former wife—has divorced me." I made an involuntary sound of astonishment, and Herbert held up his hand. "You know the consul here. Such a nice obliging fellow," he added sarcastically. "Through him

I fixed up all the necessary papers about six weeks ago. It was a very simple matter." His body sagged in the chair he had taken by his bed. "A matter of forms and signing my name over and over."

"I can't believe it!"

"Oh, it's all my fault," he said hoarsely. "She wanted to come along from the beginning, but I was against it. Too rough for a woman, too hard to begin in a new country unprepared. Let me get a foothold first, I begged her. I'll get a job, find a place to live, then send for you. She was adamant. We fought and fought over it, but I finally convinced her—convinced her for good as it turned out."

She had wanted to go with him; he had wanted to go alone, then summon her when the path was smoothed out. It was all so familiar. So like my lovely Lisa in Paris, who had resumed a momentary importance later as I used her as an excuse for not taking a wife either in Santa Morena or Rojas. But what was it Don Socrates had said about just this question? Something like: "A woman who loves her man does not ask whether he is for or against her going with him; she goes with him. She sleeps with him on straw, if there is no other bed. She eats it, if she has to, but she goes with him!" That wasn't quite it, but close enough. And I thought with a pang of the Indio woman and her vigil at *El Cementerio*. She was still with Pierre.

"I'm sure you're not to blame, Herbert," I said reassuringly. "How much did she fight, how hard was it to convince her? Some people have made up their minds to capitulate long before they argue heatedly against it. I'm sure you—"

I stopped talking as Herbert just looked at me. It was stupid of me to hurt my friend like this, to add pain to insult when the best thing was to shut up and listen. And yet how strange to feel that he was just as weak as I was— perhaps he always had been. Herbert's glance was still on me, hard, bright, and knowing for an instant as of old, then just as suddenly I saw his eyes well with tears.

"A fine fellow you are," he said softly. "You're polite and only succeed in destroying the last vestige of my ego. But I had it coming, Martin, and I thank you for it. It's good for me. As a matter of fact, I've often thought about it myself. You know, it really was not so hard to convince her. But you are the first to make me face the unpleasant truth."

It had not been my intention at all, and yet how often the truth is spoken lightly or in jest. I'd come out with it innocently and unknowingly; it had cleared the air for Herbert, but the credit belonged to Don Socrates, not to me. Now Herbert stood up, looking relieved, and I was startled.

322

"Let me help you unpack, Martin. You can have the lower drawers of the dresser. I don't use it. I have so few things. Anyway, what are your plans?"

"Plans? Oh, they haven't quite jelled yet."

"Plenty of time. By the way, Karl's giving a party at his house tomorrow night. All the people from the boat will be there and they'll want to see you. You'll come, won't you?"

"I'd love to," I said heartily, to cover my fear of meeting my friends and judges. "How is Karl anyway? I forgot to ask."

Herbert opened a drawer and stared at it. "I don't know how he is. Financially, he seems to be doing fine, but there's some trouble between him and Maria. Sometimes I think it's my fault . . ."

My God! What was happening to all these people?

"You mean that you and Maria—"

"Don't be ridiculous! I won't deny that I haven't been lonely and miserable enough to think about it, but that's not it. I'm afraid that Karl worries that my wife's example may tempt Maria. She's not happy here, not herself at all, but then none of us is."

I got up, shaking my head, and began to walk up and down the room, marveling at the soft carpet underfoot and, at the same time, uncomfortable and perplexed.

"I don't understand it at all. I'm all mixed up, Herbert. I came back here thinking that you people must have solved all your problems."

"What do you think we are? It's naive and unrealistic to think that anyone ever solves *all* his problems."

"Well, the major ones," I said defensively.

"They're all major, Martin. Every one of them."

*　*　*

Just as I promised myself, I went to the movies that night. It was some shrill, blatant, chromium-plated Hollywood concoction of no significance whatsoever, but I loved every minute. The women were so beautiful, the men so handsome, their clothes so smart, the settings so luxurious, and their problems so petty and so easily resolved for the inevitable happy ending fadeout. The next morning I was up early and spent all day doing the town alone, peering in store windows, staring at pretty girls, pounding the sidewalks, sipping the soft drinks I enjoyed, and in general enjoying the amenities and comforts of civilization.

I was still dazed and exhilarated as Herbert and I joined the men and women gathered in Karl's living room that evening. Most of us were still young people, but young people with a difference. Life had clawed and scratched us, and we looked older than our years. Hurt eyes, lined faces, and the wary expression of a losing boxer shrinking from the next telling punch. I was warmly greeted, handshakes from the men, kisses from the women, and made much of. Then we perched informally on stools, chairs, and trunks and drank wine. The conversation was lively until, at a signal, all present quieted and turned toward our host.

Karl was older than most of us, a solid, serious man who felt things deeply. He was sitting on a box covered by a little throw rug, and as he stood up, holding his wineglass high, he towered over everyone in the room. He cleared his throat and stared about the room at his guests through the thick lenses of his eyeglasses, an owl on the alert and ready with a pronouncement.

"My friends," he said slowly, "two years ago on board a ship carrying us across the Atlantic Ocean, we came together and founded this little circle. We had left behind a continent, a sorely missed homeland that no longer had friendly words, much less homes for us. Humiliations and a common grief brought this group together and kept it together. Then, after we reached La Paz, one of our number left us. Now he has come back and today our circle is complete once more.

"Martin has come back to us from the jungle. He must have had great courage and tenacity to endure an existence so different from even our own new life here. Now let us give Martin a royal welcome!"

He raised his glass in a toast, their welcome rang through the room, and everyone drank his wine. I sat uncomfortably on a draped footstool as everyone stood around me. Mentally, I was even less at ease. All these men and women were nicely dressed. They did not starve. They had found new homes, probably all as modest as Karl's, but still homes. They had jobs, found places for themselves, succeeded as well as they could. And yet something vital was missing. I had seen it in Herbert and felt it as soon as I had come into this room. Something I couldn't put my finger on and, oddly, something much worse than what I considered my self-defeat in the jungle. "A roof over the head is not enough," Pierre had told me, and the futility of Pierre's existence seemed to fill the atmosphere of this room.

They were looking at me now, waiting for my reply. I stirred, stumbled to my feet, and tried to put together some words for their warm welcome.

"First, I want to say thank you. I wish I knew what to say, but, uh, all the time I was in the jungle, I longed to be here in the city with all of you. Out there, I used to tell myself, among the people who speak my language

324

and think as I do, I'm sure I could find out what ails me, what is driving me on. Well, I guess I'll have to see my way clear now that I am here. I am glad to be back with you. Thanks very much."

At one time I had thought that nothing would make me happier than being back among them, but I knew that this wasn't true. I had broken the mold, cast away the pattern, and while I was back in the circle, I was no longer of it. I wondered if they felt the change in me, but I had no time to dwell on this as they overwhelmed me with questions about the jungle, the people in the deep interior, how I carried on my medical work, how I managed to pass the days and months, and all the rest of it.

My account was a labored one, but, from their fascinated expressions, no one seemed to mind my lame descriptions. I tried to describe the glory of the pampas at dawn and in the moonlight. I told how I accepted cattle in place of regular fees and the problems of raising a large herd. I told them of the houses I had lived in, the food, the dangers from wild animals, my early struggles with the *curanderos,* of my wonderful assistant Rudolfo, and about operations I had performed in difficult circumstances. It came hard at first, as I drained my memory, but then everything came back and poured out, spurred by the look of unmistakable admiration and near envy in every face. And I went on with little stories about the people—Don Socrates and Don Arnulfo and *El Cura* and Pierre and how he had died.

I don't know how long I kept on, but my throat was dry when I finished. Nobody said a word, the silence was pregnant, and Karl's footsteps heavy as he crossed the room for the bottle and refilled my wineglass. I drank, looking about me uneasily, but still no one volunteered to speak. Then Karl cleared his throat and seemed to speak for all of them.

"It must be wonderful to be able to make your own way, be your own master."

His words and the way he said them absolutely overpowered me. I felt so weak in the knees that I sat down again on my uncomfortable stool. I had another glass of wine, my friends came over for a word one after the other, and soon the conversation became general again. Momentarily alone, I opened the door to the outside balcony, which I had seen on arriving, slipped out into the brightly clear crisp night air, and put my elbows on the railing. How good and clean it smelled! In the distance I could see the icy peak of Illimani standing out in sharp contrast against the inky sky. It was at least a hundred kilometers away, but I felt I had only to stretch out my arm to touch it. White clouds, wallowing great masses and feathery wisps, surrounded the majestic, wind-battered summit.

The sight had a magnificent grandeur reminding me of my early student days when my school friends and I, our imaginations kindled by the tales of the ancient Greek gods and heroes, aspired to great things and great deeds. And tonight in La Paz I was standing on a balcony watching the clouds take the shape of warriors like Achilles and Agamemnon hurrying into the tumult of the Cordillera battle. The dust whirled upward by these heroes clashing on legendary battlefields must have formed just such clouds as now sailed past Illimani, while the peak stood by serenely like Mount Olympus, the home of Zeus, father of the gods. The scene, the memories of my childhood, and the thought of heroes doing battle gave me pleasure, but suddenly I was conscious that someone had joined me on the balcony. It was Karl's wife, Maria.

"What do you see out there, Martin?" I pointed to the peak of Illimani, the cloud formations, and explained how they reminded me of Greek heroes in battle. "I don't see anything," she said. Then, more softly, "You're lonely, aren't you?"

"Yes." I shrugged and kept my eyes on the battle in the clouds. "Of course I'm lonely. Why shouldn't I be? You people have each other; you all have a husband or wife. You share your days and, at night, when your worries get too much for you, all you have to do is reach for each other."

"Do you really believe it's that easy, Martin?"

"No," I said. "But it must help."

"Things are not always what they seem," she said in a low voice. "After we were married, I think Karl and I were the happiest people on earth. We had two years of heaven, then came the disaster we all know too well, and we had to leave Europe. Then came the change. The Karl I knew disappeared. He withdrew into himself. And here in La Paz life was not easy for us until he got this job as an accountant. I thought that would help, but he only became more unreasonable and jealous. Martin, I feel I am losing him more every day."

I looked away from the battle in the clouds. Maria had been pretty, gay, vivacious, bubbling with youth. Her looks had faded. She looked worn and worried and tired. I was her friend as well as Karl's, and I was a doctor. I took a deep breath and expelled it.

"You're lucky, Maria, and you don't realize it. Karl is a wonderful man and he loves you, but there are things you must take into consideration. A woman's life is filled by her love for her man, her children, her home, all those things. With a man it's different."

Maria sighed. "I know."

"No, you don't know. A man's love for his woman is important, too.

326

It's vital, like being born or breathing, but it's not all. It's only half his life. Backed by this love and the stability of his home, a man goes out into the competitive business world to fight, assert himself, and bring home the bacon of success. But if half a man's life is shaken, if the other half is cut off, uprooted, or destroyed as happened to Karl—and to all of us for that matter—his character undergoes a change. It can't help doing so. When this happens, some of us are able to adapt ourselves, however painfully, in conventional ways, and this is called normal adjustment to changed circumstances. Others, even more painfully, are forced to adapt themselves in ways that people are apt to consider eccentric. My sympathy goes to the last because, personally, I believe that the eccentric way, the strange way is the more normal. It is more natural to that particular individual. And in our times, who is to tell what is normal, what is abnormal?"

"Oh, Martin," she said doubtfully.

"You still don't get what I'm driving at, Maria?"

"No."

"Karl has lost his country, his profession, his position, not through any fault of his own, but because of acts of rank injustice. My God, you know how rank! Well, then, what else could crush a legal mind of the stature of your husband's? His whole world has been shattered by bad faith, and he cannot help but wonder if there is more to come. These are the worries and fears that wrack him every minute. And, I tell you, Maria, there is another thing he is afraid of: that one day you might leave him, too. He has a logical mind, and he must have some assurance that you will stay by his side. So he is preparing for all eventualities. Karl is proud. He has to pretend not to care."

I looked up at my cloud battlefield. The godlike struggle in the upper air had diminished in fury. The large mass had come to a standstill, small clouds breaking away to pursue their own course across the dark sky.

Maria looked at me numbly. "I don't understand. I don't understand any of it."

"It sounds complicated, but it isn't—or perhaps it is always clear to the detached observer so easily able to advise others. But I'm not so detached, Maria. I care for both of you. Be good to him then. Karl needs you so terribly now. Every minute of the day and night, you must make him feel that you are with him. Then not only will he show the love he has for you, but he'll also worship you."

"Martin!"

Something in her voice made me stiffen. I turned toward her, holding my breath. She hadn't been listening to me.

327

"Yes, Maria." It was the patient voice I would use on a disturbed patient. "What is it?"

"Take me away from here. Please, please, take me away."

A small sound of shocked surprise escaped my lips.

"I can't bear it any longer! Oh, you don't know how it is to have to stand by helplessly while Karl's spirit is dying and we drift apart just when we need each other so much. Oh, God, I have to get away from myself, to forget myself so I can get back a little strength and courage."

She broke down, fought the sobs choking her voice, and I said the first soothing thing that came into my head.

"It's no good talking like this, Maria. No good at all. You must—"

"What? Don't talk to me like a psychiatrist! *Help me!* Take me to the jungle with you, Martin," she pleaded. "Take me where there are only malaria and tigers and rattlesnakes to fight. Take me there until I can face myself again and come back cleansed and reborn as you are."

Once again I was shaken and pleased to think that Maria or anyone could believe that such a thing had happened to me in that isolated province. But I had no time to indulge myself with Maria so upset.

"Don't quit, Maria," I said firmly. "That's the unforgivable sin toward others, life, and, particularly, yourself. This is not the time to desert each other or, worse, to forget oneself. Stay with Karl, do you hear me? Stay with him!"

Perhaps I was too harsh. She broke into wild sobbing, I moved closer, and suddenly Maria put her head on my shoulder.

"You have become such a hard man," she said through her tears. "And now you hate me—I know you do—and you shouldn't. Karl, myself, you, and the others were all like fallen leaves caught up in a tumult and sent flying to the four winds. Now the rest of us still whirl around in space, our sorrows, our loves, our ambitions, our lives withered in us as we spin on and on into nowhere. But you were luckier, braver, and stronger than we were— you conquered the tumult and yourself."

On the face of it, all this about myself was incredible. I felt a warm glow inside, but I didn't believe it. That was simply not what had happened, and it would be a kindness to disabuse her.

"You are making up things, Maria. It is good to hear compliments about oneself, but this time they are simply not true."

"You are wrong. I saw it in you as soon as you came in. It's in the way you walk, talk, and look. You are not the Martin who left us."

"Whichever Martin I am, I still don't like myself," I said lightly. Ah,

Maria took us all so seriously, I thought. If only she could talk to my false priest a few minutes. "The jungle may have made a few changes for the better, but like the others I am still not a whole man. I don't suppose any of us ever will be with part of us always remaining in Austria. That's a fact we're going to have to accept and live with for our own peace of mind."

"Don't talk any more, Martin. Just hold me tight."

So I held her and watched the clouds darken and hide Illimani's peak. After a while, Maria's body stiffened in my arms, she dried her tears, and went back to her guests without saying a word. As she went inside a shaft of light glared across the balcony, then there was darkness again as the door shut behind her. The air was cold, and I shivered. I knew it was warm and bright and cozy where the party was, but I preferred my balcony. They were there, I was here, and I had to admit I was more at home in the cold and dark overlooking La Paz and the mountains.

Most of the others had to go to work the next day, and the party broke up early. I was glad in a way because it had tired me more than anything I had done since arriving in the city. It had been fun and it hadn't been fun. I couldn't tell how much of each, but I wouldn't have missed it for anything. I missed Maria somehow as we left, but I did shake hands with Karl and thank him for the party. He seemed to hate to see me leave and kept my hand in his a long time.

"What are you going to do now, Martin?" he asked. "Don't say that you don't know because you must have thought about it. You *must* tell me."

I looked at him and the words came so easily that I told myself the thought had been in my mind all along.

"I want to practice medicine and probably become a specialist of some kind. That means further study and a country with opportunities. I think I'll go to New York. Of course, there are still a lot of details I'll have to work out, but—"

"You'll do it! I know you will." He squeezed my hand hard. "Good-by, Martin. I won't tell the others. You better do it yourself."

Herbert and I left together as we had come. Deep in our own thoughts, we walked down the street that led from the upper part of the city toward the plaza. Accustomed to the tropics for so long, I felt the chill night air now and turned up my coat collar. We walked on through the silent, empty streets, our footsteps clattering loudly on the cobbled pavement between the houses.

"Do you know what a phantom leg is, Herbert?" I said abruptly.

"No."

329

"It's a surgical term. An amputee often feels pain where his amputated leg once was; he feels it long after the leg is gone. I was thinking of Karl in this connection. The trouble is over the amputation of his old self. He can't get over it, and Maria has to suffer with him and for him."

"Um," said Herbert.

We crossed the plaza.

"I talked with Maria," I went on. "I defended Karl warmly, although right now I must admit I don't feel as warmly about it. After all, there has to be a limit to his pain even if time alone were to effect a cure. And there is no complete cure, and it is up to him to help time along. He can't go on and on suffering. He has no right to make his wife's life miserable either. If he doesn't like his life as it is, then it's up to him to do something about it. Somebody should wake him up and tell him that."

"Who?" said Herbert sarcastically. "The grocer who came over with us? The tailor? The butcher? The farmer? They don't understand his problems because they don't have them. Most of the intellectuals in our circle have the same trouble in one degree or another. Not everybody has the courage you did! Many of us gave so much to one life that there is not enough left for another."

I could think of no suitable reply. Besides, I wanted to linger on the idea of myself as a brave and courageous man. Karl, Maria, all the others, and now Herbert seemed to think of me as a sort of hero, a warrior good and true who had fought the good fight against terrible odds. Well, maybe I had and maybe I hadn't, but I had done something they envied.

We went beyond the plaza, crossed the street, and walked into a sort of quadrangular park where there were benches and beds of low shrubs. I stopped in the center and so did Herbert, eying me questioningly. Across from us, a group of men and women were chatting animatedly in front of a brightly lighted movie house. On either side, large store windows, also brilliantly lighted, displayed elegant merchandise. A monk passed, and my eyes followed him as he went down the sidewalk, climbed the steps, and, head bowed, entered the portals of the ancient cathedral.

"Let's go to bed," said Herbert. "I'm tired."

"In a minute," I said. "You go ahead. I'll catch up with you."

He left, and I took a deep breath. Perhaps it was true. If it was, I'd have to get used to it. Certainly, compared with my friends, I was my own master, and I would go to the United States and continue with my medical career. It seemed to me that those who had stayed behind in La Paz were like people hanging on the outside of a fast-moving train already filled with

330

passengers, desperately clutching for a handhold. While I, with no train to cling to, had in a way built my own primitive train and given it locomotion and direction. By God, I was free at last and my own man! Wanting to scream my triumph to the skies, I lifted my face and stared at the still brilliant carpet overhead.

Looking off at the horizon, way up on the slope of the valley, I could see a light crawling along, unmistakably an engine's single great eye. I seemed to hear the faint rattle of an outgoing train of the Trans-Andean Railway, to see a trailing line of smoke, curling like the white hair of my false priest. Remembering *El Cura* sobered my elation. Know thyself, he would warn me now, and you will not lose sight of yourself or others. True, true. But my suffering compatriots, still entrenched in their emotional misery, made a poor yardstick.

How weird the sky over La Paz! The edge of the plateau, with its dusky play of light and shade, reminded me of *El Cementerio,* and the sky above shone like the sky on that terrible night when I buried Daguero. Then, as life had suddenly waned from Daguero's stricken eyes, this light, too, went out. And the engine's headlight had gone out, too. It had crossed the rim of the valley and was rolling ahead on flat ground.

For another minute a single shaft of light remained in the sky, reflected from somewhere over the horizon. Now it moved forward, pointing like a huge finger to way out yonder where Don Socrates lived—and Carlotta and Elena. And Arturo and the *curandero* called Malvenido. Pointing to Rojas where my horses and cattle grazed on the pampas and where Rudolfo guarded my house and, I hoped, was reflecting on his medical education; where a man needed no printed license to serve and be useful. And to Santa Morena embraced by its renowned *currichi* with its purifying plants. They said, I remembered, that anybody who tasted of this water must return to it, and I wondered about this, but not for long.

It was late. The lights of the movie house were still on, the people still chatting by the marquee. I didn't want to see a movie, and I no longer felt tired. But I had told Herbert I'd catch up with him. So I took one last look at the sky and started for his room. I walked all the way without overtaking him. He had left the door unlocked, but it was dark inside and I supposed he was asleep or pretending to be. I undressed in the dark and went quickly to bed, but not to sleep. I could hardly wait for the night to pass. I had so much to do. So much. And I was impatient to begin at last.